The British Isles: A Systematic Geography

EDITORIAL COMMITTEE

Editor
Professor J. Wreford Watson
University of Edinburgh

Professor W. G. V. Balchin, University College of Swansea
Mr Ian Cox, C.B.E., Shell International Petroleum
Mr G. R. Crone, Royal Geographical Society
Professor W. G. East, Birkbeck College, University of London
Professor E. Estyn Evans, Queen's University of Belfast
Professor Emrys Jones, London School of Economics and
   Political Science
Professor W. R. Mead, University College London
Professor A. E. Smailes, Queen Mary College, University of London
Professor R. W. Steel, University of Liverpool
Dr H. Thorpe, University of Birmingham

Liaison Members

Professor L. Dudley Stamp, C.B.E.
Professor J. A. Steers, University of Cambridge
Professor M. J. Wise, M.C., London School of Economics and
   Political Science
Brigadier L. J. Harris, C.B.E., Directorate of Military Survey

Honorary Secretary

Dr J. B. Sissons, University of Edinburgh

Honorary Secretary, Executive Committee

Professor T. H. Elkins, University of Sussex

The British Isles
A Systematic Geography

edited by

J. WREFORD WATSON, Ph.D., M.A., F.R.S.Can.

Professor of Geography at the University of Edinburgh

with

J. B. SISSONS, M.A., Ph.D.

NELSON

THOMAS NELSON AND SONS LTD
36 Park Street London W1
P.O. Box 2187 Accra
P.O. Box 336 Apapa Lagos
P.O. Box 25012 Nairobi
P.O. Box 21149 Dar es Salaam
77 Coffee Street San Fernando Trinidad

THOMAS NELSON (AUSTRALIA) LTD
597 Little Collins Street Melbourne 3000

THOMAS NELSON AND SONS (SOUTH AFRICA) (PROPRIETARY) LTD
51 Commissioner Street Johannesburg

THOMAS NELSON AND SONS (CANADA) LTD
81 Curlew Drive Don Mills Ontario

First published June 1964
Reprinted 1965, 1967, 1969, 1970

17 133046 3

Printed and Bound in Great Britain by
Hazell Watson & Viney Ltd, Aylesbury, Bucks

Preface

By L. DUDLEY STAMP

*Chairman of the British National Committee
for Geography*

*Formerly President, International
Geographical Union*

When the 12th International Geographical Congress met in Britain in 1928 at London and Cambridge, a volume entitled *Great Britain*: *Essays in Regional Geography* was published for the occasion under the editorship of the late Professor Alan G. Ogilvie of the University of Edinburgh. For more than thirty years that book remained the standard work on the regional geography of Britain—indeed until it was replaced in 1962 by the publication of *Great Britain: Geographical Essays* edited by Jean Mitchell, and which follows similar lines. It seemed to the British National Committee for Geography of the Royal Society, the sponsoring body for the 20th International Geographical Congress 1964, that the occasion should be marked by a volume of a different character.

Apart from the main meetings in London, pre-Congress and post-Congress specialist symposia and study-tours embrace all parts of the British Isles—England, Wales, Scotland, Northern Ireland, and the Irish Republic—and it is appropriate therefore that this volume should concern itself with the whole of the British Isles The Committee felt that the time was opportune for a stocktaking or inventory of the present state of British Geography. There is not a University in the British Isles which ignores geography, in the majority there exists an Honours school, linked in some with the natural sciences, in some with the liberal arts, in some with the social sciences, in some with all three, in still others standing alone. In most, too, there are facilities for graduate work. Though British geographers as a whole insist upon the unity of their subject and in particular stress its position as bridging the gulf between science and the arts and its continuity in study from the past through the present to the future, it is recognised that there is room, indeed need, for specialisation. Individual University departments are often associated, through the interests of their members of staff, with certain aspects of the subject. Accordingly in the series of essays which follows one topic after another is taken up and the present state of knowledge analysed and assessed by one of the leaders in the particular aspect of geography concerned.

There have been many changes and developments since 1928. Not least is the widespread appreciation of the value of geographical studies in school, college, university, and research institute, and especially as a training for a wide variety of careers. Those who have studied geography develop a balanced view of life, of national and of international affairs and become good world citizens. They are to be found in all walks of life and it is appropriate that some of the chapters of this book should be by those outside our universities.

All over the world there is a growing realisation that natural resources are far from limitless, that their proper utilisation demands objective study and a planned development or conservation. Inevitably a major trend has been towards the application of geographical methods of research to these current problems: applied geography becomes a natural addition to a basic training and passes uninterruptedly into physical planning. It becomes impossible to stop at the present day: trends leading into the future become naturally part of the field of study.

Those who receive their geographical training in the British milieu are exceptionally fortunate. Visitors from overseas who remember only the relatively small extent of the British Islands are apt to overlook that the islands can truthfully be described as a microcosm. It would be difficult, indeed impossible, to find any comparable area on the earth's surface exhibiting such a wide range of natural environments, and where such varying responses have been evoked from a succession of human inhabitants. In the geological build scarcely one of the great periods is unrepresented: the greater part was ice-covered in the last Ice Age, but some areas escaped; periods of union with the great Eurasian land mass alternated with periods of separation, with a consequential complex history of faunal and floral invasion. Not only have the climatic fluctuations of post-glacial time added to the bewildering complexity of the story, but the climate of today places the British Isles in a peculiarly intermediate position: if Mediterranean plants flourish in the southwest, Arctic-alpine vegetation and tundra characterise the high plateaux of the north. From pre-historic and through historic times successive waves of human invaders have adapted their own particular ideas to local environmental conditions. Even today this process has not yet ceased. In the present post-war period the peaceful invasion from the West Indies and West Africa poses new problems and demands new adjustments: current population trends have upset completely the calculations of only a decade or two ago.

Those who work in this exciting world, this little world of the British Isles, have frequently had varied experience overseas and bring to bear on their studies the advantages accruing from that experience. But they come home to realise that the broad scale of preliminary studies of vast lands must give place to a painstaking investigation of minutiae. It is in the value of their detailed studies, especially field studies, that British workers show their qualities of leadership.

It is our hope that this collection of essays will demonstrate to our visitors in 1964 and to many who will come after them not only the fascinating story of our islands but also the progress which has been made to date in the unravelling and the narration of that story.

Acknowledgments

Figures 17 and 18 are reproduced by courtesy of the Royal Geographical Society. Figures 45 and 48 are reproduced with the sanction of H.M. Stationery Office and Crown Copyright is reserved.

Contents

List of Figures

I

THE INDIVIDUALITY OF BRITAIN
AND THE BRITISH ISLES

PART of the individuality of Britain is the individuality of its parts. Therefore, it is difficult to assess the character of Britain *as a whole*. Britain is made up of regions distinctive enough to have cradled nations of their own. Powerful physical divides, and cultural divisions equally as powerful, have conspired to make it a country of countries. This is perhaps the first of its distinguishing features.

In the north, for example, a broad mountain barrier—the Cheviots—together with long-established rivalries culminating in the struggle between Scots and English, helped to separate Scotland from England. The differences between the two are real. To the north lies a country that is chiefly upland, to the south one that is predominantly lowland; to the north are the only large emptinesses in Britain, embracing some of the most isolated and retarded communities in western Europe, whereas to the south is one of Europe's most densely settled and most highly developed regions; to the north resources and population are limited—with 33% of Britain's area Scotland has only 11% of its population, but to the south resources such as soil, coal, iron, and ease of communication are generous, and population full: Scotland has therefore had only a limited chance to expand, and England has come to dominate the affairs of the British Isles.

Culturally, the two are distinct. Scotland still has its Celtic fringe and many relics of its Norse occupation. England has been very largely Anglicised. The north is strongly Calvinistic and even its smallest villages may be peppered with churches disputing between them the true Reformation; to the south, the Anglican church is predominant, many villages gather about only the one spire, and even where Free Church 'chapels' have contested the Englishman's allegiance, they are far more likely to be congregational than Presbyterian. The north is proud of its separate legal tradition and of its independent system of education—its four great universities are older than any in England except Oxford and Cambridge and have customs and forms of their own, whereas in the south a different type of law and a unique kind of education based on boarding schools and the collegiate university, have worked out different ways of life. Finally, separate methods of holding and using land—there is much less 'free-hold' property in Scotland than in England, and much more land 'in feu' from 'superiors' who have a considerable say in its development—have had different effects in forms of settlement, the location of industry, and the organisation of trade.

In Ireland there are also appreciable differences between north and south, in spite of the fact that there is not the nice coincidence between physical and political frontiers. True a broad belt of drumlins and other glacial hills does lie between the two, but it is the different political orientation rather than any physical divide that has come to count. The border—not unlike the Iron Curtain between West and East Germany—has been made increasingly effective, because of different policies of national affiliation, land use, development, and trade. The practice of Northern Ireland has been to strengthen the natural, cultural, and economic ties with Britain, thus separating itself from the South.

Those ties are strong. From early post-glacial times when northern Ireland was actually joined with Scotland, it has had as close links with its northern as with its southern neighbour. As Freeman (1959, pp. 46-7) has shown, structurally, economically, and socially the core of northern Ireland is an extension of the Midland Valley of Scotland. The two became inextricably linked with the Scotch Plantation in Ulster, bringing an aggressive Protestantism, and Anglo-Scots ideas and systems of land-holding from southwest Scotland to northeast Ireland. Later coal from Ayrshire and steelplate from Clydeside and Barrow became the basis for the great ship-building industry of Belfast. Strong economic attachments also came to be made with the industrial areas of Lancashire. Generally, Northern Ireland has given much greater stress to industry than Southern Ireland, and is more developed and more densely settled for its size.

Cultural differences have been widened by recent events. The North still has a Protestant majority, in spite of the 'revenge of the cradle' by which the Romanist minority is striking back; the South has an insignificant Protestant minority—indeed, compared with Britain it has an all-but 'monolithic' structure; the North has eschewed the revival of Erse attempted (though without much success) in the South, and educationally northern schools and Queen's University are linked up more closely with those in Britain than in Eire.

Cultural forces help to explain the astonishing survival of Wales which, in spite of being open to a much larger neighbour in England, is independent in many aspects. The strong Celtic renaissance in Wales has strengthened the Celtic core of the country, a core which has a very real existence as Bowen (1959, p. 5) has shown, protected as it is by mountain fastnesses, and looking out to the Atlantic fringe. True, the northeastern and southern industrial areas are closely integrated with neighbouring ones in England, and the English tongue and Wesleyan faith have made deep inroads into the life of the land; nevertheless there is a *felt* identity, which most surely separates off the principality, and which must, therefore, be taken into account in measuring geographical individuality.

All this being the case, it may be asked how Britain as a whole can be treated as an entity?

The answer is that all its parts, however much they differ from each other, also share something with each other, in sharing major aspects of the whole of the British Isles. No one part is different enough to be free of the problems or to be lacking in the opportunities experienced by all the parts together, joined into the British Isles. Each has its own image yet, in a surprising way, each bears the image of the other. Their individuality as parts cannot obscure the part they play in expressing the individual character of Britain as a whole.

In the first place, they share with it the destiny of belonging to a group of islands. Now islands are, in general, more clearly marked than other regions and, with their defining seas, tend to develop distinctive traits, not masked by the transition zones that so often lie between areas on a continent. Where Russia begins and ends has baffled the Russians themselves who, having few natural frontiers, have had to furnish their own. Germany, too, with no definable metes and bounds, has had to probe to the west or drive to the east in search of its ultimate sphere. Britain, however, has had a distinct and distinguishing front, which has helped it, and each of its constituent parts, to achieve a unique sense of identity. One knows where Britain begins and ends. Scotland, Wales, and the two Irelands also have a clear idea of their spheres, on all but one frontier at least.

Insularity is thus at the basis of British individuality—so much so that many British scarcely have the sense of being European, and it is now taking a great adjustment on their part to think in European terms. In common parlance, to cross to the continental mainland is to 'go to Europe', as much as to cross the Atlantic is to 'go to America'. Ever since Shakespeare gave expression to the feeling, the British have believed themselves fortunate in being

> This fortress built by Nature for herself
> Against infection and the hand of war;
> This happy breed of men, this little world;
> This precious stone set in the silver sea
> Which serves it in the office of a wall,
> Or as a moat defensive to a house,
> Against the envy of less happier lands.

Such insularity doubtless cuts Britain, and its constituent parts, off from many of the advantages as well as disadvantages of life on the mainland, and it was slow to receive the benefits of Rome, the blessings of Christianity, or the burgeoning of the Renaissance. Yet this gave it time to test and absorb the best from the continent and allowed it, meanwhile, to mature more evenly.

Indeed, in this last respect, insularity was to be a source of strength. Once people and ideas came to Britain they were compelled to come to terms with each other, and they were able to do so largely because they were not interrupted by frequent interference from outsiders such as often held back the growth of unity on the mainland. Britain thus became 'the tight little isle', free to develop on its own, in its own way. Consequently, it was able to knit the larger part of the archipelago into a truly united kingdom where diversity contributed to unity, and where all its parts were brought together in a highly integrated manner of life.

Insularity was not to mean parochialism, however; for, as Sir Halford Mackinder (1902, p. 11) has pointed out, it went along with universality. Seas do not only cut off, they open out. Britain may have been at the end of the road from the continental viewpoint, but it was at the opening of the Atlantic and the oceans of the world. Time changed the character of the English moat, making the surrounding waters not a means of defence so much as a vehicle of expansion, and Britain carried its trade, its missionaries, its colonisers, and its flag to the four quarters of the earth.

This soon involved Britain, and all its member countries, in the world's business, and it discovered in the words of John Donne that insularity could not mean isolation. 'Every man is a piece of the continent, a part of the maine (ocean). If a clod be washed away by the sea, Europe is less—as well as if a promontory were. Any man's death diminishes me, because I am involved in Mankind. And therefore never send to know for whom the bell tolls: it tolls for thee!'

Of few people could these words be more apt than of the British, since they have now become one of the most completely 'involved' nations in the world, deeply implicated in what happens in lands bordering on the Atlantic, Indian, and Pacific oceans. This is, today, an essential feature of Britain's character, and may be seen throughout its landscape. In the centre of London is a Parliament, having fostered similar great institutions in Canada, Australia, and New Zealand, in India, Pakistan, Ceylon, and Malaya, in West, East, and Central Africa, and in the West Indies; and one is not surprised to find, almost under the shadow of Westminster tower, the great 'Houses' of the Commonwealth clustered together.

Yet it is not only in London, but in every part of the country, that one has the sense of the universality of the life and experience of Britain. In fact, the extensions of British power gave exceptional scope for the people of Scotland, Wales, and Ireland, often with only the most limited opportunities in their own country, to find a new horizon abroad. In this they were greatly enriched by what happened to the Islands as a whole; and so in every major seaport are mementoes of those who ventured forth with the Hudson's Bay or the East India or the United Africa companies; while in almost every village (could this be said of any other country in the world?) stand the memorials of those who lost their lives in the seven seas and on the seven continents. As Housman put it so eloquently

It dawns in Asia, tombstones show,
  And Shropshire names are read;
And the Nile spills his overflow
  Beside the Severn's dead.

Actually, although this universal aspect of Britain's character has only been developed in the last three and a half centuries, there has always been an embracive element in Britain's life, which has made it representative of much beyond its own borders. Britain was not just the end of the road for Europe; it was a great road-meeting, where European lines of development met and linked. Here the Mediterranean road west, up through Iberia or the south of France, crossed the central European way west, the German 'hellweg', that line of westward-drifting folk that followed the löss from the Ukraine to the English channel along the foothills of Hercynean Europe; and here, too, the northern path to the west from Scandinavia across the North Sea to Britain's eastern coasts and northern and western isles converged on the earlier trails.

Britain was Europe's first America. It was the beckoning frontier,

5

it was the second chance, it was the last refuge to hundreds and thousands of adventurers, homesteaders, and refugees from Europe over hundreds and indeed thousands of years. Horace Greeley's advice 'Go West, young man' was almost as appropriate for Europe up to medieval times as for America in modern times; it could well have been used by prophets among mesolithic hunters and neolithic farmers, iron-age herdsmen, and dark-age seafarers, urging the dispirited or encouraging the adventuresome of the Mediterranean, the North European plain, and the Baltic to find a new lease on life in the British hesperides.

There is a sense in which the whole of at least western Europe funnels into the British Isles. The lines of its major structures, the trends of relief and drainage, the migrations of many of its plants and animals, and the movement of man and his ideas, are to a remarkable degree focussed on these Islands.

With the exception of the Fenno-Scandian shield, the main structures of Europe continue westward into the British Isles. The great north plain of Europe, though interrupted by the North Sea, re-appears in the lowlands of eastern England. North of it are the rounded worn-down remnants of the Scandinavian mountains, split by rift valleys, which are continued through the Caledonian ranges and troughs of Scotland, northern England, north Wales, and northern Ireland. The warped and much-faulted uplands of Hercynean Europe are continued in the swell of the Pennines, in the plateau of south Wales, and the southern heights of Ireland; while farther south, the Alpine trend of folding is carried west in what Wooldridge (1939, pp. 15-35) calls the Alps of England, a series of flexures which, though insignificant beside their continental counterparts, have notably affected the pattern of drainage and settlement. Indeed, all these structures have been effective in guiding settlers to Britain, making it a focus of folk wanderings. Moreover, each structure has affected more than one of Britain's component parts, and thus has involved the individual regions in the fortunes of the whole.

· In this, the coasts have also helped, since many of the coasts of Europe lead to and are repeated in the British Isles, or their several parts. The fjords of Norway, running from the heart of the mountains to off-shore skerries and the deep Atlantic swell, are found farther west in the much-indented shores of Scotland and northern Ireland. The 'ria' coasts of Spain or Brittany, with mountainous peninsulas thrusting out between sea-drowned valleys, are seen again in southern Wales and Ireland. The coast of recently-found-

6

ered estuaries and slowly sinking strands, sweeping through west Germany and Holland, reappears in the submerged river mouths and wide shallow bays of eastern England. The long lines of white chalk cliffs in Picardy are mirrored in the white cliffs of Kent. The first sight of Britain is so often the last sight of Europe, resurrected.

The seas that flow about her shores also bring Europe to her gates. The Baltic and Norwegian waters, co-mingling in the North Sea, have brought northern settlers, ideas, and trade. The Bay of Biscay and the English Channel have carried Iberian and French influences to west and south. Some of Europe's greatest rivers like the Seine, Meuse, Rhine, and Elbe are matched across narrowing seas by British rivers widening into estuaries at Southampton, London, and Hull. Such connections have been of the greatest importance. As Trevelyan (1926, p.xxiii) writes, 'Britain has always owed her fortunes to the sea, and to the havens and rivers that from the earliest times opened her inland regions to what the sea might bring. Long before she aspired to rule the waves, she was herself their subject, for her destiny was continually being decided by the boat-crews which they floated to her shores.'

Once people landed, they found the texture of the ground in Britain very like that of western Europe. The northern and western parts were strewn with the glacial hills and sleughs so characteristic of northern Europe. Indeed the Scandinavian ice deflected the ice-streams that moved down from the Grampians. Meltwater channels in northern England were not as spectacular as the urstrom-täler of northern Germany, but their sinuous marshy courses must have struck a familiar note to Anglo-Saxon colonisers. Meanwhile the ice-free portions of the chalk scarps and clay vales in the south were very similar to those known by migrants from the Boulonnais or the Paris basin.

In the same way, northern and southern fauna and flora have long had their outposts in the British Isles, making some parts of the archipelago strikingly similar to the mainland. This, too, may have attracted settlers, or helped them to feel more at home once they were established. Arctic char have to this day a few relict communities in Scottish lochs, and the halibut, cod, haddock, and herring of Norden move well down the coasts of Britain and Ireland. There they come up against the hake, sole, mackerel, and pilchard of warmer, southerly waters. The seals that sport themselves off the Lofoten and Faroe Isles play about Hebridean shores; while periodically Portuguese 'men-of-war' invade the southern resorts, endangering bathing on the Cornish Riviera.

The annual migration of the birds in like manner brings to the Islands echoes of arctic and sub-tropical climes. In spring the skies creak with long skeins of geese flying north to their polar haunts; while the cuckoo and the nightingale fill the woods with their return from the south, reminding one of

Dance, and Provençal song, and sunburnt mirth.

Brought back, too, is 'the truant swallow, circleting the river to meet his mirrored winglets,' whose swift coming and so swift departure evoke a sweetness and a sorrow that are at the heart of the English summer.

The fact is, the British climate shows the most delicate adjustment between warmth and coolness—between southern and northern Europe. Although said to be temperate and equable, it is tempered by being balanced, as it were, on a razor's edge. A season of storms where the storm-tracks are a hundred to a hundred-and-fifty miles south of their usual course will lead to a preponderance of cold sectors over Britain and can bring a wretched, rainy, raw summer of sub-arctic weather; a shift of the storm-tracks by as much again north can usher in an all-but Mediterranean summer, where one warm wave after another drenches Britain with sun.

One result of this has been a changefulness of conditions that from time to time has challenged and stimulated men, calling forth frequent re-adjustments, both in Britain as a whole and in each of its parts. Although British people may count on avoiding extremes, they have to adjust themselves to repeated variations, and this may well be one of the factors behind their ability to adapt themselves to different circumstances, their knack of 'making do', their ingenuity and initiative, which have stood them in good stead in other vicissitudes than those of the weather!

In a climate so finely balanced, fairly small ranges of relief can make a great deal of difference in vegetation and soil. In Wales, north England, and Scotland from about 1,600 ft. (500 m.) up, one is in an all-but arctic realm, bare of trees save for the occasional stunted birch or wind-scythed pine, where cotton-grass moor and sphagnum moss abound, and where, on stonier ground frost polygons and stripes are found, not unlike the tundras of Norway and Iceland. True, forests once climbed higher than they do, but with their destruction by man, the balance was tipped in favour of bog, and a bleak arctic landscape became the result. Even where determined efforts have been made to reforest the uplands, the effect is still that of the *boreal* lands, with Sitka or Norwegian spruce or Norwegian larch marching in serried ranks from hill to hill.

By contrast, in sheltered lowlands in the south and west are relics of a warmer clime where, as Buchan pointed out, one may come upon vivid slopes of arbutus thickets as the moor falls to the sea. Here box and laurel, the sycamore and walnut are at home, while such exotics as oleander and the tulip-tree, veronica and wistaria, the vine and the fig, apricot and peach can all be raised, and in the sea-side parks elephant grass and palm lift up their foreign fronds on high.

It is not surprising, therefore, that people from many parts of Europe came to see a home from home in the British Isles and that this grew to be one of the most distinctive of British features. The fact that Mediterranean men must have found the southern plains and western coasts of Britain not unlike their previous haunts in France and Spain; or that Alpine men discovered in the beech and oak forests of eastern and central Britain conditions not unreminiscent of those along the Danube or Rhine; or that Nordic men came across peat haggs and mossy moors and pine-clad hills not dissimilar from Baltic heights or Scandinavian mountains—this fact undoubtedly helped the transfer of life and allegiance from continent to archipelago. In any case, Britain became the focus of fusion of Europe's chief racial streams, and out of the initial conflict and ultimate co-operation thus engendered, it came to possess a dynamism and a unity that are at the root of its character. There are few populations in Europe more diverse and yet whose elements are more evenly balanced than those of Britain. Again, in this respect what is true of the whole country, re-occurs in each of its parts; each has experienced invasions from the three main sources of European migration and settlement.

It was not only in ethnic fusion, however, that Britain found new strength and richness of character, it was also in the clash of cultures and their eventual adjustment to each other. The language people came to speak is shot through with Teutonic and Latin elements; the common speech is, perhaps, more basically German, the educated tongue significantly French. Here and there, especially in the west and northwest, it may have Celtic words incorporated into it, while in the north old Norse and in the east Danish usages survive; here is, indeed, a veritable cross-section of life from the Gulf of Lions to the North Cape. Welsh, Gaelic, and Erse still survive in hilly or remote areas along the Atlantic border, and although they are not powerful enough to divide the Islands, they add greatly to their variety.

Of even greater significance have been the religious differences

9

that stamp the Isles with such diverse characteristics. In the strong Roman Catholic affinity of southern Ireland, scarcely shaken even when the Dark Age plunged Britain back into paganism; in the equally strong Calvinist connections of northern Ireland and of Scotland, now the heart of the Presbyterian world; and in the episcopalian and congregational or 'independent' orders of Protestantism in England, where 'church' and 'chapel' vie with each other—the faith of the Islands reverberates with the chief claims of religious experience in western Europe. Once more, these claims and counter-claims are found in each of the member countries, tying them in with Britain as a whole.

In the same way, the common law of England, going back to Germanic origins, and the Roman law of Scotland, with Franco-Latin affinities, also testify to great European traditions lodged side by side in Britain. Indeed, as Graham Clark (1940, p. 2) writes, 'Hardly a major wave of civilisation has surged across Europe but sooner or later it has broken upon our shores.'

This is seen imprinted in the land itself, through the various systems of land tenure and settlement that lend such variety to the British scene, reflecting as they do Anglo-Saxon, Anglo-Norman, Celtic and Norse traditions. The Anglo-Norman manorial village predominates in rural England, lowland Wales, and eastern Scotland, with its manor house, its lord's demesne, its ancient strip-holdings whose rigs may still be seen corrugating many a field although the lands have long been consolidated into large tenant farms, and with its villages of farm workers and rural functionaries. Associated with it may be a number of free-hold farms, now growing in number as death-duties break up estates, and compel owners to sell off tenant farms to their occupiers.

In the west and north are many older survivals. The 'trevs' of Cornwall, representing small clusters of buildings which are more than a farm but less than a village, still cling to hill or sea-side cliff, to which they were pushed by the advent of the Saxon villages with their two- or three-field systems. In Wales (as for example in the Vale of Clwyd) the old clan system of 'sharelands' may yet be seen, by which the arable basis of the clan was divided among the chief and his heirs, and the clansmen received a 'rig' or two scattered among the open fields of the sharelands. However, as these units got divided up more and more, impoverished heirs sold out and, as Glanville Jones (1961, p. 4) points out, the arable land became consolidated under moneyed proprietors, not necessarily clan leaders and their relatives. This gave rise to 'relatively large well-consolidated, and thus *isolated*, farms,' and also to the Gallo-Norman manors and tenant farms of medieval and later times. Another significant trend was the division between bond-men, working the manorial demesnes, and the free-men, who continued to have rigs in the shareland.

Ireland also has its contrasts between what were once free and bond, but the main contrasts were perhaps between the wild-land or the sown. Earlier land-tenure systems stressed pastoral holdings, and a man's social status was measured in herdsman's terms—'He has the grass of 40 cows.' But later, as the arable tail came to wag the pastoral dog in Ireland, it was the unit of land that an ox-team could plough that grew to be important.

In Scotland, the plough-team unit also became significant, and has left its mark on many a field and rural lot. As Barrow (1962, p. 129) has said, it played a specially strong role in southeast Scotland, the ploughgate being the amount of land that a team of oxen might be expected to plough in any one year, and the oxgang being an eighth part of this. Although these units have gone, their names remain, indicating the importance of the Anglo-Saxon system. In the northwest, by contrast, the clan system persisted till the end of the eighteenth century, but its small holdings, connected with little hamlets or 'clachans' (with their cultivated rigs in large 'in-by' fields, and grazing lands in hilly 'out-by' fields), gave way during the highland clearances to large estates focussed on manor house and village. The crofting system, based on small individually-operated rented crofts, with little enclosed arable plots behind the houses going up to common grazing land on the hills, is an echo of the past, presenting long, strung-out clachans on the raised beaches of the west. In the outer Hebrides, non-aristocratic but usually substantial family settlements, asso- ciated with the suffix -stadir, and small holdings linked with the suffix -setr, show strong Norse influence, as do the vestigial signs of strip-holdings in Orkney and Shetland, where udal tenure ruled until the fifteenth century and left Norwegian relics in the landscape.

The fact that none of these various land systems is confined to any one part of the British Isles, but that, on the contrary, they are common in smaller or greater measure to each of them, has again strengthened the character of Britain as a whole, which has had to work out its modern system by striking a balance between these older ones. Although England is dominantly Anglo-Norman, it has its Celtic and Scandinavian affinities; the Celtic ways have remained operative longer in Wales, Ireland, and Scotland, but in each of these countries the Anglo-Norman tradition is also strong. Norse relics are present in Scotland, but likewise in northeast Ireland, and the Isle of Man. The blend is such as to create a characteristically British pattern, the parts contributing to the whole, yet the whole being more than just the sum of its parts.

Within these various systems of using the land the actual uses have created striking differences, from the deer 'forests' and sheep pastures of the high lands, through the commercial woodlands of the hill-slopes, to the cattle and sheep-rearing farms of the lower uplands and the stock-fattening farms of the fodder-rich lowlands; or again, from the dairying done in the more humid west to the cropping that is characteristic of the drier east. It often astonishes the visitor what sharp differences occur in British farming within such a very short space. Writing of the Vale of Blackmoor, lying in the downlands of Wessex, Hardy says: 'The traveller from the coast, after plodding northward for a score of miles over calcareous downs and corn-lands, is surprised and delighted to behold, extended like a map beneath him, a country differing absolutely from that which he has passed through. Behind him the hills are open, the sun blazes down upon fields so large as to give an unenclosed character to the landscape, the lanes are white, the hedges low and plashed, the atmosphere colourless. Here, in the valley, the world seems to be constructed upon a smaller and more delicate scale; the fields are mere paddocks, so reduced that from this height their hedgerows appear a network of dark green threads overspreading the paler green of the grass. Arable lands are few and limited; with but slight exceptions the prospect is a broad rich mass of grass and trees.'

Farm areas often appear still more individual by being the centres of unique breeds of cattle and sheep. British farming has a remarkable record for its number of local breeds, and, as Mead indicates more fully in a later chapter, these lend both a distinct character to their locality, and also a pattern to the Islands as a group.

As Stamp (1955, pp. 121-2) points out, 'Over a very large part of Britain each area has its characteristic breed of cattle (or sheep). In some cases the attachment to a particular district is extraordinarily strong. Thus over North Devon the sturdy Red Devons hold undisputed sway: it is possible to draw a sharp line across the country, to the south of which supremacy passes to the lighter-coloured South Horns. The curly coated broad white-faced Hereford cattle still dominate the rural scene in the county from which they take their name: similarly the Galloways seem almost to exclude other breeds in parts of Galloway. If the popular dairy breed the Ayrshire is now found in many parts of Britain it is still true to say that it reigns supreme in Ayrshire itself.' Names such as Aberdeen-Angus, Lincoln Red, Sussex, Guernsey and Jersey, famous in many cases far beyond the British Isles, are still redolent of the little areas in Britain that cradled them forth; while as for sheep, their roll call sounds like the geography of the chief scarps and uplands of the country. Swaledale and Rough Fell, Penistone and Wensleydale bespeak parts of the Pennines, Herdwicks are typical of the Lake District, Cheviots of the Scottish borders, and Clun or Radnor of the border hills of Wales; there are Southdown, Dorset Down, Hampshire Down, and Oxford Down, each of them from their own sward-covered cuestas; while the Leicesters and Lincolns of the eastern wolds, and the Devon Longwool and Dartmoors of the southwestern uplands likewise tell of the importance of local differences in the British scene.

Mining, industry, trade, and transportation have produced an even greater variety, from the heavy iron and steel industries of Margam, Sheffield, and Middlesbrough; the shipbuilding of the Clyde, Tyne, Mersey, and Belfast estuaries; the chemicals of Cheshire; cotton and engineering of Lancashire; woollens of Yorkshire; potteries of Staffordshire; motor-car manufacturing of the Midlands and the aircraft industry of Gloucester and Bristol; to the great variety of production in London—the British Isles show an almost unparalleled range of industrial activity.

Yet although variety is a marked feature of the British Isles, it has not been developed at the expense of unity, or, at any rate, interdependence. A major aspect of Britain's character is the unity which it has been able to achieve out of diversity. This has not been an easy thing to create, and the existence of the Irish Republic shows that unity can be precarious to the point of breaking down. Yet whether there was political union or not there has always been mutual dependence between the several parts of the Isles, diverse though they may have been. At almost every stage of their development and in each of their main sections, the British Isles have come up with 'core areas' around which some degree of integration has been reached.

In mesolithic times, the British 'Mediterranean' became the focus of life and settlement. Fisherfolk seeking sites on low raised beaches from which to catch shell-fish and do in-shore fishing swarmed along the mild western coasts of Cornwall, Wales, Man,

Ireland, and Scotland. Though widely scattered they were kept together by the waters of the Irish Sea. Later, in the tragic times of King Mark, Tristan, and Isolde, these western lands once again touched hands across the middle sea. In the same way, in the legends of Cuchulain, Fingal, and Deirdre of the Sorrows, both Ulster and Argyll were linked across what Dr Chadwick (1952, p. 106) has called the 'Celtic Pond'. Later still, at the height of the Norse invasion, the kingdom of Man and the Isles again awoke the unities latent in the British Mediterranean. Queen Elizabeth found this sea her chance to draw Ireland into the English sphere, while later yet, the closeness of Loch Ryan to Belfast Lough, of Southwest Scotland to Northeast Ireland, was the basis for the Ulster Plantation.

Meantime, another area had emerged as a centre of developments: this was the meeting place of the English scarp-lands, at Salisbury Plain. From here the Cotswolds and Chilterns ran away to the north, and the Wessex, Surrey, and Sussex Downs to the south and east. Along some of these downs, early Neolithic colonists moved into the country. Here the people of the bronze age developed the so-called Wessex culture. In the Middle Bronze Age 'was forged in Britain a native civilisation,' as Daniel (1952, p. 30) remarks, 'which is the first of our national glories. We see in it now not only the bronze tools and gold ornaments that survive, but also the magnificent ritual sites like Stonehenge and Avebury.' Set on the sweeping downs, these, in their awesome grandeur, were among Europe's greatest monuments. In the iron age that succeeded, downland sites were again important as seen in the many hill forts crowning the scarps and, more especially, in the figures of giant men and white horses cut into the side of the chalk. Thus the Heroic Age of British colonisation seized on the great natural routeways of the downs, and fanned out over the English plain in star-like patterns of movement. The chalkways dominated the British scene, villages emerged strung out along the spring line between chalk and clay, with farming above, and fowling and fishing below. In drier spells, settlement moved down towards the vales, in wetter periods it climbed up on to the chalk uplands, but its general pattern was the splay of the scarps.

As each new invasion crossed from the continent and felt its way along the downs, pushing farther west and north, it drove preceding people to the remoter shores, and so the lines of new advance over the English plain tended to cut across the older lines up the Irish Sea. Hence the seas, instead of continuing as a highway, became a hide-out; the Atlantic fringe grew into what Fox (1932, p. 88) has called the zone of survival, a refuge for lost people and lost causes. The English plain evolved, by contrast, as a zone of replacement, where new cultures succeeded to old. Part of the British nature has thus been to cling to the old, part to welcome the new; part to find a place for minor peoples and causes, and part to accept dominant strains and come to terms with rising forces. Again, since this had to be done in each country within the Isles, it strengthened the development of these traits in Britain as a whole.

The rising forces of the English plain, that is, of the *plain* itself, of the river terraces and later the river bottoms, began with the Belgic invaders, who with their broad-bladed, ox-drawn plough, the *caruca*, started to advance down the valley sides. Romanised cultivation continued the trend. Yet these early dwellers had come in among downland settlers and as Stamp (1955, p. 26) reminds us, 'the areas of closest village settlement and most intense agricultural activity were (still) over the chalklands of . . . Salisbury Plain and Cranborne Chase.' The main value of the English loamlands, bottoms, and fens, was left to Anglo-Saxon, Dane, and Norman to discover, who took over the great estuaries and river basins.

The most important of these soon became the Thames, opening out toward the continent, and with upper arms breaching the chalk, to reach to the heart of the country. London, at the first bridgeable site above the estuary and commanding a remarkable array of gaps through the chalk became, from Roman times, the outstanding centre of the lowlands. It thus displaced both the Irish Sea, core area of the early sea-board settlements, and also the Salisbury downs, centre of chalkland colonisation.

The new hub sent out wheel-like spokes of power that took in both chalkland and sea to embrace, at length, the whole of the Islands. The Romans saw that the extensions of power up the Thames to the Severn in the west or the Trent in the north, would divide the upland masses of Cornwall, Wales, and North England from each other and thus allow them to be encircled, isolated, overcome, and subordinated to the English plain. Considerably later the growth of Wessex to be the leading English kingdom led to the unification of Severn and Trent and the Southampton and London basins, eventually centred in London. The struggles that culminated in this triumph are often referred to as the Wars of the Hegemony; but it was not so much the hegemony of one English group over the others that was established, as the hegemony of the plain of England. The Normans saw this and, again using the gaps through the chalklands, they drove from the London basin to the lower Severn, to the Cheshire plain, and to the vale of York and so surrounded Wales and outflanked the Pennines.

It may seem surprising that they did not then move away from London, which is after all quite eccentric to the country as a whole, up to the Midlands and develop a site, the like of Birmingham, which would have been geographically more central. But although the Midlands were more central they were less suitable because of their ancient relict uplands and less fertile stretches of sandstone. Moreover, access to the continent was at least as important, if not more so, than accessibility from the rest of England. Thus London held its own, even after expansion had reached as far as the Irish Sea and the Normans stood at the gates of Ireland. The way in which the great English plain projects itself between Wales and the Lake District over to the central plain of Ireland led, almost inevitably, to the establishment of an English sphere of influence—the Pale, around Dublin—and the subsequent absorption of the neighbouring country. In the same way, the extension of the English plain up the plain of Lancastria and the Vale of York towards the Solway lowlands and the Scottish midlands, helped in the subjugation of Scotland. The fortunate historical circumstances which eventually led to a union of the English and Scottish crowns united those two lands. Later still, the establishment of the Protestant succession in Ireland at the Battle of the Boyne, permitted the Scottish Plantation in Ulster, by which people living in the Midland Valley of Scotland crossed the narrow waters to link up their fortunes with a similar landscape in the Belfast basin. The British Isles were united.

This was essentially through the westward and northward projection of the power of the English plain to the plains of Ireland and Scotland. Unity has come in the end to be a greater force than diversity; much more of the British Isles is united than divided. And basically this has been because there was a strong node in the British plain, and within that plain in the London basin, for the forces of unity to use and develop. Although diversity was enough to produce individual regions like Wales, Scotland, and Southern and Northern Ireland, it could not outweigh the unity given to the whole by the predominance of England. Even when Southern Ireland separated itself out politically, it still had to acknowledge the close ties that bound it to the progress and welfare of the Islands as a group. In this respect the Islands have been more fortunate than most parts of Western Europe where, with the exception of France, few areas have had the assistance of a single commanding structure to enable them to develop unity and strength.

The projection of English strength at last led altogether beyond Britain. This was almost to be expected since the same gaps that bypassed Cornwall, encircled Wales, and outflanked the Pennines, opened out beyond Severn mouth, the Mersey inlet, and the Firth of Clyde to the great reaches of the Atlantic; and so, once Europe took to the oceans, the main line of British expansion led to North America, the West Indies, and West Africa. The exploitation of the English plain meant, in the hands of an aggressive and adventurous people, the penetration of plains oversea, and the beginnings of the British Empire.

The move into the Atlantic world greatly helped the development of the western ports, and advanced places like Bristol, Cardiff, Liverpool, and Glasgow. Yet it did not displace the east because trade with Europe increased at the same time. All the European seaboard nations were becoming great traders and, while they sought expansion through colonies dominated by the operation of the Mercantilist Policy, they did more than simply import raw materials from and export manufactured goods to their growing empires; they traded with each other—often in empire goods, but also in home-grown and home-made products. London became an exchange centre for the whole west coast of Europe, and held its own in the empire trade in addition.

And it continued to hold its own even after the industrial revolution, based on coal and iron, worked a transformation in the country and led to the rise of the Midlands, of Lancashire and Yorkshire, of Northumberland and Durham, of central Scotland, and of south Wales as active and populous areas. By this time London was well entrenched, and much of the development of the coal-based areas was instigated from London, or integrated by London, and therefore increased London's importance as the nerve-centre of finance and commerce. A great upsurge of manufacturing began in London itself to make the metropolis, in time, Britain's chief industrial centre. Consequently, London has continued to exert its central and centralising influence.

The migration to the coalfields has been, of course, one of the outstanding features of Britain, and early saw the decline of the iron industry in the Forest of Dean, and of the woollen industry in Gloucestershire and Norfolk, in favour of Sheffield, and the textile towns of the West Riding of Yorkshire. Gradually the north came to vie with the south, and Blake's 'dark satanic mills' grew to replace 'England's green and pleasant land'. But there was not as much of a break as has often been imagined. What happened was a pulling-out of south to north rather than a displacement of south by north. Today, the south is once more coming into its own. The coal mines of the shallower parts of the northern coalfields are being abandoned. Northern textiles, especially Lancashire cottons, are being cut down. Northern people are drifting south, ard there is a major swing of the population towards London. The result is that Manchester and Liverpool, Leeds and Sheffield have been drawn, along with Birmingham, into a great industrial complex, now centred on London, which really 'carries' the country, creating a huge Y-shaped area packed with roads, railways, factories, and cities that links northwest, northeast, and south together in a new and massive way.

Without the ability of the London 'core' to link together the other parts of England, and the parts of Wales, Ireland, and Scotland so intimately connected with England, it is doubtful whether a truly British way of life and identity would have arisen in the British Isles. The peripheral forces might have been too much for the magnetism of the centre. But that magnetism has grown with each period, and has drawn all parts of the British Isles to it, in one manner or another. In this, it has drawn into itself many Scottish, Welsh, and Irish, North of England, Midland, or West Country traits, making Britain much the stronger for the strength of its individual regions; but at the same time it has been able to impose the image of the greater Britain on all the lesser Britains, and so to create a truly British individuality.

Thus stage by stage, the seizure of the continental coign of Britain, the mastery of its interlocking plains, the encirclement of the uplands, the use of the Atlantic approaches, and the integration of all these round the great node of London, saw the rise of a centralising power in the British Isles that came to link and cement together most of its parts, making something distinctive out of Britain as a whole. It became at one and the same time a European, an independent, and a world reality. Embracing much of the life and experience of a continent which, in western Europe, was focussed on Britain; insular enough to be free from repeated outside attack and to be left alone to work out its own destiny, yet destined through its seas to find universal contacts that involved it deeply in world affairs; enriched by a great variety of landscapes and cultures, and yet strengthened by certain basic and prevailing unities, Britain has slowly but firmly built up a definite character

18

of its own, which, although it has changed with time and progress, has always gone back to the same and abiding geographical verities.

References

BARROW, G. W. S., 1962. Rural Settlement in Central and Eastern Scotland, *Scot. Stud.*, **6**, 2, 123-44.
BOWEN, E. G., 1959. Le Pays de Galles, *Trans. Inst. Brit. Geogr.*, No. 26, 1-24.
CHADWICK, N. K., 1952. The Celtic West, in *The Heritage of Early Britain* (ed. KNOWLES, M. D.), London, 104-127.
CLARK, J. G. D., 1940. *Prehistoric England*, London.
DANIEL, G. E., 1952. The Peoples of Prehistoric Britain, in *The Heritage of Early Britain* (ed. KNOWLES, M. D.), London, 11-32.
FOX, C., 1932. *The Personality of Britain*, Cardiff.
FREEMAN, T. W., 1959. Two Landscapes—Southwest Scotland and Northeast Ireland, in *Geographical Essays* (ed. MILLER, R., and WATSON, J. W.), Edinburgh, 46-67.
JONES, G. R. J., 1961. The Evolution of Rural Settlement in Wales, in *Records of Symposium on Rural Settlement*, School of Scottish Studies, Edinburgh, 1-19.
MACKINDER, H. J., 1902. *Britain and the British Seas*, London.
STAMP, L. D., 1955. *Man and the Land*, London.
TREVELYAN, G. M., 1926. *History of England*, London.
WOOLDRIDGE, S. W. and LINTON, D. L., 1939. *Structure, Surface and Drainage in South-east England*, Pubn. No. 10, Inst. Brit. Geogr., London.

2

BRITISH GEOGRAPHERS AND THE GEOGRAPHY
OF BRITAIN

THE twentieth-century geographers of Britain have drawn upon a fund of interest in the British Isles created by map makers, compilers of gazetteers, essayists and others from earlier centuries. However, the development of a truly geographical interest awaited the recognition of what H. J. Mackinder called 'the new geography' and about which he lectured to the Royal Geographical Society in January 1887 under the title 'On the scope and methods of geography.' Shortly afterwards he was appointed to a Readership in Geography in the University of Oxford, and the subject was recognised in Cambridge too. The modern period in the development of geography as a subject fit to be taught in the universities of Britain had begun, and new developments, leading in many different directions, were soon to be seen. Some of these were especially concerned with the quest for a better understanding of Britain by British geographers, and have borne fruit during the twentieth century.

In 1896 H. R. Mill proposed a scheme for a geographical description of the United Kingdom, based on the maps of the Ordnance Survey, and consisting of a separate memoir for every sheet of the map on the scale of one inch to a mile. Four years later he expressed the hope that eventually a series of similar memoirs—400 in all—would be produced and then 'combined and condensed to form a handbook of the geography of the British islands as a whole' (Mill, 1896).

In 1902 two books of great importance appeared. One, Lord Avebury's *The scenery of England and the causes to which it is due*, had affinities with volumes published by A. Geikie and D. Mackintosh a generation earlier. The other was Mackinder's *Britain and the British Seas*, in the series 'The Regions of the World' that he himself edited; three-quarters of the book is concerned with systematic geography under chapter headings such as 'the submarine platform', 'the uplands and lowlands', 'the physical history of Britain', 'British weather', 'racial geography', 'historical geography' and 'economic geography'. The relatively brief, essentially regional portion is that section that seeks 'to obtain the full effect of the composite environment . . . as exhibited in the topography of the several divisions of the country': and four chapters discuss Scotland, Ireland, southeastern England and northwestern England (including Wales).

The volume was well received, Mill welcoming it 'with a pleasure enhanced by anticipation and not diminished by perusal'. Thirty years after its publication the writers of another geographical work on the British Isles referred to Mackinder's book as 'a landmark in the progress of thought in the country' (Stamp and Beaver, 1933, p. 1); and S. W. Wooldridge (1950, p. 9) paid tribute to 'Mackinder's brilliant sketch,' noting that 'there is hardly a chapter of that inspired and germinal book which has not been the subject of notable development and expansion in first-class specialist studies.'

Mackinder in a 'note on authorities' refers to four 'among the numerous general descriptions of the British Isles' but significantly only one of the four, G. G. Chisholm, was British. Geographers were but few, and some believed, with P. M. Roxby, that 'the geographer's parish must indeed be the world.' There was not, however, a complete lack of geographical publication concerned with Britain, though the authors were not always professional geographers. A. D. Hall and E. J. Russell's *Agriculture and soils of Kent, Surrey and Sussex* (1911), the work of two soil scientists, was described some years later by a geographer as 'one of the best geographical studies in southeastern England' (Ormsby, 1928, p. 483). In the same year O. J. R. Howarth's *A geography of Ireland* was published, and of several important papers appearing at this time Roxby's study of the historical geography of East Anglia (1908-09) has become a classic of British regional geography. Roxby (1913-14) went further and argued the case for a full survey of the agricultural geography of England on a regional basis. There was in fact at this time considerable fieldwork activity at both undergraduate and post-graduate levels with the increasing number of students taking courses in geography, notably those reading for the Diploma in Geography in the University of Oxford.[1] Of dissertations undertaken at this period and later published special note may be taken of that concerned with the one-inch sheet of the Andover district by O. G. S. Crawford (1914), a classicist who turned to geography and whose subsequent career in the Ordnance Survey as Archaeology Officer added so much to the geographical

[1]It should be noted that there were no Honours Schools of Geography in Britain until they were established in the University of Liverpool in 1917 and in the University College of Wales, Aberystwyth, shortly afterwards.

knowledge of the prehistory and early history of the British Isles. Yet despite these manifestations of the work of British geographers it must be noted that the volume on the British Isles in the six-volumed *Oxford survey of the British Empire*, edited by A. J. Herbertson and O. J. R. Howarth and published in 1914, was written largely by contributors whose training had not been in the field of geography.

During the First World War many geographers became members of the armed forces or were attached to the Intelligence Division of the Naval Staff, but, while most of their work was on regions outside Britain, the geography of Britain was not neglected. Considerable thought was given, for example, to the undertaking of regional surveys, while C. B. Fawcett made a valuable contribution to the thinking about the post-war organisation of local government in a paper, 'Natural divisions of England', published in 1917 and subsequently expanded into a book, *Provinces of England* (1919): of this book a reviewer (*Geogr. J.*, 1920, **55,** p. 318) suggested that it was 'apart from its purpose . . . of more use as a text-book of English geography than some which make the claim', and forty years later it was re-issued, with a new introduction, because of its continued relevance to current problems of the regional division of Britain.

In the decade immediately following 1918 there were rapid developments in geography in many British universities. Noteworthy publications of this period included Ll. Rodwell Jones's *North England : an economic geography* (1921), and in the same series J. Bygott's *Eastern England* (1923); L. B. Cundall and T. Landman's *Wales: an economic geography* (1925); and H. R. Ormsby's *London on the Thames* (1924). But the first substantial work dealing with the whole of the British Isles to appear after the First World War was—perhaps significantly—the work not of a British, but a French, geographer, A. Demangeon, whose volume on Britain, *Les Iles Britanniques* (1927), was the first of the great *Géographie Universelle* series. The full effect of this work was not felt until its translation by E. D. Laborde twelve years later (Demangeon, 1939), by which time conditions had changed considerably and several comprehensive geographical works on Britain had been published.

The next major step forward was associated with the holding of the twelfth International Geographical Congress in Britain in 1928. Just as the Congress of 1964 has been responsible for stimulating the compilation of the present volume, the work of 23 university geographers, so the holding of the 1928 Congress in Britain challenged British geographers to produce *Great Britain: essays in regional geography*, edited by A. G. Ogilvie, and written by twenty-six authors. A 'Joint Regional Studies Committee' of the British National Committee for Geography was formed under the chairmanship of Sir John Russell. The editor explained how, with an increase in Departments of Geography from three in 1902 (when Mackinder's book was published) to twenty-seven in 1927— and with a regional spread extending from Exeter in southwestern England to Aberdeen in northeastern Scotland—it seemed possible to prepare 'a new composite volume . . . dealing with Great Britain region by region, . . . thus permitting the expression of local characteristics'. The success of the work was immediate and its value for many years increased, rather than diminished, with the passage of time. A reviewer (*Geogr. J.*, 1930, **75**, 266) described it as 'a valuable and authoritative work, since each author, being familiar with his assigned district, can describe it with a fullness and confidence that no single writer could provide for the whole island.' There is indeed the widest variety of approach and treatment. A recent comment on this diverse group of essays in the preface of another collection of geographical essays on Great Britain (Mitchell, 1962, p. xi) may serve as the considered judgment of British geographers more than a third of a century after the first publication of the Ogilvie volume: it 'stands enduring, a testimony to the Britain and to the geographers of its period.'

Much of the research undertaken in Britain during the last three decades has sprung from the ideas expressed and the problems posed by the twenty-six authors of 1928. The period immediately following the Congress was marked by a new awareness by geographers of the relevance of parts of their work to Britain's social and economic problems, especially during the years of depression that affected Britain along with most other parts of the world from about 1930 onwards. Thus some geographers began to attempt a national survey, 'to take stock of the natural resources of the British Isles, and show broadly what use has been made of those resources in the past, and to analyse the present position' (Stamp and Beaver, 1933). Such was the beginning of what became the Land Utilisation Survey of Britain (Stamp, 1950). The Ordnance Survey had already issued an *Agricultural Atlas of England and Wales* and a second edition was published in 1932, shortly after the preparation by geographers of the atlases for Scotland and Ireland. Then in 1933 there appeared the first edition of a work now in its 10th edition, *The British Isles: a geographic and economic survey*, by L. D. Stamp and S. H. Beaver. 'Again and again', the preface notes (p. ix), 'one gets a glimpse of vast home resources as yet but little utilised, or capable of much more intense utilisation . . . But the future is fraught with possibilities of progress.' In these words of introduction one is given a highly significant comment on the outlook of some British geographers towards the geography of their country at a time of economic difficulty when Britain had not yet, in their own words, 'emerged from the Great Depression' (Stamp and Beaver, 2nd. ed., 1937, p. vii).

C. B. Fawcett (1934) described the book as 'perhaps the most important work on the geography of these islands published since the War . . . Almost every one of the thirty-five chapters would be expanded into a large volume if the survey became exhaustive'. In complete contrast to *Great Britain: essays in regional geography*, most of the chapters adopted a systematic approach. There were in addition chapters on the agricultural regions of Scotland and of England and Wales as well as accounts of London and (in more recent editions) of the Irish Republic and of Northern Ireland. That this work has continued to be so widely used during the thirty years of its existence is a testimony to the need for, and value of, such a survey which clearly filled a notable gap in British geographical literature.

The publication of this volume on the British Isles coincided—quite fortuitously—with another significant event in the history of British geography, the foundation of the Institute of British Geographers. The early history of the Institute was largely concerned with the need for more outlets for the publication of the research done by professional geographers in Britain, much of it about their own country (Buchanan, 1954); but in its pre-war publications—restricted to monographs—only L. E. Tavener's *Land classification in Dorset* (1937) and S. W. Wooldridge and D. L. Linton's *Structure, surface and drainage in south-east England* (1939) were specifically concerned with parts of Britain. After the war, however, the publication policy was radically altered 'to include publication of shorter papers, and particularly papers read at its own meetings' (*I.B.G. Trans.*, 1946, **11**, p. viii); in consequence the Institute has issued many research papers, a high proportion of them devoted to topics concerned with, or illustrated by, the geography of the British Isles, particularly of England and Wales (Steel, 1961). Perhaps no one body has done more to stimulate and, in some measure, to co-ordinate geographical research in Britain than the Institute, and certainly no journal has published more of the original work done by British geographers on Britain as a whole during the past three decades, notably since 1946 when the publication of its *Transactions and Papers* was resumed. A high proportion of the work on Scotland, however, continues to appear in the *Scottish Geographical Magazine*, and on Ireland in *Irish Geography*, while some journals with regional interest have been started in recent years, such as the *East Midland Geographer*. Much research work on the British Isles has also been published by the Royal Geographical Society in its *Geographical Journal*, the mother of British geographical publications, and, especially since the Second World War, by the Geographical Association in its journal, *Geography*.

The period of the Institute of British Geographers' existence has coincided with a quite remarkable growth of the subject in Britain which has been marked by developments in universities, training colleges and schools—as well as in other directions—that are so varied it is by no means easy to trace the different strands by which British geographers have helped to extend the knowledge of their own country. In the years immediately before the war more and more departments of geography were established in the various universities and most of them proceeded to investigate the main geographical features of their local areas while at the same time their students were introduced to the study of the subject in the field. Besides these activities, which added very considerably to the knowledge of the geography of Britain as recorded in the Congress volume of 1928, British geographers can, in retrospect, be seen to have been particularly concerned with three main branches of the subject—economic geography (and in particular the Land Utilisation Survey of Britain), historical geography, and physical geography (especially geomorphology); while shortly before the war there was a growing interest in the relations of geography to national and regional planning. Developments in some of these fields are traced and documented in the present volume, and detailed analysis is, therefore, unnecessary here.

Economic Geography

The Land Utilisation Survey of Britain was established in 1930 at a time when great changes were occurring in British agriculture and when much farm land was being taken over for other uses. Its objective has been described by L. D. Stamp, its founder and Director, as 'a national stock-taking of land resources, using the methods familiar to all geographers, relying essentially on field work and direct observation. The immediate aim . . . was to record the then existing use of every acre of England, Wales and Scotland' (Stamp, 1951, p. 374). The whole of the field work was carried out by unpaid volunteers, mostly geographers, and drawn almost entirely from universities, colleges, and schools: most of it was completed between 1931 and 1933. The first two sheets at a scale of one inch to a mile were issued early in 1933 and publication went on steadily until the whole of England and Wales had been covered in 140 sheets: for Scotland one-inch sheets were published only for the more populous parts. Information covering the whole of Great Britain was placed on two sheets on the scale of 1 : 625,000 (about ten miles to one inch) which were published in 1941.

In addition ninety-two reports, nearly all written by geographers, were produced between 1937 and 1947 under the title of *The Land of Britain*. It was 'under [E. C. Willatts's] eagle eye and able guidance [that] the bulk of the Survey's work was done' (Stamp, 1948, p. 450), but the credit must at least equally be given to Professor Stamp who subsequently played a great part in stimulating the Commission of the International Geographical Union to propose a World Land Use Survey which draws heavily upon British experience. Apart from the value of the Survey in terms of national planning the contribution that it made to the understanding of the agricultural geography of Britain is incalculable, and it is significant that in the 'sixties a second land-use survey of Britain is at present in progress (Coleman, 1961).

The industrial geography of Britain also received some attention from British geographers, notably from those working in London and in the civic universities in the industrial parts of the country. A. Wilmore's survey (1930) was of a general nature, and much fuller detail was given in the relevant chapters of Stamp and Beaver's book. Some carried out research in connection with development programmes prepared for areas particularly hit by depression and unemployment during the 'thirties: G. H. J. Daysh's work with the Cumberland Development Council and the North-East Development Board is a particular example of this type of activity.

Mention must, however, be made here of one of what a reviewer (*Geogr. J.*, 1949, **114**, 203) called the sadly limited number of outstanding books on our geography, W. Smith's *An economic geography of Great Britain*. This work, though not published until after the war, was 'the product of many year's inquiry and research' (Smith, 1949, p.v.) and drew the lineaments of the economic geography of Great Britain . . . on the eve of the late war'; but data from later years were added 'wherever available and, in relation to the theme of the work, whenever significant' (p. xv). Smith did not claim, even for the pre-war years, 'to paint a complete picture of the economic geography of Great Britain'. 'A single individual,' he wrote 'cannot be equally familiar with the whole of such a complex panorama' (p. v). After a decade and a half his study of the antecedents of the present economic geography followed by a systematic analysis of conditions in agriculture, industry, transport and trade remains a standard authority in this field despite the tremendous economic changes in the years since the book first appeared.

Historical Geography

Work in historical geography is especially associated with H. C. Darby, who was the editor of the fourteen studies (and author of two) that appeared in 1936 as *An historical geography of England before A.D. 1800*: all the contributors except Eilert Ekwall of Sweden were members of departments of geography in British universities. The preface speaks of 'the reconstruction of past geographies' and of 'a sequence of cross-sections taken at successive periods', though the editor himself in a more recent paper (Darby, 1960, p. 149) has suggested that 'some chapters are concerned not so much with cross-sections as with the events and developments that produced changes—the Anglo-Saxon settlement, the Scandinavian settlement, the draining of the Fens, the growth . . . of London'. The volume stimulated a great deal of further work, the amount of which is suggested by the extensive documentation accompanying Darby's reflections on the book after more than twenty years (Darby, 1960, pp. 156-9). Among the contributors to the volume the publications of E. G. R. Taylor, J. N. L. Baker, and Darby call for particular mention: Taylor's for her knowledge of British geography and geographers of earlier periods (Taylor, 1930, 1934); Baker's for the light he has shed on the progress of geography in recent centuries and on the special contributions of particular British geographers (e.g. Baker, 1948, 1955, 1963); and Darby's both for his studies of the English Fenland (Darby, 1940a, 1940b) and for his painstaking extraction and analysis, with the help of many colleagues, of the geographical evidence of the Domesday Book. The results of this work are appearing in a series of six volumes of which four have so far been published (Darby, 1952; Darby and Terrett, 1954; Darby and Campbell, 1962; Darby and

Maxwell, 1962). Thus although, in Darby's own words (1960, p. 151), 'the end of the Domesday project is not yet in sight, . . . it is not far below the horizon'.

Other geographers have made important contributions to the reconstruction and the understanding of the landscape of Britain at both earlier and later periods. There has, in particular, been a growing awareness of the significance of the late eighteenth century and the nineteenth century to the proper appreciation of the geographical conditions of the present century. This has resulted in some important publications based upon the Reports of the Board of Agriculture from 1793 onwards, the acreage returns of 1801, and other sources of agricultural data (e.g. Henderson, 1936, 1952; East, 1937; Thomas, 1959). In addition many of the County Reports of the Land Utilisation Survey have short but useful studies of agriculture at earlier periods. The successive census reports of Great Britain issued for each decennial census since 1801 (except for 1941) provide a wealth of material for geographical analysis, some of which has been published (e.g. Darby, 1943; C. T. Smith, 1951; Lawton, 1953). Recently there has also been an awakening of interest in the study of the remains of the Industrial Revolution—many of which are in danger of decay and loss—and geographers are collaborating in the study of what has been termed 'industrial archaeology' (E. R. R. Green, 1960; Lawton, 1962). Much historical geography of counties, individual settlements and small areas has also been published, either in semi-popular form (e.g. Balchin, 1954; Millward, 1955), or in geographical periodicals (cf. Steel, 1961, pp. 136-7), in journals that are not primarily for geographers, and in local historical periodicals.

Physical Geography

Many British geographers, as well as many workers in cognate fields such as geology, botany, and soil science, have contributed to a fuller understanding of the physical geography of the British Isles. In the field of climatology, for example, work has been developed from the data made available by the Meteorological Office and from earlier publications such as the *Rainfall Atlas of the British Isles*, published by the Royal Meteorological Society. Special mention may be made of the remarkable series of rainfall records collected from about 1860 for many places in Britain by the British Rainfall Organisation, a body of voluntary observers whose work was directed first by G. J. Symons and then by H. R. Mill until his retirement in 1919 when oversight of the work was assumed by the Meteorological Office: the Organisation's series of annual volumes of *British rainfall* are a mine of climatological information. A *Climatological Atlas of the British Isles* was published by the Stationery Office in 1952, and some of the special peculiarities of British weather conditions were studied in *British weather in maps* by J. A. Taylor and R. A. Yates (1958). Some of the aspects of applied climatology have been discussed by S. Gregory (1954) and in a number of interdisciplinary conferences held in recent years, and A. Garnett and others have made important contributions to the investigation of air pollution, especially in some industrial districts in England. Closely related to these studies is the concern shown by geographers such as Balchin and Gregory for the future water supplies of the country, again particularly in those areas where the industrial water demand is especially high. G. Manley's *Climate and the British scene* (1952) and other studies (e.g. 1959) throw much light on the variations of British climate during glacial and post-glacial times.

Geographers have not until recently followed up to any extent the lines of research suggested by A. G. Tansley (1911, 1926, 1939) whose works have long been recognised as the standard authorities for the study of ecology: since the war, however, more botanical work has been undertaken from a geographical point of view, and under the general title of biogeography—a term at least as old as Humboldt but of relatively recent usage in British geography—a growing number of university departments, as well as bodies like the Nature Conservancy and the Soil Surveys of England and Wales and of Scotland, are encouraging the geographical study of both vegetation and soils, employing amongst other things techniques such as that of pollen analysis (e.g. Oldfield, 1960).

It is, however, in the field of geomorphology that British physical geography has been strongest and most active and has produced such a large number of research workers. During the nineteenth century there was a traditional link between some branches of geology and geography, particularly physical geography, and the visit of W. M. Davis to Britain, which led to his famous paper of 1895 on 'The development of certain English rivers' in southeastern England (*Geogr. J.*, 1895, **5**, 127-46), has been said to have 'revived interest in British landforms, at the same time giving it a new direction' (Wooldridge, 1952, p. 297). The study of landforms was especially encouraged in those universities whose departments of geography had sprung from, or were particularly closely associated with, departments of geology, and between the wars considerable work was done in certain areas on physiographic evolution (Ogilvie, 1924), erosion surfaces and denudation chronology (Miller, 1935), coastal morphology (Steers, 1927), and drainage systems (Linton, 1932, 1933). The references given are to typical examples of the very considerable volume of literature published not only in recognised geographical periodicals but also in geological publications. In *Structure, surface and drainage in south-east England* (1939), Wooldridge and Linton stated a strong case for the prosecution of regional geomorphological studies which many of their own students, with numerous other geographers trained elsewhere, accepted and attempted to carry out during post-war years. Two valuable books covering broad fields and written by senior workers were published soon after the war: L. D. Stamp's *Britain's structure and scenery* (1946) and J. A. Steers' *The coastline of England and Wales* (1948). Useful contributions on smaller themes began to appear regularly in various journals which moved Wooldridge (1950, p. 10) to say, 'though the unitary geomorphology of Britain is yet to be written, I feel that I can safely promise that it will be written when I survey the very considerable efforts of our younger physiographers'. Perhaps E. H. Brown's *The relief and drainage of Wales* (1960) may be regarded as an important first instalment. In 1952 Wooldridge indicated in a survey of the changing physical landscape of Britain some of the special problems concerned with the formation of the essential elements of the landscape by subaerial and submarine agencies throughout Tertiary times. In subsequent years there has been an outpouring of geomorphological research papers: perhaps more papers on geomorphology have appeared than on any other branch of the subject in post-war years, the majority of them being concerned with parts of the British Isles. The relevant chapters in the present volume, by G. T. Warwick, D. L. Linton, and J. B. Sissons, with their bibliographical references, are adequate testimonies to the drive and enthusiasm of British geographers in the field of geomorphology.

Geographers and Planning

The proper interest of British geographers in the planning of their own country can be traced back to some of the works of Patrick Geddes, including *Cities in evolution* (1915) in which he proposed the use of the term 'conurbation' as 'an expression of the new form of population grouping' (pp. 14-15) and to the work of geographers like C. B. Fawcett (1917, 1919, 1921). Fawcett's (1932) study of aspects of the 1931 census continued earlier work and emphasised the tendencies towards increased urbanisation in Britain.

In 1937 a Royal Commission was appointed to inquire into the distribution of the industrial population of Great Britain (Cmd. 6153, 1940). To the work of this commission geographers made a considerable contribution. The Royal Geographical Society's memorandum included a considerable number of maps prepared by a group of geographers: seventeen of these maps and a memorandum were published in the *Geographical Journal* (1938, **92**, 22-39; 499-526). The memorandum argued strongly in favour of an official national atlas, similar to those published by many other countries: one that would represent a complete national stocktaking of the country's physical, economic, and social resources. Subsequently a committee of the British Association reported on its preliminary ideas, and 'plans for a national atlas' were discussed at a Royal Geographical Society meeting in December 1939 (Taylor, 1940). But no immediate action followed, partly because of the problems involved in such a large project, but more particularly because by then the Second World War had begun. British geographers were faced with other tasks, many of them outside their own country, though much of their pre-war interest in planning and mapping was reflected first in their war-time activities and later in the spurt of progress in the subject that marked the post-war period.

As in the First World War a large series of elaborately produced Geographical Handbooks was prepared by the Naval Intelligence Division of the Admiralty, but all the volumes were concerned with areas outside Britain. Nevertheless, some geographers were called upon to study aspects of their own country, notably in the interests of war-time organisation and in preparation for post-war planning. Shortly before the war E. W. Gilbert (1939) had argued the case for 'practical regionalism in England and Wales' suggesting that geographers should 'use all their endeavour to ensure that the foundations of the regional system of administration are co-ordinated on a good geographical basis'. The regional division of the country for Civil Defence purposes underlined the range and complexity of the regions recognised by a variety of official and non-official bodies, and was further discussed by a group of geographers in 1942 in the light of war-time experience (Taylor, 1942; see also Gilbert, 1948, 1951).

Of greater importance in the long-term was the participation by geographers, together with economists, sociologists and others, in numerous discussions and conferences concerned with the background to regional planning and the likely problems of post-war Britain. Most notable of all was Stamp's service as vice-chairman of Lord Justice Scott's Committee on Land Utilisation in Rural Areas [of England and Wales] (Cmd. *6378*, 1942). The report of the committee included three important maps—land classification, population changes between 1931 and 1938, and types of farming— and showed geographers 'that the principles for which they have so long fought are thus being . . . fully recognised' (Stamp, 1943, p. 20). Certainly it has been a document that has had considerable influence on the post-war planning of many parts of rural Britain.

Many geographers were associated with the Ministry of Town and Country Planning from its establishment in 1943, as research, regional planning, and maps officers as well as in other capacities. Thus it was this Ministry (and its successor, the Ministry of Housing and Local Government, set up in 1951) that started to publish the valuable series of maps of Britain, generally at the scale of 1 : 625,000 and covering the whole country in two sheets. Many of the maps, of which nearly thirty have so far been published, owe much to geographers, and particularly to E. C. Willatts, for many years Maps Officer at the Ministry. In many ways they constitute a national inventory in cartographic form, and their range is being further extended from time to time: some of the material has been incorporated in an *Atlas of Britain*, prepared under the guidance of an editorial board of geographers and published by the Oxford University Press in 1963.

Much of the work done by geographers in the field of war-time planning has never been published because of its detailed or confidential nature, though some papers on Scotland were published by A. G. Ogilvie (1944, 1945, 1946), and in a volume edited by G. H. J. Daysh (1949) there is a wealth of geographical data for certain areas of Great Britain written by geographers who had been planners during the war. There were also special investigations, some of which were completed or followed up after the war. Examples include Steers' detailed study of the 2,751 miles of coast in England and Wales (Steers, 1944, 1948) and S. H. Beaver's work on minerals and planning (Beaver, 1944). The latter was followed by studies of the problem of derelict land (West Midland Group, 1948) and of sand and gravel exploitation in the London basin (Wooldridge and Beaver, 1950), while more recently there have been investigations of subsidence problems in industrial areas (Wallwork, 1956, 1960).

There have also been numerous surveys prepared for planning

purposes where the participation of geographers has been notable: examples are Middlesbrough (Glass, 1948), Birmingham and the Black Country (West Midland Group, 1948), and Herefordshire (West Midland Group, 1946). The analysis of urban fields suggested by A. E. Smailes (1947) was developed in the Ministry of Town and Country Planning (Green, 1950) and in universities (Bracey, 1952, 1953), while more recently such analyses have been further elaborated and refined by geographically-trained officers. Here indeed there are branches of geographical study that have received continuous attention from the pre-war period through the war into the post-war years of Britain's recovery and rehabilitation. Buchanan's view (1954, p. 14) is that the enhanced reputation of the subject at the end of the war owed much to the recognition of geographers' contributions to the war effort. So today there is greater participation by geographers than ever before in the counsels of the nation. Geographers are serving as members of the National Parks Commission, the Nature Conservancy, and the Field Studies Council.

Miscellaneous

In keeping with the variety of the geography of Britain, British geography has shown amazing diversity as well as marked progress in many different directions during post-war years. There has been expansion in nearly every university, as well as a great extension of fieldwork, most of which is concentrated upon parts of Britain itself. In consequence a great amount of data is in course of collection, and geographers are now better able to appreciate the complexity of the areas in which they live and work. It is therefore of special interest to look at some of the publications in the regional field that have appeared since the end of the Second World War.

Just as in pre-war years the synoptic view of the British Isles taken by the French geographer Demangeon had preceded—and enriched—the British views of the same area later, so it was the two-volumed study of the whole of the British Isles *Die Landschaften der Britischen Inseln* by the Austrian geographer J. Sölch (1951, 1952) that first appeared in the immediate post-war period. This large work, with its remarkably comprehensive bibliography, is no generalised picture of the country as a whole. As one reviewer put it: ' . . . it has been the personalities of our little neighbourhood units that have captured his affectionate interest'. 'Probably few of us have done as much foot-sore geography in so many parts of Britain as did Sölch' (*Geography*, 1951, **11**, 269-70).

British geographers meanwhile were writing about smaller portions of their country. T. W. Freeman drew on his extensive first-hand knowledge and on the results of numerous student excursions in his *Ireland* (1950), a penetrating study revealing a sympathetic understanding and a geographical view of the complexity, charm, and problems of both Eire and Ulster. Nearly half of the book is concerned with the topical approach to Ireland as a whole: the remainder consists of chapters describing the twelve regions recognised by the author. Wales received rather different treatment from a team of geographers working under the editorship of E. G. Bowen (1957). As specialists in various fields, the contributors each wrote on a particular aspect of the geography of the Principality and then described one or more of the nine regions into which the country was divided.

In contrast, apart from one or two advanced school texts, no comprehensive works on Scotland alone and as an entity have appeared. There are, however, numerous papers on geographical conditions in Scotland, notably in the pages of the *Scottish Geographical Magazine*, which amplify important pre-war contributions such as those on agriculture by C. P. Snodgrass (1932, 1933) and those on coal-mining and population by P. R. Crowe (1927, 1929). Geographers have also participated in the *Third Statistical Account of Scotland*, now in preparation, and there have been three comprehensive British Association handbooks on large tracts of Scotland, all edited by geographers: A. G. Ogilvie's *Scientific survey of south-eastern Scotland* (1951), R. Miller and J. Tivy's *The Glasgow Region* (1958), and A. C. O'Dell and J. Mackintosh's *The Northeast of Scotland* (1963).

These last volumes were specially prepared for meetings of the British Association for the Advancement of Science and form part of a valuable series of regional handbooks. Before the Second World War a small booklet was prepared for most university and other towns where the Association held its annual meeting but the contribution of geographers was in most cases small, though there were some notable exceptions. The pattern for the enlargement and illustration of these volumes was set by the *Scientific survey of north-eastern England*, prepared for the Newcastle upon Tyne meeting in 1949 (Isaac and Allan, 1949). In subsequent years geographers have been responsible for the editing of the following volumes, in addition to the three for parts of Scotland already mentioned: Birmingham (Wise, 1950), Belfast (Evans, 1952), Liverpool (Smith, 1953), Oxford (Martin and Steel, 1954), and

Sheffield (Linton, 1956). Even in those volumes not produced under the guiding hand of a geographer-editor, there has been valuable geographical material, as in those prepared for the meetings held in Bristol (MacInnes and Whittard, 1955), York (Willmott, 1959), Cardiff (Rees, 1960), Norwich (Briers, 1961), and Manchester (Carter, 1962).

Another series designed to cover the whole country more evenly and more geographically is the 'Regions of Britain' series of fourteen volumes under the editorship of W. G. East, of which three volumes have so far been published: *North England* by A. E. Smailes (1960), *The Highlands and Islands of Scotland* by A. C. O'Dell and K. Walton (1962), and *The East Midlands and the Peak* by G. H. Dury (1963). Regional volumes in the 'New Naturalist' series by geographers include *The Weald* by S. W. Wooldridge and F. Goldring (1953) and *The Peak District* by K. C. Edwards and others (1962). Edwards is editing a series for the Geographical Association, 'British landscape through maps', in which geographical descriptions are given of selected Ordnance maps. The series, of which two or more are published each year, is unlikely ever to provide complete coverage for the whole country but it has already proved itself a most valuable way of encouraging geographers in training— in schools, training colleges, and universities—to study regional geography in the field in their own country.

There have also appeared two volumes on the whole of Great Britain, one (embracing Ireland as well) by a single author, the other a collection of essays by selected writers, all of them geographers. G. H. Dury, whose research work has been mainly in the field of geomorphology, has in *The British Isles: a systematic and regional geography* (1961) written about an area that is 'highly industrialised, intensively cultivated, and deeply committed to production for export'. *Great Britain: geographical essays* (1962), edited by J. B. Mitchell, is a large work of more than 600 pages, to which twenty-eight geographers have contributed. In the editor's words (p. xi) 'the essays . . . are very different in their themes; to impose uniformity would be to distort'; and because 'no claim is made that each is a geographical region, still less that the areas selected for study . . . are in any sense *the* geographical regions of Great Britain' (p. xi), there is no formal analysis of regional frontiers and sub-divisions, and no map showing the areas is printed. The editor stresses that it is not a new edition of the Ogilvie volume of 1928, though in its inception and general arrangement there are some obvious affinities.

The present volume, prepared by the British National Committee for Geography for the International Geographical Congress of 1964, is the latest, and perhaps the most ambitious, effort by British geographers to provide a geographical picture of their own country. In concept it differs markedly from the volume prepared for the last Congress held in Britain. Far more is known about the geography of Britain as a result of the intensive research undertaken during the last third of a century. There have also been significant developments in British geographical thought in recent years, as in other countries, and this has modified some of the earlier ideas about regional geography. Perhaps many, even most, British geographers would still subscribe to the sentiments expressed by Sir John Russell in the Introduction to the *Essays in regional geography* prepared for the previous Congress, 'The purpose of regional geography is to describe the regions of a country as they are and to discover the causes that have made them what they are' (Ogilvie, 1928, p. xvii). But today many would feel that it was also important—some would claim more important—to present systematically for the country as a whole some of the major geographical aspects of the British Isles to which so much research has been devoted in recent years. Perhaps this composite study reflects, in its chapter headings and in its authors, some of the significant features of the trends in British geography today, just as other work by some of the authors represented here, and the volume of essays collected under Miss Mitchell's editorship, are reminders of British geographers' continuing interest in the description and analysis of specific areas of their country.

Individual concepts of the scope and purpose of geography may vary enormously: there may be widely differing ideas about the desired form for an exposition of the geography of any tract of country, whether large or small: great enthusiasm may be shown for work in the field, and excellent descriptions of landscape in all its diverse and exciting aspects out-of-doors be given to appreciative professional colleagues and to patient, even long-suffering students. But one fact stands out above all others from this survey of the concern of British geographers for the study of the geography of their own country: it is that the writing of the geography of one's own homeland—even of one's own immediate environment that may be so very familiar, possibly all too familiar—is one of the hardest tasks that a geographer has to face. It is surely significant that, with a few exceptions (which are not always particularly successful efforts), only a handful of individuals has had the courage to write books on Great Britain or the British Isles as a whole: so much of the work considered in this chapter has been done by groups of geographers working together or by individuals writing in a restricted and specific systematic or regional field—often in close touch with students of other disciplines whose investigations have, as numerous references throughout this volume make clear, so markedly fertilised and improved British geographical studies.

This volume gives, therefore, an indication of what a team of British geographers believes should be known about the geography of the British Isles in the sixties of the twentieth century. It is their hope that these studies will help professional colleagues and other visitors from oversea, as well as their fellow-countrymen, to appreciate more keenly and to understand more really the inter-weaving of the strands of physical and human geography—in time as well as in space—that help to constitute the geographical mosaic of this relatively small but quite remarkably diversified portion of the earth's surface, the British Isles.

References

BAKER, J. N. L., 1948. Mary Somerville and geography in England. *Geogr. J.*, III, 207-221.
— 1955. Geography and its history. *Adv. Sci.*, **12**, 188-98.
— 1963. *The history of geography.*
BALCHIN, W. G. V., 1954. *Cornwall: an illustrated essay on the history of the landscape.* (The making of the English landscape series).
BEAVER, S. H., 1944. Minerals and planning. *Geogr. J.*, **104**, 166-93.
BOWEN, E. G. (editor), 1957. *Wales: a physical, historical and regional geography.*
BRACEY, H. E., 1952. *Social provision in rural Wiltshire.*
— 1953. Towns as rural service centres: an index of centrality with special reference to Somerset. *Trans. Inst. Brit. Geogr.*, **19**, 95-105.
BROWN, E. H., 1960. *The relief and drainage of Wales: a study in geomorphological development.*
BUCHANAN, R. O., 1954. The I.B.G.: retrospect and prospect. *Trans. Inst. Brit. Geogr.*, **20**, 1-14.
COLEMAN, ALICE, 1961. The Second Land Use Survey: progress and prospect. *Geogr. J.*, **127**, 168-86.
CRAWFORD, O. G. S., 1922. *The Andover district.*
CROWE, P. R., 1927. The population of the Scottish lowlands. *Scot. Geogr. Mag.*, **43**, 147-67.
—— 1929. The Scottish Coalfields. *Scot. Geogr. Mag.*, **45**, 321-37.
CUNDALL, L. B., and LANDMANN, G. P., 1925. *Wales: an economic geography.*
DARBY, H. C., 1940a. *The medieval Fenland.*
— 1940b. *The draining of the Fens.* (2nd edition, 1956).
— 1943. The movement of population to and from Cambridgeshire between 1851 and 1861. *Geogr. J.*, **101**, 118-25.
— 1952. *The Domesday geography of eastern England.* (2nd edition, 1957).
— 1960. An historical geography of England: twenty years after. *Geogr. J.*, **126**, 147-59.
— and CAMPBELL, E. M. J. (editors), 1962. *The Domesday geography of south-eastern England.*

THE BRITISH ISLES

— and MAXWELL, I. S. (editors), 1962. *The Domesday geography of northern England*.
— and TERRETT, I. B. (editors), 1954. *The Domesday geography of midland England*.
DAYSH, G. H. J., and others, 1949. *Studies in regional planning*.
DEMANGEON, A., 1939. *The British Isles*. Translated by E. D. Laborde.
EAST, W. G., 1937. Land utilization in England at the end of the eighteenth century. *Geogr. J.*, **89**, 156-72.
FAWCETT, C. B., 1917. Natural divisions of England. *Geogr. J.*, **49**, 124-41, with folding map following p. 160.
— 1919. *Provinces of England: a study of some geographical aspects of devolution*. Revised, 1960, with an introduction by S. W. WOOLDRIDGE and W. G. EAST.
— 1931. British conurbations in 1921, *Sociological Review*, **14**, 111-22.
— 1932. Distribution of the urban population in Great Britain, 1931. *Geogr. J.*, **79**, 100-16.
— 1934. Review of L. D. STAMP and S. H. BEAVER, The British Isles: a geographic and economic survey, 1933. *Geogr. J.*, **83**, 54-55.
FREEMAN, T. W., 1950 *Ireland: its physical, historical, social and economic geography*.
GEIKIE, A., 1865. *The scenery of Scotland viewed in connection with its physical geography*.
GILBERT, E. W., 1939. Practical regionalism in England and Wales. *Geogr. J.*, **94**, 29-44.
— 1948. The boundaries of Local Government Areas. *Geogr. J.*, **111**, 172-206.
— 1951. 'Geography and regionalism', in G. TAYLOR (editor), *Geography in the twentieth century*.
GLASS, R., 1948. *The social background of a plan: a study of Middlesbrough*.
GREEN, E. R. R., 1960. Industrial Archaeology. *Antiquity*, **34**, 43-8.
GREEN, F. H. W., 1950. Urban hinterlands in England and Wales: an analysis of bus services. *Geogr. J.*, **116**, 64-88.
— 1951. British bus services. *Geogr. Rev.*, **41**, 645-55.
GREGORY, S., 1954. Accumulated temperature maps of the British Isles. *Trans. Inst. Brit. Geogr.*, **20**, 59-73.
HENDERSON, H. C. K., 1936. Our changing agriculture: the distribution of arable land in the Adur Basin, Sussex, from 1780-1931. *J. Min. Agri.*, **43**, 625-33.
— 1952. Agriculture in England and Wales. *Geogr. J.*, **118**, 338-45.
H.M.S.O., 1940. *Royal Commission on the distribution of the industrial population*. Cmd. 6153.
— 1942. *Report of the Committee on land utilisation in rural areas*, Ministry of Works and Planning, Cmd. 6378.
LAWTON, R., 1953. 'Genesis of population', in W. SMITH (editor), *A scientific survey of Merseyside* (British Association), 120-31.
— 1962. Industrial archaeology. *Geogr. J.*, **128**, 121-122.
LINTON, D. L., 1932. The origin of the Wessex rivers. *Scot. Geogr. Mag.*, **48**, 149-65.
— 1933. The origin of the Tweed drainage system. *Scot. Geogr. Mag.*, **49**, 162-75.
MACKINTOSH, D., 1869. *Scenery of England and Wales*.
MANLEY, G., 1959. The late-glacial climate of North-west England. *Lpool. Manchr. Geol. J.*, **2**, 188-215.
MILL, H. R., 1896. Proposed geographical description of the British Islands based on the Ordnance Survey, *Geogr. J.*, **7**, 345-65.
MILLER, A. A., 1935. The entrenched meanders of the Herefordshire Wye. *Geogr. J.*, **85**, 160-78.
MILLWARD, R., 1955. *Lancashire*. (The making of the English landscape series).
MITCHELL, J. B. (ed.), 1962. *Great Britain: geographical essays*.

OGILVIE, A. G., 1924. The physiography of the Moray Firth coast. *Trans. Roy. Soc. Edinb.*, **53,** 377-405.
— (ed.), 1928. *Great Britain: essays in regional geography* by 26 authors, with an introduction by Sir E. John Russell.
— 1944. Debatable land in Scotland. *Scot. Geogr. Mag.*, **60,** 42-5.
— 1945. Land reclamation in Scotland. *Scot. Geogr. Mag.*, **61,** 55-84.
— 1946. Land reclamation in the Outer Isles. *Scot. Geogr. Mag.*, **62,** 26-8.
OLDFIELD, F., 1960. Late Quaternary changes in climate, vegetation and sea-level in Lowland Lonsdale. *Trans. Inst. Brit. Geogr.*, **28,** 99-117.
ORMSBY, H., 1928. Review of A. DEMANGEON, Les Isles Britanniques, *Geogr. J.*, **71,** 482-3.
ROXBY, P. M., 1908, 1909. Historical geography of East Anglia. *Geogr. Teacher*, 284-92; **5,** 128-44.
— 1913-14. The agricultural geography of England on a regional basis. *Geogr. Teacher*, **7,** 316-21.
SMAILES, A. E., 1947. The analysis and delimitation of urban fields. *Geogr.*, **32,** 151-61.
SMITH, C. T., 1951. The movement of population in England and Wales in 1851 and 1861. *Geogr. J.*, **117,** 200-10.
SMITH, W., 1949. *An economic geography of Great Britain.*
SNODGRASS, C. P., 1932. The influence of physical environment on the principal cultivated crops of Scotland. *Scot. Geogr. Mag.*, **48,** 329-47.
— 1933. Stock farming in Scotland and its relation to environment. *Scot. Geogr. Mag.*, **49,** 24-34.
SÖLCH, J., 1951, 1952. *Die Landschaften der Britischen Inseln.* Erster Band, England und Wales. Zweiter Band, Shottland und Irland.
STAMP, L. D., 1943. The Scott Report. *Geogr. J.*, **101,** 16-29.
— 1948. *The Land of Britain, its use and misuse.*
— 1950. 'Land use surveys with special reference to Britain', in G. TAYLOR (editor), *Geography in the twentieth century*, 372-92.
— and BEAVER, S. H., 1933. *The British Isles: a geographic and economic survey.* 2nd edition, 1937, and subsequent editions.
STEEL, R. W., 1961. A review of I.B.G. publications, 1946-60. *Trans. Inst. Brit. Geogr.*, **29,** 129-47.
STEERS, J. A., 1927. The East Anglian coast. *Geogr. J.*, **69,** 24-43.
— 1944. Coastal preservation and planning. *Geogr. J.*, **104,** 7-18.
— 1948. *The coastline of England and Wales.*
TANSLEY, A. G., 1911. *Type of British vegetation.*
— 1926. *Practical plant ecology.*
— 1939. *The British Islands and their vegetation.*
TAYLOR, E. G. R., 1930. *Tudor geography, 1485-1583.*
— 1934. *Late Tudor and Early Stuart Geography, 1583-1650.*
— and others, 1940. Plans for a national atlas. *Geogr. J.*, **95,** 96-108.
— 1942. Discussion on the geographical aspects of regional planning. *Geogr. J.*, **99,** 61-80.
THOMAS, D., 1959. The acreage returns of 1801 for the Welsh borderland. *Trans. Inst. Brit. Geogr.*, **26,** 169-83.
WALLWORK, K. L., 1956. Subsidence in the mid-Cheshire industrial area. *Geogr. J.*, **122,** 40-53.
— 1960. Some problems of subsidence and land use in the mid-Cheshire industrial area. *Geogr. J.*, **126,** 191-9.
WEST MIDLAND GROUP, 1946. *English County: a planning survey of Herefordshire.*
— 1948. *Conurbation: a planning scheme for Birmingham and the Black Country.*
WILMORE, A., 1930. *Industrial Britain: a survey.*
WOOLDRIDGE, S. W., 1950. Reflections on regional geography in teaching and research. *Trans. Inst. Brit. Geogr.*, **16,** 1-11.
— 1952. The changing physical landscape of Britain. *Geogr. J.*, **118,** 297-308.
— and BEAVER, S. H., 1950. The working of sand and gravel in Britain: a problem in land use. *Geogr. J.*, **115,** 42-57.

3

THE MAPPING OF THE BRITISH ISLES

THE map of the British Isles has developed to meet the contemporary requirements of travellers by land and sea, administrators, soldiers, scholars, geographers, and planners, approximately in that order. In the early stages progress was influenced by developments on the Continent, but in the last century Britain has contributed substantially to the science of cartography, and has set its own standards.

The earliest surviving maps of the British Isles are portions of the standard medieval mappa mundi, of which the best known example is the Hereford World Map of c. A.D. 1300. This was almost certainly derived from a late Roman world map. Though little evidence has survived, there was undoubtedly a continuing interest in mapping the British Isles from at least the thirteenth century onwards. The rivers, as channels of trade, received particular attention. The other element was derived from itineraries, indicating the relative positions of towns on the main routes. The four maps of the British Isles by Matthew Paris, the St Albans historiographer (c. A.D. 1250), display these features. Though crudely drawn, they are proof that a cartographic convention had been established. The cardinal points are indicated, and although the maps are not drawn to scale, they contain evidence that the cartographer was aware of this problem. A fine example of late medieval mapping is the 'Gough Map' in the Bodleian Library. Dated approximately A.D. 1360, it is the first to show an outline of England and Wales approximating to reality. The basis of the map is a surprisingly accurate representation of the road system of England and Wales, both for direction and for distances. Though no scale is directly stated, it is approximately 1 : 1 million. Scotland is poorly represented, as a long tongue extending far to the north. The general excellence of the English section has suggested that observed latitudes had been employed in its compilation, but there is no positive evidence for this.

There were almost certainly several copies of the Gough Map in circulation, for its influence can be traced down to the sixteenth century; it was no doubt the 'official' map of the Kingdom, used by the royal administrators. At this period, a type of nautical chart—the portolan chart—had also been evolved, based upon the use of the magnetic compass and the estimation of distances. This, however, had little apparent effect on the development of the land map.

The fifteenth century witnessed little progress in mapping in the British Isles. However, the Renaissance stimulated advances in mathematics and astronomy in western Europe, and MSS of Ptolemy's *Geographia* had been recovered; these together brought about a revival of cartography. This perhaps mainly influenced progress in large-scale property surveys and the like, but it also stimulated mapping on smaller scales.

In England the demands of administration and national defence under a centralised monarchy, and an awakening interest in the country's history, prompted the Tudor monarchs to patronise mapping in Britain. One of the earliest instances of this continental influence was the appointment by King Henry VIII of a German, Nicholas Kratzer, as royal horologer. Kratzer lectured on Ptolemy's *Geographia* at Oxford, and was in correspondence with Albrecht Dürer about a new map of Britain. It is not known what the result of this was, but it is perhaps not without significance that the first 'modern' map of the British Isles dates from ten years later. This is the Cotton MS map (Aug. I, i-9) in the British Museum. It is the first map other than Ptolemy's to show the country on a projection (a simple type with converging meridians, evolved in the fifteenth century) and to have a scale of miles. It is also remarkable as presenting the first recognisable outline of Scotland and the Isles. The central meridian runs approximately through Exmouth, the meridians being numbered from Ptolemy's origin in the Canaries.

In the next four decades, a number of maps were produced and some of them published. Though a knowledge of the theory of triangulation was spreading, it is improbable that it was used in their compilation. Most of the sources would appear to have been literary—itineraries, sailing directions, lists of ports, etc. The accepted configuration (largely from the Gough Map) was also amended from such material. Maps of this type included those by George Lily (1546), Humphrey Lluyd (1583), and Gerhard Mercator (1564) from information supplied by an anonymous Englishman.

Associated with this was a movement towards regional mapping, which was to prove a more fruitful approach. Antiquarian scholars, with their interest in the distribution of early monuments and place-names, were to the fore, but the work eventually received official approval. Lawrence Nowell had proposed a series of county maps in c. 1560, but it remained for Christopher Saxton with a patron's backing and the approval of Queen Elizabeth I, to carry the project through successfully between 1574 and 1579. His county maps of England and Wales, many engraved by craftsmen from the Low Countries, appeared as an atlas in 1579, which was accompanied by a general map of England and Wales put together from the county surveys. It is unlikely that Saxton made extensive use of current techniques of triangulation. No doubt he obtained much of his data by riding the roads, and compiling a route traverse. One of the few details we know is that he had authority to ascend church towers and other view points in Wales; no doubt he took bearings of other prominent features, and interrogated local inhabitants on the topography of the neighbourhood.

Table 1.   The Accuracy of Early British Mapping Compared

	Cotton	Lily	Saxton	Actual latitude
London	51° 45′N	52° 15′	51° 33′	51° 31′
Berwick	55° 7′	56° 32′	55° 45′	55° 47′
Difference	3° 22′	4° 17′	4° 12′	4° 16′
Lancaster	54° 20′	55° 0′	54° 4′	54° 4′
London	51° 45′	52° 15′	51° 33′	51° 31′
Difference	2° 35′	2° 45′	2° 31′	2° 33′

The scale of the Saxton map is approximately 1 : 1·8 million. A striking feature is the general accuracy of the latitudes, shown in Table 1. These figures suggest that the positions of many of the towns were based on observations for latitude with astrolabe or cross-staff. Longitudes are less accurate, as would be expected. The difference of longitude between London and Land's End is 5° 37′: read from the Saxton Map it is 6° 15′. This is more an index of the accuracy with which distances were measured, as it is not the result of astronomical determination of longitude. The longitudes appear to be calculated from the meridian of the eastern Azores. The popular atlas of county maps was John Speed's 'Theatre of the Empire of Great Britaine', 1611 and later editions.

These were largely founded on Saxton and other contemporary cartographers, but Speed added inset city plans and some archaeological detail.

Saxton's general map of England and Wales was to remain the standard map for almost two centuries. A large-scale version, approximately 1 : 500,000 based upon his county surveys was issued in 1583 in twenty sheets. On this, a 'small mile' was taken to be equivalent to one minute of latitude. The plates of this map were subsequently obtained by Philip Lea, who added roads and a little additional detail in 1688. The map continued in circulation for over one hundred years, a 'corrected' issue by Bowles and Carver appearing as late as 1763. Another version of this map was that known from a phrase in its title as the 'Quartermaster's Map'. The plates were engraved by Wenceslaus Hollar and the map published by Thomas Jenner in 1644, no doubt to meet increasing demands of travellers in that troubled time. It was still circulating in 1662, and twenty-six years later John Garrett published a revised edition having the roads added mainly from Ogilby's 'Britannia'. Like those of Philip Lea's version, the plates had a long life for John Rocque used them for another issue in 1752.

In Scotland, there was at the close of the sixteenth century a considerable amount of cartographic activity associated with the names of Timothy Pont, who was inspired by the example of Saxton to map many areas, and his successor Robert Gordon of Straloch. Pont's work only received publicity when, edited by Gordon, it appeared in Blaeu's *Atlas* of 1653. The general map, put together by Gordon, and also published by Blaeu, remained standard for a century.

In Ireland there was in the later sixteenth and early seventeenth century much mapping in connection with military and colonising operations, but little of this found its way into published maps. Some of it however was included in a map of Ireland by Battista Boazio, engraved by Renold Elstrack, and published in 1599. Since it was adopted by Dutch publishers and included in later editions of Ortelius's atlas, it became the most widely circulated map of Ireland for some decades. The best map of Ireland of this epoch was undoubtedly that produced by Sir William Petty, as a result of the surveys he undertook in connection with the Cromwellian land settlement. This map, warmly praised for its accuracy by John Evelyn, appeared in the atlas volume, *Hibernia depicta* published in 1673.

Most of the maps of the British Isles, here and abroad, during the seventeenth century were compiled from material of varying value. The principal source for detail for England and Wales was the road-book of John Ogilby bearing the title 'Britannia, or the Kingdom of England . . . actually surveyed', 1675. This consisted of a series of strip maps for the principal roads, indicating distance and direction, with details of villages, gentlemen's estates, and landmarks lying within a short distance of the route. These maps were essentially compilations of disparate pieces of survey fitted together without any kind of rigorous overall control. In the later seventeenth century two developments, one incomplete, the other abortive, pointed the way to further progress. The first was the initiation of a systematic survey of the coasts of Britain.

Until the end of the century, the publication of charts in Britain was of little significance. Some publishers had used old engraved plates obtained from Holland and the general standard of their output was low. The first step towards remedying this was taken by Captain Greenvile Collins, who, with official backing, carried out surveys eventually published in *Great Britain's Coasting Pilot*, 1693, and reprinted as late as 1792. Similar but less extensive work was done in Scotland by John Adair. Real progress, however, began with Murdoch MacKenzie's survey of the Orkneys in 1742, which was based on a rigid triangulation. When he retired, MacKenzie had charted Ireland, and the west coast of Britain from the Orkneys to the Bristol Channel. The methods he had evolved were practised by his son, and other hydrographic surveyors throughout the second half of the century. The turning-point in the charting of the British coasts came with the foundation of the Hydrographic Department in 1795, and the appointment of Thomas Hurd as Hydrographer. Hurd was responsible for the establishment of an official surveying service, and for the issue of the naval charts to the mercantile marine.

The second development was prompted by advances in survey techniques evolved in France which are particularly associated with the Academy of Sciences (founded 1666) and later with the Cassini family. This involved determining the length of an arc of meridian and this was carried out in 1669-70 by Jean Picard, using a carefully measured base, a system of triangles and observations for latitude. (The figure obtained for a degree was approximately 69 miles 783 yards or 111·7 km.). The meridian of Paris was then extended through the country, and a map of France, the first to depend upon systematic and rigorous survey, was published in

44

1693. Subsequently, Caesar François Cassini de Thury, with royal support, began a triangulation of the whole country that formed the basis of a topographic survey of France—the famous Cassini map, on the scale of 1 : 86,400.

These events had some repercussion in Britain. As early as 1635, Richard Norwood had obtained a surprisingly accurate figure for the arc of meridian based, not on triangulation, but on the simple measurement of the roads between London and York. In 1686 Edmond Halley, prompted by contemporary work in France, attempted without success to measure a meridian arc by triangulation. He was frustrated in this by the wooded character of the countryside and his ill-success in finding local persons to identify his sighting points. Robert Hooke, with his usual versatility, was also interested in such projects, being a sponsor of John Adams's plan of 1681 for a survey of England on the half-inch scale based on meridians after the French pattern. Adams had published in 1677 a large map of England and Wales in 12 sheets ('Angliae totius tabula'), showing the roads as straight lines, with distances, between towns. He compiled this in connection with his 'Index villaris', based on the 'Hearth books'. A much reduced version was popular during the eighteenth century, at least fourteen issues appearing before 1794. The map does not appear to be based upon original surveys, and it was doubtless his experience of the untrustworthiness of the available material that led Adams to put forward his plan. This project received the support of the Royal Society, and Adams proceeded to measure a twelve-mile base in King's Sedgemoor, Somerset, and to carry his system of triangles, some of which had sides of fifty miles, through the West Country and into Wales. He also determined, for the first time in England, many triangulated altitudes. By 1684, he claimed to have travelled 25,000 miles (40,000 km.). The finances of such an undertaking proved too much for one individual, and no sheet was ever engraved; Adams's scheme, which anticipated in some degree the Cassini map, had to wait for almost a century before it was placed, with the establishment of the Ordnance Survey, on a sound basis.

The awakening interest in science and natural history, embodied in, and stimulated by, the Royal Society, founded in 1660, was reflected in considerable activity in local county studies, and several volumes included maps of the particular county. The earliest of these were Dr Robert Plot's volumes on Oxford, 1676 and Staffordshire, 1686. It was soon apparent that such work, dependent on the efforts of a few individuals and hampered by financial difficulties, could never cover the whole country systematically. Ogilby's scheme to produce 'A description of the whole world', of which the 'Britannia' was one volume only, met with similar difficulties; and of the county series planned for England and Wales, only Kent and Middlesex appeared (in 1672).

The work of mapping contemporary England, in default of a co-ordinated scheme, therefore fell to the private county surveyors. These men, generally trained as estate surveyors, extended their activities to producing maps of their own and neighbouring counties, and relied upon the local nobility and gentry to recompense their labours. These maps were on larger scales than those of their predecessors; the scale of One Inch to One Mile (1 : 63,360) gradually became popular, and was ultimately adopted by the Ordnance Survey for their first general map. These maps were usually based on a system of triangulation developed from a base measured by a chain or 'perambulator' wheel. Angular measurements were made with the magnetic needle or with the graphometer, a simple instrument embodying a compass and two sighting vanes. The detail was sometimes plotted on the plane-table.

The expanding economy of the country stimulated the demand for maps other than those whose main feature was the depiction of roads. The growth of population, the development of industry, and new forms of transport were rapidly changing the face of the country, and these maps are now of great value to students of the historical landscape of England. Characteristic are Henry Beighton's Warwickshire, 1725, John Rocque's Surrey, and John Cary's Middlesex, 1786. Many were stimulated by the prizes offered by the Royal Society of Arts for 'accurate actual surveys' from 1759 onwards. Cary was surveyor of roads to the General Post Office, and his road distances were used to amend his maps. One of his important works was his 'New map of England and Wales with parts of Scotland', 1794, 5 miles to one Inch (1 : 316,800).

During these years, developments were taking place which were to lead to the establishment of the Ordnance Survey and the first systematic general survey of the British Isles. A close connection between the county surveyors and the early work of the Ordnance Survey has been demonstrated by R. A. Skelton. The two founders of the Survey were General Wm. Roy and the third Duke of Richmond. Roy in 1747-55 had carried out a military survey of Scotland on the scale of one inch to one thousand yards (1 : 36,000) and in 1776 had produced a scheme for a general military map of England, which was never proceeded with, owing to the outbreak of the

American War. His interest in the project continuing, he was charged with the measurement of the Hounslow base in 1784, undertaken to link England with the Cassini triangulation of France. He later put forward plans to make this the foundation of a general survey of the British Isles. Roy died in 1790 before his proposals were implemented. The initiative then passed to the Duke of Richmond, Master-General of the Ordnance 1782-95. The Duke had already shown his interest in survey; the technical assistants for the measurement of the Hounslow base had been furnished by him, and he had reorganised the Board of Ordnance, introducing into its service two surveyors who had worked for him privately in Sussex, Thomas Yeakell and William Gardner. The foundation of the Ordnance Survey dates from June 1791, when the Duke of Richmond took 'His Majesty's pleasure for proceeding with the Trigonometrical Operation begun by the late Major General Roy'. It is important to note that William Gardner who had led a surveying party in the Plymouth area for the Board in 1787, continued to serve it until his death in 1800, and completed the drawing of the One Inch map of Kent published by Faden at the Tower on 1 January 1801. The work and style of the eighteenth-century surveyors had therefore a direct influence upon the early Ordnance Survey maps.

The work of the Ordnance Survey proceeded under two heads: the extension of a network of triangulation from the Hounslow base, and the execution of the survey for the One-Inch Map. By 1795 a double chain of triangulation had been carried to Land's End, and fifteen years later most of England and Wales had been covered. Three bases of verification were measured between 1801 and 1817, but in order to extend the Survey over the British Isles and to establish the accuracy of the whole system, two principal bases were measured, the Loch Foyle base in 1827 and the Salisbury Plain base in 1849. By 1832, the triangulation was complete and the results published in the 'Account of the observations and calculations of the Principal Triangulation &c.' 1858. A test base, subsequently measured at Lossiemouth, showed that the probable error was in the neighbourhood of one inch in one mile. When it was decided to put all mapping on one projection, a new primary triangulation was carried out in 1936-38, 'which indicated the excellence of the old'. The first sheet of the One-Inch Map, covering Kent and part of Essex, appeared in 1801 (second edition 1807) with the title 'General Survey of England and Wales, an entirely new and accurate survey of the county of Kent, with part of the

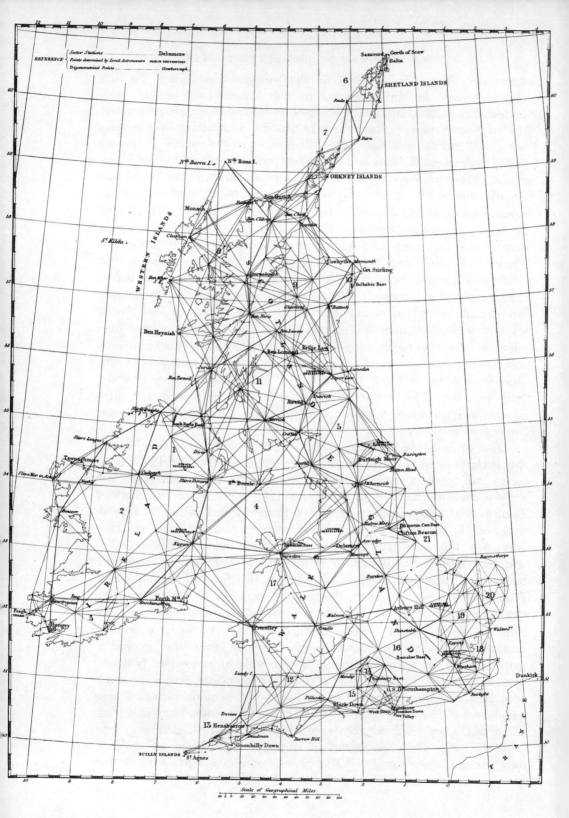

Fig. 1   GENERALISED DIAGRAM OF THE FIRST PRINCIPAL TRIANGULATION OF THE ORDNANCE SURVEY
(Ordnance Trigonometrical Survey, Principal Triangulation, 1858, Plate XVIII).

County of Essex. Done by the Surveying Draughtsmen of His Majesty's Honourable Board of Ordnance, on the basis of the Trigonometrical Survey'. By 1825, southern England, up to the boundary of Yorkshire and Lancashire had been mapped. A decision was then taken of great importance for the future of the Survey—namely the mapping of Ireland on the scale of Six Inches to the Mile (1 : 10,560), to meet the requirements of local taxation. Practically all the resources of the Survey were directed to this objective, which was finally completed in 1846. Experience in Ireland showed the great value of the Six-Inch scale, and it was therefore decided to adopt it for northern England and Scotland.

One shortcoming of this early work was that counties or groups of counties were mapped on separate meridians. This introduced many complications in making the marginal areas fit. The demand for large-scale maps was now becoming insistent; with the growth of the towns problems of sanitation, for example, demanded attention, and the 'railway mania' had shown the need for a comprehensive survey. These demands also emphasised the necessity for precise data on relative heights, and levelling was accordingly begun in England in 1849, the heights being referred to mean tide level at Liverpool. Previously heights shown had been obtained by measuring vertical angles. (Since 1922, the datum is mean sea level at Newlyn.) Parliament however was extremely reluctant to vote the large and continuing expenditure requisite for a national survey, and controversy as to suitable scales to be adopted became violent. Finally, in line with decisions taken at an International Statistical Conference at Brussels in 1853, after the work of the Survey had been practically brought to a standstill, and following two Committees and a Royal Commission, it was decided to complete the One-Inch Map, to map the whole country on the Six-Inch scale, and to map the cultivated areas on the scale of 1 : 2,500 (twenty-five inches to the mile). The sheets of the One-Inch Map (completed in 1870) were to be revised from the Survey for the larger scales. These are the lines upon which the Survey has since worked. In the middle of the century there was much interest in cartographical technique. Contours were introduced in 1843, and experiments in layer shading carried out. In 1880, engraving on copper was abandoned and reproduction by zincography introduced, permitting the freer use of colour.

The Ordnance Survey as it functions today was now firmly established, and it is not the purpose of this essay to trace its subsequent history in detail. Some important points however may

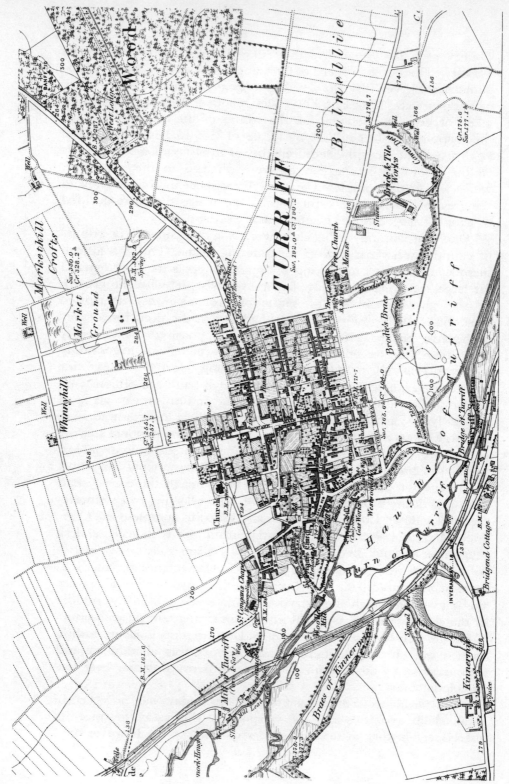

Fig. 2 A SAMPLE REPRODUCED FROM THE ORDNANCE SURVEY 6-INCH MAP, FIRST EDITION.

be noted. Throughout much of its history it has been hampered by lack of funds, which has resulted in severe curtailment of its activities, and failure to keep its maps revised. This was particularly marked in the inter-war period 1919 to 1939. However, the absolute necessity for a comprehensive and up-to-date series of national maps and plans is now generally recognised, particularly in connection with national and local planning. Provision is now made for the maintenance and revision of a comprehensive integrated series of maps, ranging from the Ten Miles to One Inch (1 : 633,600) to the Fifty-Inch (1 : 1,250) and including a map at 1 : 25,000 scale or approximately two and a half inches to the mile. The projection employed is the Transverse Mercator with a central meridian at 2° W. A National Grid based on the metre and with an origin southwest of Land's End is superimposed on Ordnance Survey maps, following the report of the Davidson Committee (1938).

During the early decades of the nineteenth century, before the Ordnance Survey One-Inch map was completed, county surveyors enjoyed a final spell of prosperity. Using the data of the Great Triangulation, a number of them published maps of counties at or near the One-Inch scale. The most distinguished was Christopher Greenwood, who between the years 1817 and 1834 published thirty-five such maps, the greater part of a projected atlas of England and Wales. Eventually, however, such private mapping became unremunerative. A special case was the Half-Inch map of Britain, produced with layer colouring by John Bartholomew and Co., Edinburgh, by arrangement with the Ordnance Survey.

The production of specialised maps of the British Isles has a long history, extending back at least to the manuscript maps of Anglo-Saxon England produced by Lawrence Nowell, and the map of the Saxon Heptarchy published by John Speed in his 'Theatre of the Empire of Great Britaine', 1611. In the mid-nineteenth century great interest was displayed in mapping many distributions. August Petermann produced in 1852 a map of the incidence of cholera and H. D. Harness compiled some interesting maps of population distribution and railway traffic flow for Ireland in 1837. The Land Use Survey of Britain, initiated by L. D. Stamp in 1933, published maps, based on the One-Inch Ordnance Survey, of the land use of the greater part of Britain. A second such survey, organised by Miss A. Coleman, is now engaged in the same task and is publishing maps, so far confined to England and Wales, on the scale of 1 : 25,000.

A continuously-developing National Atlas of Britain on the scale of 1 : 633,600 is published for the Ministry of Housing and

Local Government by the Ordnance Survey. The latter also produces the maps of the Geological Survey on several scales and has published in addition a fine series of archaeological and historical maps. Among other special maps mention should be made of 'The Climatological Atlas of the British Isles', published by the Meteorological Office in 1952, and of the 'National Atlas of Disease Mortality' prepared by the Royal Geographical Society, 1963. The 'Atlas of Britain', 1963, by the Clarendon Press, provides many distribution maps of British geography, economics, and sociology on uniform scales and style, and is the present end-product of a long tradition of special mapping based on national surveys of various kinds.

References

ANDREWS, J., 1961. *Ireland in maps; an introduction.* Dublin.
ANDREWS, M. C., 1924. The map of Ireland A.D. 1300-1700. *Proc. Belfast Nat. Hist. Soc.,* **1**.
BRITISH MUSEUM, 1928. *Four maps of Great Britain designed by Matthew Paris about A.D. 1250.*
CLOSE, Sir C. F., 1932. *The map of England.*
— 1926. *The early years of the Ordnance Survey,* Chatham.
CRONE, G. R., 1956. *Map of the world in Hereford Cathedral by Richard of Haldingham, c. A.D. 1280.* Royal Geographical Society.
— 1961. *Early maps of the British Isles, A.D. 1000-A.D. 1579.* Royal Geographical Society.
FLOWER, R., 1935. Lawrence Nowell and the discovery of England in Tudor times. *Proc. Brit. Acad.,* **21**, 14.
FORDHAM, Sir H. G., 1928. Christopher Saxton of Dunningley. *Misc. Thoresby Soc.,* **28**.
GILBERT, E. W., 1958. Pioneer maps of health and disease in England. *Geogr. J.,* **124**, 172-84.
HARLEY, J. B., 1962. *Christopher Greenwood, county map-maker.*
HARVEY, P. D. A., and THORPE, H., 1959. *The printed maps of Warwickshire, 1576-1900.*
LYNAM, E., 1950. English maps and map-makers of the 16th century. *Geogr. J.,* **116**, 7.
NORTH, F. J., 1937. *Humphrey Lloyd's map of England and Wales.* Cardiff. Nat. Mus. of Wales.
ORDNANCE SURVEY, 1938. *Final report of the Departmental Committee.*
PALMER, H. S., 1873. *The Ordnance Survey of the Kingdom.*
PARSONS, E. J. S., 1958. *The map of Great Britain, c. A.D. 1360, known as the Gough Map.* Bodleian Libr. and R.G.S.
ROBINSON, A. H. W., 1962. *Marine cartography in Britain.*
ROBINSON, R. H., 1955. The 1837 maps of Henry Drury Harness. *Geogr. J.,* **121**, 440-50.
ROYAL SCOTTISH GEOGRAPHICAL SOCIETY, 1936. *The early maps of Scotland.* 2nd ed. Edinburgh.
SKELTON, R. A., 1962. The origins of the Ordnance Survey of Great Britain. *Geogr. J.,* **128**, 415.
TAYLOR, E. G. R., 1937. Robert Hooke and the cartographic projects of the late 17th century. *Geogr. J.,* **90**, 529.
— 1930. *Tudor Geography, 1485-1583.*
WINTERBOTHAM, H.St J. L., 1934. The national plans. (The Ten-foot, Five-foot, Twenty-five inch, and Six-inch scales). *Ord. Surv. Prof. Pap. New. ser.,* **16**.

4

CLIMATE

THE weather and climate of the British Isles result from moving
disturbances within the extra-tropical Westerlies. These disturbances, consisting of a series of cyclonic and anti-cyclonic systems,
are related to the main circumpolar jet stream. Both the jet stream
itself at high altitudes, and the related disturbances at lower
altitudes, are essentially mobile phenomena, fluctuating rapidly
in space and varying in frequency and intensity throughout the
seasons of any one year, and from year to year for any given season
(Barnes et al., 1956). This highly variable character of pressure
patterns, typical of all areas within the Westerlies, is intensified
in the British Isles off the coast of mainland Europe. This position
ensures the periodic impact of pressure systems from the east,
such as boreal anticyclones in winter (Cornish, 1947), as well
as the omnipresent influence of relatively warm oceanic waters.
These modify the thermal and moisture characteristics of all air-
masses approaching the country. This highly critical position in
relation to weather-producing mechanisms ensures considerable
variability in climatic conditions within the rather firm limits
imposed by latitude and the surrounding sea surfaces.

Each of the atmospheric systems affecting the British Isles
tends to produce its own complex of weather conditions. Many
attempts have been made to classify these weather complexes, so
as to express British weather in a limited set of categories. Writers
have classified the pressure distribution rather than the weather
itself. Thus Lamb (1950) defined seven 'weather types', of which
two were stationary anticyclonic and cyclonic types while the other
five were a mixture between air-mass conditions and the directions
from which moving depressions approach the British Isles. Examples of these are shown in Figure 3. The relationship between
these 'types' and actual weather conditions is at best only of a
general nature. This is partly because the whole question of intensity
of development is omitted from the classification, partly because there
are marked seasonal differences in the weather associated with the
one 'weather type', and partly because at any one moment in time
the same 'type' will give different conditions in different localities.

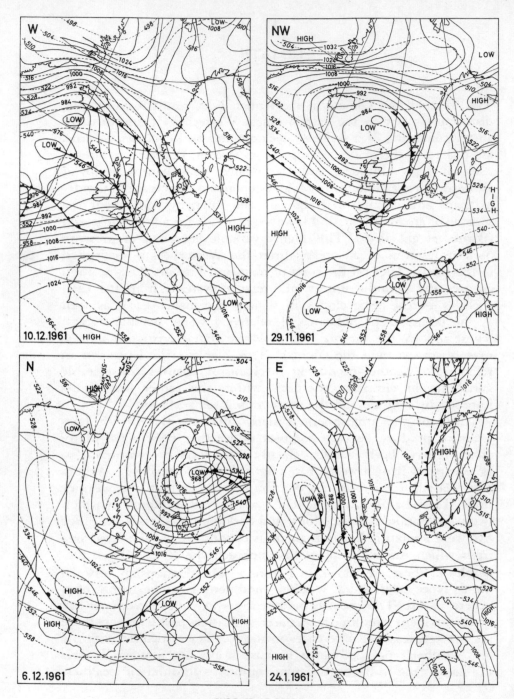

SURFACE AT 0600 H
----1000—— Surface isobars (in millibars) •—•— Warm front ▲—▲ Cold front ▲—▲ Occluded front

UPPER AIR AT 0000 H
----546---- Isopleths of 1000-500 mb. thickness (in geopotential decametres)

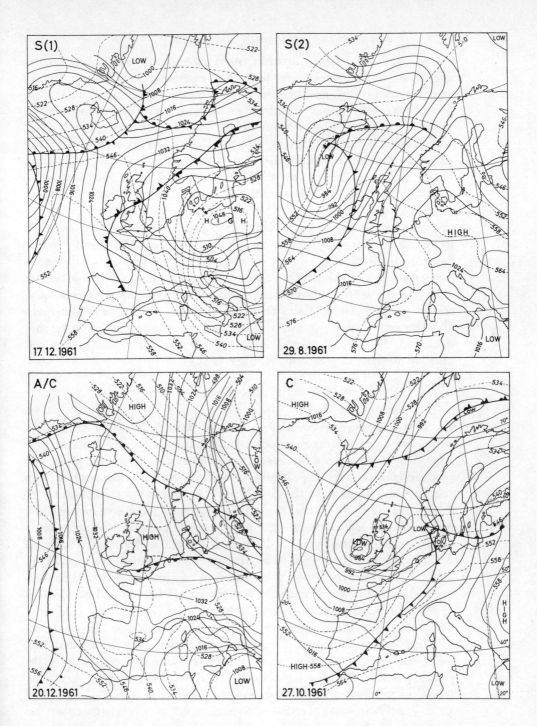

Fig. 3. WEATHER TYPES AFFECTING THE BRITISH ISLES (types after Lamb, 1950; maps based on the *Daily Weather Reports* and the *Daily Aerological Reports* of the Meteorological Office).

Studies of actual, as distinct from theoretical, conditions resulting from these 'types' are few. An example is Belasco's (1945, 1952) work on temperatures at Kew. In central Scotland a detailed comparison of actual weather at several stations indicates the great importance both of east-west location and of purely local topographical factors (Barry, 1957). Paton (1951) shows that the showery weather normally associated with northwesterly (maritime polar) air often gives way to blue skies and good visibility over southeast Scotland, as a result of the air's mountain passage. Furthermore, easterly conditions yielding continental polar air in winter are, as a result of the air's North Sea journey, 'decidedly less cold in southeastern Scotland than in southeastern England', while frontal rain from depressions moving from the west or southwest is 'very much reduced along the east coast'. Any generalisation for the country as a whole is therefore virtually impossible. Consequently, this essay will stress salient features only, especially since the main characteristics of the climate have been presented in considerable detail in the *Climatological Atlas of the British Isles* (1952), and also by Bilham (1938) and Manley (1952).

Temperature

The temperature conditions of the British Isles are controlled primarily by the source regions of air masses affecting the country, modified by the temperatures of the seas across which these masses pass before reaching our shores. In winter, cold air approaches from the east and southeast, the north and the northwest. In the first of these cases (Fig. 3. E) the dry stable nature of the air maintains low temperatures far to the west, especially when associated with anticyclonic conditions over the British Isles, while the relatively small extent of the North Sea and its lowish temperatures (41-45°F, 5-7·5°C, in January) limit the degree of modification that it undergoes. Again, the narrowness of the Straits of Dover and of the seas to the northeast and southwest helps to explain the very low temperatures then often obtaining in southeast England. In contrast, cold air originating over Greenland and farther west approaches from the northwest (Fig. 3. NW). It is markedly warmed by its passage across the North Atlantic Drift, with sea-surface temperatures off northwest Britain above 46°F (8°C) in winter and above 54°F (12°C) in summer. So, although cold in a relative sense, the air can never be exceptionally cold. As this maritime polar airstream is, on average, the most common air mass affecting the British

56

Isles in all months, even in southeast England (Belasco, 1952), the thermal character of the North Atlantic Drift clearly affects the lower limit of British temperatures. Cold air of northerly origin, i.e. maritime arctic air (Fig. 3. N), is the least common source of cold conditions. The sea surface is again a modifying factor, though the shorter trajectory, coupled with lower initial temperatures over the Arctic basin, do lead to very low temperatures at times, especially over exposed northern coasts. In contrast, the onset of stormy conditions (Fig. 3. W and C), usually associated with the periodic arrival of maritime tropical air, leads to phases of mild weather when temperatures rise well above 50°F (10°C) even in January.

These various tendencies create a temperature distribution in winter that only partially reflects latitudinal differences, for relative exposure to easterly and westerly influences, and the contrast between areas close to and more removed from the sea, largely eliminate the effect of northerly or southerly position. Thus in January and February, one of which is the coldest month on average everywhere in the British Isles, mean monthly temperatures are about 40°F (4·5°C) not only along the coasts of northwestern and northern Scotland, but also along the whole of the east coast as far south as the Thames estuary. In contrast, mean temperatures of 41-45°F (5-7°C) extend along both southern and western coasts, the higher values occurring especially over western and southwestern peninsulas. However, mean sea level maps indicating coldest conditions slightly inland from the east coast are rendered of limited value by relief features.

The influence of these is shown clearly in terms of absolute minimum temperatures. Thus, whereas all areas of the British Isles recorded values as low as 20°F (−7°C) in the period 1907-40, most areas experienced at least one period of 10°F (−12°C) or less, while many inland and upland areas had temperatures of below 0°F (−18°C). These latter include not only the Cairngorms, where −17°F (−27°C) was recorded at Braemar at 1,111 ft. (340 m.) in February 1895, but also lowland southeast England which often receives continental polar outbursts of maximum intensity. Temperature conditions in upland areas are in fact but little known in detail. Thus of 526 stations included in the *Monthly Weather Report* for August 1961, only 19 are above 1,000 ft. O.D. (300 m.) and of these only 2 are above 2,000 ft. O.D. (600 m.). The one mountain (as distinct from upland) observatory that has existed in the British Isles was on Ben Nevis (4,406 ft., 1,300 m.), but operated only from 1883 to 1904 (Paton, 1954). Mean temperatures were below freezing point from early October to early May, falling in February to about 23°F (−5°C) and rising to 41°F (5°C) in July. There are also scattered records such as those obtained by Manley in the northern Pennines (1943). These indicate, for example, that within upland basins in winter mean daily minima for 1906-35 were below 30°F (−1°C), while mean daily maxima did not exceed 38°F (3°C). Moreover, topographic features induce intense effects under anticyclonic conditions (Fig. 3. A/C) especially where air-ponding occurs. Even so, winter temperatures in the British Isles are rather higher than those in other countries in similar latitudes, and extreme cold conditions rarely last very long.

In summer, latitudinal differences and altitudinal position assume dominance. Maritime polar air is still common, and introduces periods of below-average temperatures. Equally, maritime tropical air is frequent, but whereas in winter this provides mild spells, in summer such air normally produces only average temperatures. This is especially true over western areas, though farther east heating over land often markedly increases temperatures experienced from both polar and tropical maritime air masses. Above-average temperatures are usually produced by the onset of continental air, whether this be of easterly or southerly origin, especially if it is associated with anticyclonic developments. Southerly airstreams of southeast European or North African origin, however, provide the heat-wave conditions that sometimes occur, with temperatures above 90°F (32°C). Such incursions of continental tropical air are most common over southeast England (Fig. 3. S2) and, coupled with occasional low winter temperatures, make this area the part of the country with the greatest temperature range.

Mean monthly temperatures in July and August are lower than in most other temperate-latitude countries. Sea level values range from about 55°F (13°C) in the north to about 62°F (17°C) in the south, with values at any given latitude being higher inland than at the coast. Mean maxima, on the other hand, exceed 60°F (16°C) in almost all areas and are above 70°F (21°C) in some parts of southern England, especially inland. Mean minima, however, fall almost to 50°F (10°C) in most areas. High temperatures are exceptional features, but nearly all lowland areas have experienced values above 80°F (27°C). In the southern two-thirds of England more than 90°F (32°C) has occurred in many areas, while temperatures of above 95°F (35°C) have been recorded in some places.

The intervening seasons of spring and autumn are characterised

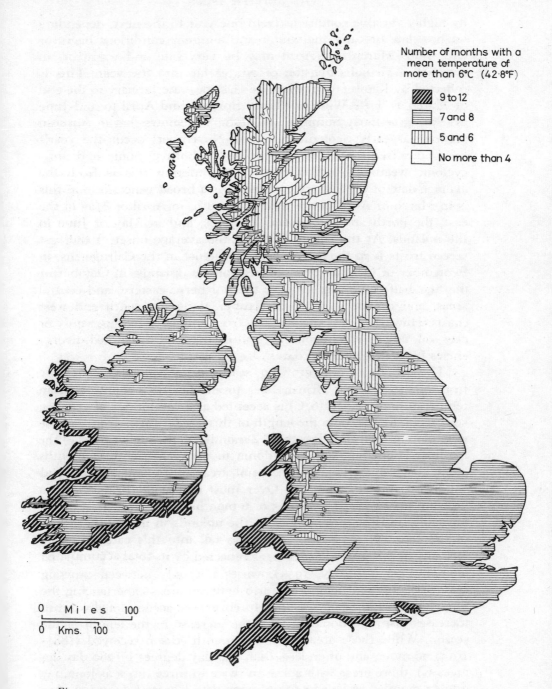

Number of months with a
mean temperature of
more than 6°C (42·8°F)

9 to 12

7 and 8

5 and 6

No more than 4

0   Miles   100

0   Kms.   100

Fig. 4.   THE LENGTH OF THE GROWING SEASON defined by the number of months with a mean temperature above 42.8°F (6°C) (after Gregory, 1954).

59

by highly variable conditions from one year to the next, depending on how late or early the winter and summer conditions begin or end. Both March and April may be very fine and warm or, in contrast, a virtual extension of winter far into the year. This is reflected by Lamb (1950) when he classifies late January to the end of March as 'Late Winter *or* Early Spring', and April to mid-June as 'Spring *or* Early Summer', while he also shows that in Autumn (defined as early September to mid-November) occur the year's maximum frequencies of long spells of both cyclonic and anti-cyclonic weather. Another way of considering this is from the average date of the last screen frosts. As a broad generalisation this is in March or April in the west and south, in April or May in the east, the north and the central lowlands, and in May or June in the uplands. At the end of summer the average onset of the first screen frosts is in the second half of August in the Cairngorms, in September or October over the rest of the uplands, in October or the first half of November over the northern, eastern, and central areas, and as late as early December along the south and west coasts. However, local site, such as frost hollow or hilltop, sandy or clay soil, city or rural exposure, will clearly lead to marked divergencies from these general dates.

The length of the growing season thus varies considerably from one part of the British Isles to another. If a monthly mean temperature of $42 \cdot 8°F$ ($6°C$) is accepted as a valid index of growing season conditions, then the length of this season varies from as little as (and in limited areas less than) 4 months on the higher parts of the Scottish Highlands and Snowdonia to between 9 and 12 months along western and southern coastal areas of Ireland, Wales, and southwest England (Fig. 4). Over most of upland Britain such a growing season lasts for some 5 or 6 months, while over most of the lowlands, and the lower slopes of the uplands in the southern half of the country, some 7 or 8 months fall into this category. The intensity of this growing season, as reflected by its total accumulated temperatures (Gregory, 1954), varies not only between growing seasons of different length but also between areas experiencing the same length of growing season. Moreover, the accumulated warmth increases disproportionately with the increase in the length of the season. While those areas with a 4 month season received (1881-1915) no more, and often less, than 500 day degrees F (280 day degrees C), those areas with a season twice to three times as long, i.e. 9 to 12 months, received 2500 to 3000 day degrees F (1400 to 1650 day degrees C). Also, whereas in western Ireland the actual value was close to the lower of these limits, in southern England it verged on the upper one. This internal variation can also be found in the other two categories of growing season shown on Fig. 4, in each case changes in intensity varying with latitude.

Local modifications as a result of relief features can also be important. The classic work of Hawke (1944) showed that even within the English lowlands, e.g. within the valleys of the Chilterns, frost frequencies comparable to those of Braemar at 1,111 ft. (340 m.) can be created, and that in such circumstances ground frosts are possible in all months. Less intense yet comparable results have been presented for Bath (Balchin and Pye, 1947), while marked local contrasts are also observable even in shallow, open, oceanic valleys on Wirral, Cheshire. Here nocturnal temperature inversions of the order of 10°F (5·5°C) are possible between points only some 90 ft. (27 m.) different in height and about ¾ mile (1·2 km.) apart (Fig. 5).

Yet further modifications are introduced by the widespread urban-industrial areas. Even such moderate-sized towns as Bath and Reading (Parry, 1956) have significant thermal effects. In Reading, for example, minimum temperature differences of 4-5°F (2-3°C) are common, while differences as great as 8°F (4·5°C) may occur. The major heat-island effect is, of course, provided by Greater London, within which the temperature pattern is both intricate and complex (Chandler, 1960, 1961a, 1962). Rural-urban contrasts in night minima were 12°F (7°C), varying from 40-52°F (4-11°C), on the night of 13/14 May 1959 when, with light winds, steep thermal gradients paralleled the edge of the built-up area. As winds increase, however, the thermal differences due to relief or urbanisation tend to be eliminated.

Precipitation

The climate of the British Isles is usually regarded as equable and wet. However, precipitation varies far more from one locality to another than does temperature, average annual values ranging from only 20 in. (500 mm.) along the Thames estuary to over 200 in. (5,000 mm.) in some parts of highland Britain. The distribution of average annual (or monthly) rainfall partially reflects westerly or easterly position, as the majority of rain-producing atmospheric systems approach from the west. This applies not only to frontal and warm-sector rain of depressions, but also to instability showers associated with maritime polar air. Only rarely do depressions

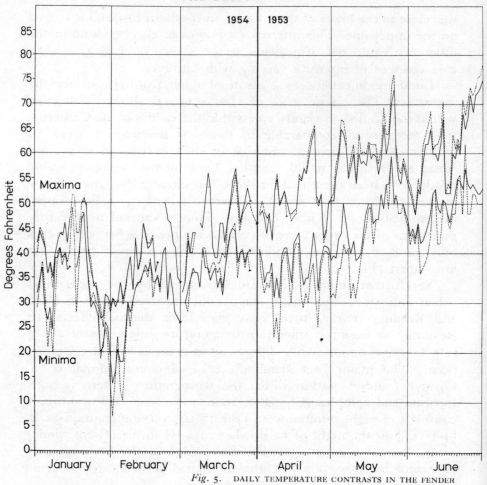

Fig. 5. DAILY TEMPERATURE CONTRASTS IN THE FENDER

approach these islands from the east, while showers from easterly airstreams, such as the continental polar in winter, are normally restricted to the coastal zone itself. This greater wetness of the western areas is accentuated by the western location of the major highlands.

In this way average annual rainfall over most of the English and Scottish lowlands is less than 30 in. (750 mm.) (Fig. 6), while over the western Highlands of Scotland, parts of the Southern Uplands, Lake District and northern Pennines, much of upland Wales, and the western hills and peninsulas of Ireland, it exceeds 60 in. (1,500 mm.). Values vary considerably from year to year, deficits of 40-50% and surpluses of 50% or more being possible. The variability of annual rainfall, expressed by the coefficient of

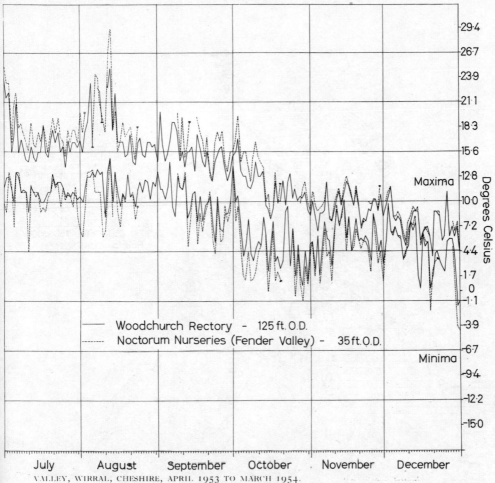

Maxima

Degrees Celsius

— Woodchurch Rectory - 125 ft. O.D.
----- Noctorum Nurseries (Fender Valley) - 35 ft. O.D.

Minima

July   August   September   October   November   December

VALLEY, WIRRAL, CHESHIRE, APRIL 1953 TO MARCH 1954.

variation, ranges from about 8% to nearly 20% (Fig. 6). It tends to
be least over northern and western areas and highest over eastern
and southern areas, although this pattern does change in detail
from one period to another (Gregory, 1955). The composite presen-
tation of mean annual rainfall and its coefficient of variation (Fig.
6) illustrates the contrast between the western Highlands of Scotland
where high average falls are associated with low variability, and
other wet uplands of the British Isles where variability is greater.
Other significant features are the increased variability (with comparable average values) as one moves from north to south in Ireland,
and the moderate to high variability of all the drier areas in Scotland
and England.

This interaction of average and variability conditions means

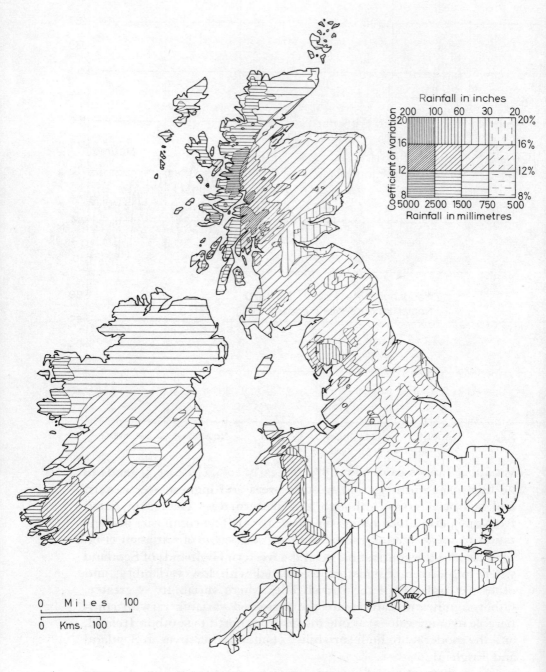

Fig. 6.   MEAN ANNUAL RAINFALL AND ITS COEFFICIENT OF VARIATION, 1901-1930.

64

The legend within the figure reads:

Rainfall in inches
Coefficient of variation
200 100 60 30 20
20%
16%
12%
8%
5000 2500 1500 750 500
Rainfall in millimetres

Miles 100
Kms. 100

that the probability of receiving given amounts of rainfall varies widely, even between areas with similar average values. For example, nowhere is a fall of over 30 in. (750 mm.) an impossibility, while conversely in only limited areas will a fall of less than this amount never occur. The British Isles can be divided into those areas where high rainfall can be relied upon [i.e. over 50 in. (1,250 mm.) in at least 70% of years]; those where low rainfall is a distinct possibility [i.e. where less than 30 in. (750 mm.) occurs in at least 30% of years]; and those intermediate areas not fitting into either of these categories (Fig. 7).

This year-to-year variability of rainfall resolves itself into periods of wetter- and periods of drier-than-average conditions. Such fluctuations over the past century or so were irregular, the phases of increase or decrease in the number of wet or dry years failing to coincide over the country as a whole. Glasspoole (1921) stressed, by means of correlation coefficients, the complete lack of relationship between fluctuations over western and eastern areas of the Scottish Highlands only some 80 miles (150 km.) apart. He showed instead the links between the western Highlands and the Lake District and Ulster, and between the eastern areas and much of lowland Britain as represented by Oxford. The frequency of wet years tended to increase from the latter part of the nineteenth century through to the 1930s at least, for all except Region 4 (Fig. 8). Certainly, for virtually the whole country, the 1881-1915 period, on which the Ministry of Town and Country Planning 1 : 625,000 Mean Annual Rainfall Map is based was drier on average than either 1901-1930 (which is represented in the *Climatological Atlas of the British Isles*) or 1916-1950, the values for which have been published under the heading *Averages of Rainfall* (H.M.S.O., 1958).

Whichever of these pictures of annual rainfall is accepted, the seasonal distribution of the rain is also important. Over most of the country the period February to April tends to be drier on average than the months on either side. Moreover, the 'high-summer' months of July and August tend to be wet, with September rather drier, before the onset of wet conditions again from October onwards. The relative balance of the wetter periods of winter and summer varies over the country, however, especially between west and east. In the west, winter rainfall tends to outweigh that of summer, while in the east there is a tendency for the reverse to apply (Mill and Salter, 1915). Such characteristics by no means occur every year, but the broad distinction drawn by Crowe (1940)

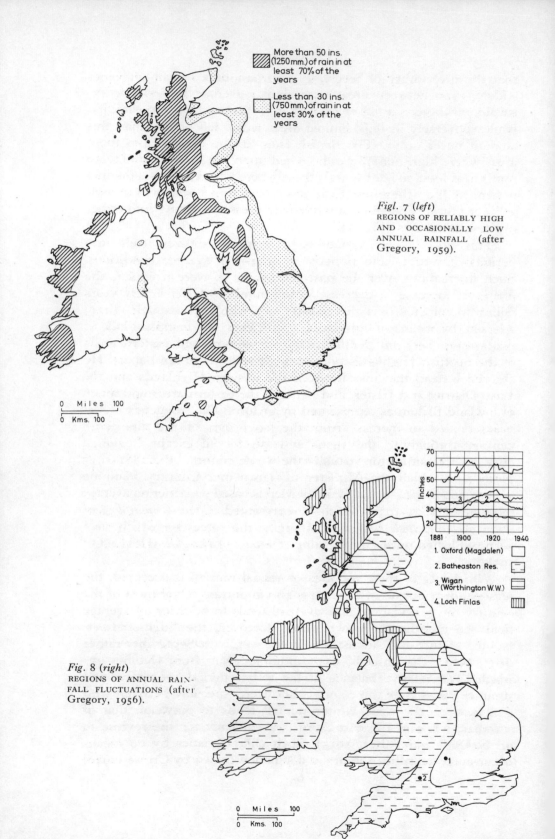

More than 50 ins. (1250 mm.) of rain in at least 70% of the years

Less than 30 ins. (750 mm.) of rain in at least 30% of the years

Fig. 7 (*left*)
REGIONS OF RELIABLY HIGH AND OCCASIONALLY LOW ANNUAL RAINFALL (after Gregory, 1959).

0   Miles   100
0   Kms.   100

70
60
50
Inches   40
30
20

1881   1900   1920   1940

1. Oxford (Magdalen)
2. Batheaston Res.
3. Wigan (Worthington W.W.)
4. Loch Finlas

Fig. 8 (*right*)
REGIONS OF ANNUAL RAINFALL FLUCTUATIONS (after Gregory, 1956).

0   Miles   100
0   Kms.   100

between areas of winter maximum, areas with a wet second half of the year, and one area with a tendency for a summer maximum (Figs. 9 and 10) is based on a frequency of occurrence of at least three years out of five.

In assessing the value of moisture income, the loss through evaporation and transpiration must also be considered. Penman (1950) estimated losses of between 15 inches (380 mm.) and 18 in. (460 mm.) per annum over most of England and Wales. These values tend to decrease northwards and westwards, but with increasing elevation the decrease of temperature and increase of humidity is partly offset by increases in wind speed. The bulk of this loss occurs during summer, and balancing this against variations in seasonal incidence of rainfall, it has been suggested that an annual rainfall of from 26 in. (650 mm.) in northern England to 36 in. (900 mm.) in southern England is needed to offset moisture loss. Thornthwaite's formulae (Howe, 1956) yield higher estimates of potential evapotranspiration, e.g. a summer-month water-need of 4 in. (100 mm.) or more, and annual values of the order of 30 in. (750 mm.). Nevertheless, periodic moisture deficits are still possible even when average rainfall is greater than 30 in. (750 mm.). In upland areas Nature Conservancy experiments on evaporation (Green, 1959) confirm the regional and altitudinal influences mentioned above.

Relationships between evaporation and rainfall are necessarily modified in terms of specific events, such as high intensity rainfall. In the British Isles this is often associated with summer thunderstorms, especially within shallow depressions in which convergence is considerable. The sea breeze front, inland from the south coast of England, may act as a generator of such storms, giving rise very occasionally to precipitation rates of up to 2 in. (50 mm.) per hour for short periods. Extreme convergence within warm sectors of depressions is also a potent factor in producing intensive rainfall especially over uplands (Douglas and Glasspoole, 1947). This, together with thunderstorm development, contributed greatly to the fall of over 9 in. (225 mm.) within 24 hours experienced on Exmoor at the time of the Lynmouth floods in 1952 (Bleasdale and Douglas, 1952). Such serious, though short-lived, floods are not infrequent in the British Isles.

Over the higher uplands a proportion of the precipitation falls as snow and is retained in this form for considerable periods. Snowfall records are mainly for lowland sites (below 200 ft. or 60 m.). The average number of days with snow falling at such altitudes

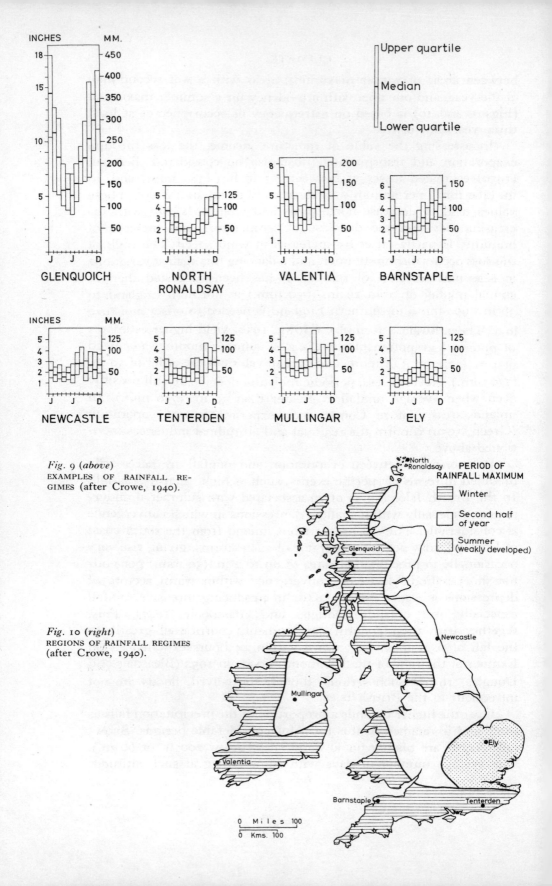

INCHES   MM.

18 ──── ── 450
         ── 400
15 ──── ── 350
         ── 300
         ── 250
10 ──── ── 200
         ── 150
 5 ──── ── 100
         ── 50

J   J   D
GLENQUOICH

NORTH RONALDSAY

VALENTIA

BARNSTAPLE

INCHES   MM.

5 ──── ── 125
4 ──── ── 100
3 ────
2 ──── ── 50
1 ────

J   J   D
NEWCASTLE

TENTERDEN

MULLINGAR

ELY

Upper quartile

Median

Lower quartile

Fig. 9 (above)
EXAMPLES OF RAINFALL RE-
GIMES (after Crowe, 1940).

Fig. 10 (right)
REGIONS OF RAINFALL REGIMES
(after Crowe, 1940).

PERIOD OF
RAINFALL MAXIMUM

Winter

Second half
of year

Summer
(weakly developed)

North Ronaldsay

Glenquoich

Newcastle

Mullingar

Valentia

Ely

Barnstaple

Tenterden

0   Miles   100
0   Kms.   100

varies from over 30 in northeast Scotland to less than 5 in southwest England, with less than 20 such days over Ireland and Wales, England other than central and eastern areas of the north, and western coastlands of Scotland south and west of Fort William. Over the uplands recourse must be had to estimates based on the limited data available (Manley, 1939). These suggest that snow lies for at least 100 days each year in many of the higher parts of the Scottish Highlands, while in parts of northern England more than 50 days a year have such a snow cover. Actual conditions are highly variable from year to year, however, with snow possible even over lowlands any time from November to the end of April, while it is not unknown in May and June; yet in some years, especially on west coasts, there may be no more than one or two days on which snow falls, and none on which it lies. In more sheltered corries at high altitude, however, snow may last the whole year (Champion, 1952).

Other features

Many other elements contribute to the characteristics of the climates of the British Isles, but these can receive no more than passing comment. The occurrence of gale force winds is, of course, a necessary corollary of the dominance of temperate-latitude depressions. These gales, often related to intense secondary depressions moving rapidly across the country from west to east, or to troughs or fronts extending southwards from the main depression, can produce winds in excess of 100 m.p.h. (160 km.p.h.) along western and northern coasts, although such speeds are fortunately rare. Nevertheless, a gust of 177 m.p.h. (280 km.p.h.) was recorded in the Shetlands on 11 February 1962. Most, though not all, of these gales have a westerly component within their direction, but even so, many east coast locations have experienced winds of above 80 m.p.h. (130 km.p.h.), and this is true of inland areas too. As a whole, northern and western coasts receive an average of 20 to 30 days with gales per year, while along the east and southeast coasts 5 to 15 days are more common. Average wind speeds, however, are not excessive, being less than 10 m.p.h. (15 km.p.h.) over central England, while there are frequent periods of calm or near-calm under anticyclonic conditions. Furthermore, many local wind phenomena often develop, from the topographically-induced 'helm' wind of Cross Fell (Manley, 1945) to the urban 'heat-island' circulations described for Leicester (Chandler, 1961b).

Despite the periodic storminess of the British climate, sunshine amounts are by no means limited. The average daily duration of bright sunshine throughout the year varies from about 3 hours in the north to approximately 5 hours in the south, or between 20% and 40% respectively of the theoretically-possible amount. In June and July these values are about 4 hours in the north and 7·5

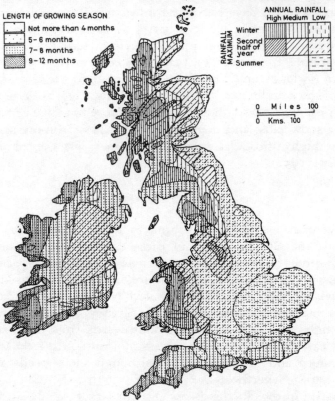

LENGTH OF GROWING SEASON
- Not more than 4 months
- 5 - 6 months
- 7 - 8 months
- 9 - 12 months

ANNUAL RAINFALL
High Medium Low

RAINFALL MAXIMUM
- Winter
- Second half of year
- Summer

0   Miles   100
0   Kms.   100

Fig. 11.   REGIONAL CLIMATIC DIFFERENCES (based on Figs. 4, 7, and 10).

hours in the south, but it must be remembered that at this time of the year length of daylight increases markedly northwards. June values for possible hours of sunshine vary from 16·22 at latitude 50° N to 18·59 at 60°N, while long periods of twilight render hours of real darkness virtually non-existent in northern areas in summer. In December average sunshine values diminish to 0·5 to 1·5 hours per day. Years vary however, so that in June 1925 at Plymouth almost 12·5 hours a day was averaged over the month, while December 1912 at Manchester yielded an average daily duration of only 0·01 hours.

Such low values in an urban area result partly from man-made pollution, many characteristics of which were studied in the Leicester survey of 1937-39 (H.M.S.O. 1945). Detailed studies of pollution in the British Isles are not numerous, but maps available for the Sheffield area (Garnett, 1957) and central Yorkshire as a whole (Eyre, 1962) stress the interacting influences of relief, meteorological circumstances, and the distribution of urban functions. As a whole, the increased frequency of fogs over urban-industrial England including London, compared with the rest of the country (some 30 to 50 days a year against less than 20 for most rural areas), as well as overall poorer visibility in towns, reflect these man-made factors. These were at their worst in the London 'smog' of December 1952 when some 4,000 people died as a direct result of toxic materials in the atmosphere. Nevertheless, fogs do occur over coastal and rural areas without the aid of man-made pollution, reflecting the frequently high moisture content in the atmosphere. Such fogs are usually of a radiational nature during winter, associated with anticyclonic development, while in summer fogs are mainly of marine origin. This contrast is demonstrated along the south coast of England, where a summer maximum of poor visibility in the oceanic west gives way to a winter maximum in the more continental east, the transition occurring in the neighbourhood of the Isle of Wight (H.M.S.O., 1940).

Regional climates

Despite the many and varied climatic contrasts within the British Isles, climatic boundaries used in major world classifications normally do not pass through these islands. The only distinction made, and then not in all classifications, is between those areas in eastern England that usually experience a moisture deficit in the summer and the rest of the country. In part this results from the tendency to ignore upland conditions, especially as regards temperature, and in a country where temperature conditions deteriorate rapidly with height (Manley, 1951) this is most misleading. Regional differences must therefore be defined in a purely British or local context. Distinctions based on 'site' e.g. coastal, upland and urban climates, were presented by Bilham (1938); those related to ecological factors were prepared by Tansley (1939).

In Figure 11 regional differences are based on rainfall in terms of probability (Fig. 7), the seasonal incidence of that rainfall (Fig. 10), and the duration of the growing season (Fig. 4). Accepting the

71

approximations involved in each of the constituent elements, and the small scale of the map, many of the major climatic relationships and differences within the British Isles are here summarised, although details are omitted. Clearly regional diversity is as much a characteristic of British climates as is temporal fluctuation. Nevertheless, their treatment is scarcely appropriate in this work, which focusses attention on the British Isles as a whole.

References

BALCHIN, W. G. V., and PYE, N., 1947. A micro-climatological investigation of Bath and district. *Quart. J. R. Met. Soc.*, **73**, 297-319.

BARNES, F. A., BASTEN, J., and FIELD, N. J., 1956. The high summers of 1954 and 1955 and the long waves in the Westerlies. *E. Midl. Geogr.*, **6**, 9-26.

BARRY, R. G., 1957. *A contribution to the study of weather types.* Unpublished B.A. Thesis, University of Liverpool.

BELASCO, J. E., 1945. The temperature characteristics of different classes of air over the British Isles in winter. *Quart. J. R. Met. Soc.*, **71**, 351-76.

— 1952. Characteristics of air masses over the British Isles, *Geophys. Mem.*, **87**, (H.M.S.O.).

BILHAM, E. G., 1938. *The climate of the British Isles.* London.

BLEASDALE, A., and DOUGLAS, C. K. M., 1952. The storm over Exmoor on 15th August 1952. *Met. Mag., Lond.*, **81**, 353-67.

CHAMPION, D. L., 1952. Summer snows around Ben Nevis, *Weather*, **7**, 180-84.

CHANDLER, T. J., 1960. Wind as a. factor of urban temperatures—a survey in North-east London. *Weather*, **15**, 204-13.

— 1961a. The changing form of London's heat-island. *Geography*, **46**, 295-307.

— 1961b. Surface breeze effects of Leicester's heat-island. *E. Midl. Geogr.*, **15**, 32-8.

— 1962 London's urban climate. *Geogr. J.*, **128**, 279-98.

CORNISH, R. T., 1947. The cold spell—January to March 1947. *Geography*, **22**, 67-76.

CROWE, P. R., 1940. A new approach to the study of the seasonal incidence of British rainfall. *Quart. J. R. Met. Soc.*, **66**, 285-309.

DOUGLAS, C. K. M., and GLASSPOOLE, J., 1947. Meteorological conditions in heavy orographic rainfall. *Quart. J. R. Met. Soc.*, **73**, 11-38.

EYRE, S. R., 1962. Fog in Yorkshire, 1959-60. *Weather*, **17**, 125-31.

GARNETT, A., 1957. Climate, relief and atmospheric pollution in the Sheffield region. *Adv. Sci., Lond.*, **13**, 331-41.

GLASSPOOLE, J., 1921. The fluctuations of annual rainfall. *Brit. Rainf.*, **61**, 288-300.

GREEN, F. H., W., 1959. Some observations of potential evaporation, 1955-1957. *Quart. J. R. Met. Soc.*, **85**, 152-8.

GREGORY, S., 1954. Accumulated temperature maps of the British Isles. *Trans. Inst. Brit. Geogr.*, **20**, 59-73.

— 1955. Some aspects of the variability of annual rainfall over the British Isles for the standard period 1901-30. *Quart. J. R. Met. Soc.*, **81**, 257-62.

— 1956. Regional variations in the trend of annual rainfall over the British Isles. *Geogr. J.*, **122**, 346-53.

— 1959. Climate and water supply in Great Britain. *Weather*, **14**, 227-32.

HAWKE, E. L., 1944. Thermal characteristics of a Hertfordshire frost hollow. *Quart. J. R. Met. Soc.*, **70**, 23-40.

H.M.S.O., 1940. *Weather in Home Waters and the North-Eastern Atlantic, Vol. II, pt. 3, The English Channel.* M.O. 446, b(3).

— 1945. *Atmospheric pollution in Leicester.*

— 1952. *Climatological Atlas of the British Isles.* M.O. 488.

— 1958. *Averages of Rainfall for Great Britain and Northern Ireland*, 1916-1950. M.O. 635.

HOWE, G. M., 1956. The moisture balance in England and Wales. *Weather*, **11**, 74-82.

LAMB, H. H., 1950. Types and spells of weather in the British Isles, *Quart. J. R. Met. Soc.*, **76**, 393-429.

MANLEY, G., 1939. On the occurrence of snow-cover in Great Britain. *Quart. J. R. Met. Soc.*, **65**, 1-23.

— 1943. Further climatological averages for the Northern Pennines, with a note on topographical effects. *Quart. J. R. Met. Soc.*, **69**, 251-61.

— 1945. The Helm wind over Cross Fell. *Quart. J. R. Met. Soc.*, **71**, 197-215.

— 1951. The range of variation of the British climate. *Geogr. J.*, **117**, 43-65.

— 1952. *Climate and the British Scene*, London.

MILL, H. R., and SALTER, C., 1915. Isomeric rainfall maps of the British Isles, *Quart. J. R. Met. Soc.*, **41**, 1-39.

PARRY, M., 1956. Local temperature variations in the Reading area. *Quart. J. R. Met. Soc.*, **82**, 45-57.

PATON, J., 1951. Weather and climate, *Scientific Survey of South-Eastern Scotland*, Edinburgh, 36-43.

— 1954. Ben Nevis Observatory, 1883-1904. *Weather*, **9**, 291-308.

PENMAN, H. L., 1950. Evaporation over the British Isles. *Quart. J. R. Met. Soc.*, **76**, 372-83.

TANSLEY, A. G., 1939. *The British Isles and their Vegetation*, Cambridge, Ch. 3.

5

HYDROLOGY

'All the rivers run into the sea; yet the sea is not full:
unto the place from whence the rivers come thither they
return again.' (Ecclesiastes 1 : 7)

IN the British Isles, with its marginal position and uneven relief,
the supply and availability of water at any point is by no means
constant or certain. Hence the interest and importance of British
hydrology.

As has been seen, rainfall is generally well distributed throughout the year, although the greater proportion is usually received
by the western parts in the winter and the eastern parts in the summer. The annual total of rainfall also reveals a broad distinction
between the wetter highland west, mainly receiving from 40-80 in.
(1,000-2,000 mm.), and the drier lowland east with 20-40 in.
(500-1,000 mm.). There is similarly a variation in evaporation over
the British Isles, and, as Gregory has shown, large parts experience
losses equivalent to about 15-18 in. (380-450 mm.) of rainfall per
year. There is thus a high percentage loss of the precipitation in
some areas. The residue either accumulates in natural overground
reservoirs such as lakes; or, where the rocks permit percolation, in
natural underground storage reservoirs: the excess forms the run-
off in the shape of springs, streams and rivers. It is this part of the
hydrologic cycle that will be considered first.

The conservation of water becomes of special importance whenever extremes are a normal experience or where the demand for
water by a growing community begins to exceed the minimum
supply available. This situation is now arising in many parts of
Great Britain and there is an increasing realisation of the need to
regard water as a prime natural resource basic to the life of the
community and meriting proper conservation measures. The utilisation of the water resources and the steps being taken towards their
conservation hence forms the second part of this chapter.

Rivers and lakes

The main outlines of the present relief of the British Isles were
fashioned in the Tertiary era and before the Pleistocene glacial

period. Whilst the majority of the rivers have therefore quite ancient origins the appearance and southward movement of the great ice sheets had a profound influence in certain areas on the drainage pattern. In the Highland zone old valleys were blocked or obliterated and new channels were cut by both ice and meltwaters, while glacial lakes in troughs and corries were produced. In the Lowland zone glacial erosion and deposition frequently resulted in ill-defined drainage patterns such as are now found in the Central Plain of Ireland.

As is to be expected from the position of the Highland zone the rivers of Great Britain are longer to the east than to the west. An apparent exception occurs in the case of the Severn, but the head-waters of this river and the Teme, Wye and Usk all flow from the Welsh Uplands eastwards towards the Thames until interrupted by the cross drainage of the Warwick Avon and lower Severn. The main water parting in Great Britain coincides generally with the main divide: it follows a north-south line through the country but keeps well to the west apart from the protuberance of the Warwick Avon. With the exception of the Severn complex, westward from the main parting short streams quickly reach the fringing Atlantic waters and there are few major rivers: in Scotland the Clyde and the Nith, in England the Ribble and Mersey, and in Wales the Dee and Teifi alone merit mention.

Eastward from the main water parting we find, in contrast, a series of longer rivers many of which are grouped into the major estuaries which play an important part in the economic life of the country. In Scotland the Spey, Don, Dee, Tay, Forth, and Tweed are all significant: descending from the impermeable rocks of the uplands these rivers are fast flowing and very responsive to precipitation. Southwards and across the Scottish border a series of streams flows eastward from the Pennines; of these the Tyne, Wear, and Tees run independently to the North Sea, then follows the most northerly of the major estuarine groupings so characteristic of the English Lowland zone. The Swale, Ure, Nidd, Wharfe, Aire, Calder, and Don all drain ultimately to the Humber, which also receives the Trent from the south. The gathering grounds of these rivers amount to over 10,000 square miles (25,000 sq. km.), or about one-fifth of the whole of England. Many of the headwaters of the Humber estuary have been impounded in the Pennines and the quality of the water throughout is generally good. Parts of the middle portions of the rivers however are to be found flowing through the Triassic sandstones which have been developed for underground supplies and there are consequently few river filtration schemes.

Continuing southward the next major drainage basin centres upon the Wash. The Witham, Welland, Nene, and Great Ouse descend into the Fens and then pass into the drowned plain of the Wash which breaches the Chalk of Norfolk and Lincolnshire. These rivers drain some 6,000 square miles (15,000 sq. km.) of extremely flat country, mostly clays with large tracts of marsh with fen, in which the natural drainage channels have been much modified by man to prevent flooding and so maintain an intensive agricultural economy. The rainfall over the catchment areas is low, the rivers are sluggish and the quality of the water is not high. Spring snow-melt sometimes produces flood hazards. East Anglia is drained by a series of short independent streams of which the Yare, Waveney, Stour, and Blackwater are the largest. Some of these streams are characterised by extensive estuarine mouths quite out of keeping with the diminutive drainage basins.

Next is the major drainage complex of the Thames, which dominates southeast England. Rising in the Jurassic Cotswolds, and gathering unto itself many small streams from the oolitic limestone and Oxford Clay Vale, it breaches the Chalk escarpment at Goring Gap. Below Reading it receives streams such as the Lee, Wey, Mole, Darent, and Medway which constitute the drainage of the London Basin and part of the Weald. Some 6,000 square miles (15,000 sq. km.) of drainage hence converge on the large and important Thames estuary. Over a quarter of the population of England and Wales are resident within this river basin and in it we find many water filtration schemes, notably those in London, Henley, Reading, and Oxford. With the exception of London however there are few impounding reservoirs giving gravity supplies, largely because of the unsuitable and over-populated ground. A moderate rainfall maintains a fairly reliable flow and the quality of the Thames water is of a good standard from the source to Teddington, beyond which the river is tidal.

The rivers draining to the English Channel are mainly short and independent streams which flow from the high ground of the Weald, Salisbury Plain and the Palaeozoic uplands of the southwest peninsula. The Rother, Arun, Test, Itchen, Avon, Stour, Exe, Dart, and Tamar are the largest, but as rivers they can claim but limited significance. Westward from Selsey Bill estuarine conditions again characterise the lower reaches of many streams.

On the west coast of Great Britain the largest drainage complex is that centred upon the Severn estuary. The area covers about three quarters of the whole of Wales and the greater portion of seven English counties making a total of some 4,400 square miles (11,500 sq. km.). The Severn, Teme, and Warwick Avon are the major rivers of the upper part of the basin, whilst into the estuary itself flow the Wye, Usk, Bristol Avon, and Parrett. The Severn Basin proper has a mean run-off of 2,200 million gallons (10,000 million l.) a day, the highest in Britain. The rainfall over much of the basin is high and, as a great deal of the drainage area comprises impermeable Palaeozoic rocks, run-off is very responsive to precipitation and flooding is not infrequent. The water is generally pure and, in the upper reaches of the Welsh tributaries, soft: these qualities, combined with the admirable impounding facilities offered by the available relief and underlying geology, explain the numerous reservoirs that have been constructed to serve the populations of Liverpool, Birmingham, Newport, Cardiff and Swansea. In the central part of the basin conditions are favourable for river filtration schemes such as those at Shrewsbury, Worcester and Cheltenham.

The most important element in the drainage system of Ireland is the river Shannon, actually the longest of all the rivers in the British Isles, since its length of just over 250 miles (400 km.) slightly exceeds that of the Thames. The Shannon rises within twenty miles of Donegal Bay and flows slowly southward through loughs Allen, Ree and Derg. At Killaloe at the southern end of Lough Derg the river passes through a section of rapids before turning westward from Limerick to an estuary some sixty miles (100 km.) in length. Across the Central Plain there is a fall of only one in ten thousand but from Killaloe to Limerick there is a drop of a hundred feet (30 m.). This has been used as the basis of the Shannon H.E.P.[1] scheme which provides power to almost all parts of the Republic of Ireland.

Elsewhere in Ireland the rivers are mainly short drainage channels from the surrounding rim of mountain masses. These either flow direct to the sea or enter the Central Plain. In Leinster and Munster the Avoca, Slaney, Barrow, Nore, Suir, Blackwater and Lee are larger and constitute a more regular system. In Northern Ireland the Bann, Foyle, and Erne are worthy of mention.

One feature of many Irish rivers is the tendency to expand into wide lakes of irregular outline. Some half of the course of the Shannon above Killaloe is made up of loughs Allen, Ree and Derg,

[1] Hydro-electric power.

and in a similar way over half of the Erne comprises Lough Erne and Upper Lough Erne. In the west loughs Corrib, Mask, and Conn flank the mountain rim of Connacht. These, along with Lough Neagh in Northern Ireland, are the largest lakes in the British Isles, although by continental standards all these must be judged quite small, for Lough Neagh, the largest, is but 153 square miles (400 sq. km.) in extent.

The lakes of Great Britain are even smaller than those of Ireland and the majority appear to be the product of glaciation: the most notable are those located in the glens of the Scottish Highlands and in the dales of Cumberland and Westmorland. Lochs Shin, Fannich, Ness, Rannoch, Tay, Katrine, and Lomond in Scotland and lakes Windermere, Haweswater, Ullswater, Thirlmere, and Derwentwater in the Lake District are the best known: many are utilised in connection with H.E.P. projects and water supply schemes or for recreational purposes. Upland Wales also possesses a number of large lakes, notably Trawsfynydd, Bala, Vyrnwy, and the Claerwen and Elan Valley complex, but all of these are man-made or man-modified in connection with power or water supply projects.

The Highland zone of Great Britain is further spattered with countless rock tarns, corrie lakes, and morainic-dammed ponds. In contrast the Lowland zone has no large lakes, for little trace now remains of the one time pre-glacial pondings of the Pleistocene period, all having been drained by natural or artificial means. Lowland zone lakes are predominantly man-made, peat digging for instance has produced the Norfolk Broads, gravel extraction has resulted in numerous residual lakes in many parts of the Thames and Trent basins, whilst reservoir construction in the London area has further added conspicuous lakes to the landscape.

Underground water resources

When precipitation falls on impermeable ground it flows off in the form of streams: on permeable ground however precipitation is followed by percolation along with run-off, and much of the water will be stored underground until such time as it issues from springs or is extracted by pumping. Whilst the terms permeable and impermeable are purely relative in the process of percolation and there is no firm dividing line, we can make a broad and fairly accurate generalisation so far as the British Isles are concerned to the effect that impermeability is associated with the older strata and permeability with the younger. This means that the Highland zone of Great Britain and much of Ireland, where Palaeozoic rocks dominate, have few underground water resources: the Mesozoic and Tertiary rocks of the Lowland zone of England on the other hand have many important natural underground reservoirs. Certain of these formations merit particular mention.

The Bunter and Keuper sandstones of the Triassic system outcrop over an area of some 1,750 square miles (4,500 sq. km.) in Lancashire, Cheshire, Yorkshire, Nottinghamshire, Leicestershire, Warwickshire, Somerset, and Devon. Where the sandstones pass under newer rocks for an area of a further 1,250 square miles (3,250 sq. km.) useful underground supplies may be tapped. Several hundred million gallons of water a day are now extracted from these reserves and the Bunter Pebble beds in particular are most prolific yielders.

The Oolitic limestones and associated sands of the Jurassic system outcropping eastward from the Triassic rocks are also of importance, more particularly in Lincolnshire, Northamptonshire, Gloucestershire, and Somerset. Some 2,500 square miles (6,500 sq. km.) of these rocks outcrop and are available for the collection of precipitation, with a further 1,000 square miles (2,600 sq. km.) of concealed rocks facilitating storage.

The greatest underground water-bearing formation in England is undoubtedly the Chalk of Cretaceous times. Some 5,000 square miles (13,000 sq. km.) outcrop and there are at least another 7,000 square miles (18,000 sq. km.) concealed and available for storage. Several hundred million gallons a day are extracted by pumping and the resource is particularly important in the water supply of Lincolnshire, East Anglia, the London basin, and the southern counties of Kent, Sussex, Hampshire, and Dorset. Up to a quarter of the population of England derives some if not all of its water supply from the Chalk, and the heavy demand of the present century has led to a steady fall in the level of the water table in the London basin: a problem that gives increasing concern as there are signs of brackish water infiltrating from the east.

Elsewhere in the British Isles special local geological circumstances may give good water reserves as, for example, parts of the lower and upper Greensand and some glacial drift deposits. There is also the rather special case of the Carboniferous limestone which, although impervious, has a propensity for swallowing surface drainage if well jointed and fissured, and in this way sometimes becomes of importance as a source of underground water.

The relationship between the amount of rainfall and the potential yield of underground water in an area of pervious rocks is clearly difficult to determine. In the Lowland zone of England where the variation in precipitation is not great, calculations suggest a potential yield of 300,000-400,000 gallons per square mile (525,000-700,000 litres per sq. km.) per day.

The use of water

An organised community needs water for a wide variety of purposes. Water is required for transportation and power, for domestic purposes and the disposal of waste products, for agricultural and industrial activities, and for recreation. The uses overlap, sometimes supplementing and sometimes conflicting with each other. Transportation of waste may preclude recreational use. Power production may impede navigation. A reservoir on the other hand may create recreational facilities. In all cases, however, conservation of the available supplies and the maintenance of a steady flow of water is desirable for a continuance of the use.

A broad division may be made in these categories between, on the one hand, those uses such as transportation, power production and recreational facilities where little water is actually consumed and where the community takes advantage of opportunities provided in the main by Nature: and, on the other hand, the remaining categories of domestic, industrial, and agricultural usage where water is abstracted from the hydrological cycle and largely consumed.

The increasing population of the British Isles and more particularly that of Great Britain, combined with a rising standard of living, has produced new problems of water conservation. For although the region as a whole has a relative abundance of precipitation, *the majority of the population actually lives where the rainfall is lowest and the surface water least*. As a consequence there has been an increasing pollution of many lowland rivers and a rising consumption of water abstracted from both overground and underground sources. The situation has now been reached where many areas in Lowland Britain must needs look elsewhere than their immediate locality for water supplies in normal years, quite apart from any difficulties encountered in drought conditions.

The increased use is to a large extent related to the increased availability of water by the organisation of piped supplies during the last century. Whilst some communities in Britain have long organised their water supply—Southampton has a charter dating back to 1420, Hull to 1447, Plymouth an Act of 1585, and London its New River project of 1613—it was not until the explosive increase of population and sudden expansion of towns accompanying the Industrial Revolution of the early nineteenth century that problems of water supply really became acute. But it was the fear of cholera after the epidemics of the middle part of the nineteenth century that really precipitated action. The Royal Commission of 1843-45 recommended that local authorities should have definite responsibilities for water supply as well as for drainage. Thereafter new water undertakings, both private and public, appeared with increasing rapidity, until by the early part of the twentieth century the number of undertakings had passed the four-figure mark, and the greater proportion of the urban communities had access to reasonable supplies of water.

Water supply thus ranks as one of the oldest of the public utilities in the British Isles. This situation explains some of the present-day difficulties, for the existing system largely grew up around the administrative unit of the parish or town and long before the concept of conservation or any ideas of wider integration had emerged. For many years local sources, which had originally determined the siting of local communities, sufficed for local needs. But the towns grew to cities and the improved availability of water led to increased consumption: turning on a tap was not the same as drawing water from a distant well or spring. The larger urban units hence outgrew their local supplies and had to look elsewhere for water. Between 1879 and 1904, Manchester, Liverpool, and Birmingham developed sources in the Lake District and Wales some 106, 68, and 74 miles (170, 110 and 120 km.) away respectively. In a similar way Glasgow, Edinburgh, Belfast, and Dublin eventually turned to neighbouring upland areas for augmented supplies.

These measures sufficed until the inter-war period, when increasing demands and consumption began to outgrow supply once again. The situation was further aggravated by a number of droughts, notably those of 1921, 1933 and 1934. These droughts, however, stimulated a fresh interest in water conservation and resulted in the appearance of Regional Advisory Water Committees in 1924, the Water Pollution Research Board in 1927, and the Inland Water Survey in 1935. Parliament also passed the Supply of Water in Bulk Act and the Rural Water Supplies Act in 1934, whilst the Central Advisory Water Committee appeared in 1937.

The concept of conservation and the idea of a wider integration of the available resources were slowly emerging.

The outbreak of the Second World War in 1939 unfortunately brought all such progress to a halt, and although new hopes were raised by the admirable Government white paper of 1944 and the Water Act of 1945, the post-war economic difficulties nullified most efforts in the field of water conservation. River Boards emerged as a result of an Act of 1948 but their powers were limited. The Inland Water Survey and the Central Advisory Water Committee began again after the war, but both lapsed for several years after 1952 as a result of economy measures. All water supply under-takings were thwarted by lack of capital.

Meanwhile the consumption of water has continued to rise inexorably. The explanation is not far to seek. Whereas the domestic consumer of 1830 used less than four gallons (18 l.) per day, by 1960 in many areas of Great Britain he used over 60 gallons (270 l.) per day, whilst 95% of a greatly increased population had water on tap. By 1960 a total supply of 2,853 million gallons (12,750 million l.) of water a day was needed from the public water under-takings in Great Britain and of this some 65% is thought to have been for domestic purposes. There is clear evidence of a relentless annual increase in water consumption with a rising rate of increase. This situation was realised in 1949 by a Committee of the Ministry of Health investigating trends in water consumption. The Com-mittee was responsible for the oft-quoted forecast that 'water undertakings would be faced by 1970 with a demand for twice the amount consumed in 1938'. Events have shown, if anything, that this forecast will prove to be an underestimate well before 1970. Some undertakings are already supplying more than double their 1938 figures and the total for England and Wales will almost certainly be doubled before the appearance of this chapter in 1964. Table 2 below shows the average daily consumption of water for England and Wales, and Scotland, over the last two decades. These figures suggest a nation-wide phenomenon rather than an exclusive-ly urban-industrial trend.

Against these figures we should set for comparison the total storage capacity (Table 3), since this gives a measure of the country's immediate reserve capacity and ability to withstand emergencies, droughts, and increased demands.

Whilst the storage capacity has grown considerably since 1938 the increase has not been at the same rate as the growth in con-sumption. This must mean that for Great Britain as a whole emer-

WATER SUPPLY UNDERTAKINGS

Table 2. Average daily consumption (gallons and litres)

	England and Wales		Scotland	
1938	1,360,905,000 galls.		246,223,000 galls.	
	6,124,072,500 litres		1,108,003,500 litres	
	percentage increase over 1938			
		%		%
1946	1,654,924,000 galls.	22	280,725,000 galls.	14
	7,447,158,000 litres		1,263,262,500 litres	
1948	1,761,210,000 galls.	29	288,230,000 galls.	17
	7,925,445,000 litres		1,297,035,000 litres	
1950	1,771,265,000 galls.	30	301,285,000 galls.	22
	7,970,692,500 litres		1,335,782,500 litres	
1952	1,864,896,000 galls.	37	318,319,000 galls.	29
	8,392,032,000 litres		1,432,435,500 litres	
1954	1,942,942,000 galls.	43	321,881,000 galls.	31
	8,743,239,000 litres		1,448,464,500 litres	
1956	2,040,092,000 galls.	50	346,924,000 galls.	41
	9,180,414,000 litres		1,561,168,000 litres	
1958	2,195,802,000 galls.	61	369,803,000 galls.	50
	9,881,109,000 litres		1,664,113,500 litres	
1960	2,466,247,000 galls.	81	386,989,000 galls.	57
	10,981,115,000 litres		1,741,450,500 litres	
1962	2,568,294,000 galls.	89	406,217,000 galls.	65
	11,557,323,000 litres		1,827,976,500 litres	

gency stocks do not give the same measure of insurance against both drought and higher demands as they did in 1938. When considered in detail of course we find that in some localities storage is temporarily well ahead of consumption, but conversely in others storage has now seriously deteriorated in relation to consumption.

Additional factors have also recently appeared to complicate the situation. Although the quantity of water supplied by the public water undertakings is large, it is completely dwarfed by the amount of water abstracted outside the public supply system for industrial purposes. The new continuous flow techniques, automation and the huge plant layouts, combined with a surge in power production, have resulted in dramatic increases in industrial water

Table 3. Total storage capacity (gallons and litres)

	England and Wales		Scotland	
1938	164,300,342,000 galls. 729,351,539,000 litres		56,082,891,000 galls. 252,373,009,500 litres	
	percentage increase over 1938			
		%		%
1946	197,523,776,000 galls. 888,856,992,000 litres	20	63,205,566,000 galls. 284,425,047,000 litres	13
1948	202,655,645,000 galls. 911,950,402,500 litres	23	64,280,334,000 galls. 289,261,503,000 litres	15
1950	208,664,652,000 galls. 938,990,934,000 litres	27	64,280,334,000 galls. 289,261,503,000 litres	15
1952	226,159,081,000 galls. 1,017,715,864,500 litres	38	65,278,224,000 galls. 293,752,008,000 litres	16
1954	239,458,961,000 galls. 1,077,565,324,500 litres	46	65,424,904,000 galls. 294,412,068,000 litres	17
1956	240,498,711,000 galls. 1,082,244,199,500 litres	46	73,306,890,000 galls. 329,881,005,000 litres	31
1958	245,219,895,000 galls. 1,103,489,527,500 litres	49	73,815,862,000 galls. 332,171,379,000 litres	31
1960	257,620,395,000 galls. 1,159,291,775,500 litres	57	75,722,214,000 galls. 340,749,963,000 litres	33
1962	261,916,173,000 galls. 1,178,622,778,500 litres	60	80,436,720,000 galls. 361,965,240,000 litres	43

consumption in the post-war years. The biggest use of water is in the electrical supply industry which at present needs something of the order of 15,000 million gallons (67,500 million l.) a day for cooling and steam raising purposes. The water requirement for direct cooling for a coal-fired power station of 2,000 megawatts, or an atomic power station of 600 megawatts, such as are being constructed nowadays, is of the order of 1,000 m.g.d. (4,500 m.l.d.). It must be borne in mind that electricity consumption in Great Britain has doubled every decade since the 1920s. The outlook for water need is indeed formidable on this count alone. Other industries are also substantial water users: the chemical industry's requirements approach 1,000 m.g.d. (4,500 m.l.d.), the steel industry 500 m.g.d. (2,250 m.l.d.) and the paper industry 650 m.g.d. (3,000 m.l.d.). It is clear that the domestic and industrial usage of water must by now be of the order of 20,000 m.g.d. (90,000 m.l.d.) and that availability of water will increasingly control the location of industry in future.

As we are considering water use in general, mention should be made at this point of the hydro-electric power schemes in the British Isles. Relatively speaking, these are not large and only represent a coal equivalent saving of little more than 2-3 million tons a year, or just over 1% of the total energy produced: the schemes are important, however, in the areas where development has taken place. In Ireland the Shannon was developed between 1925 and 1929 for H.E.P. at Ardnacrusha near Limerick and the power is distributed to all parts of the Republic. Smaller H.E.P. power stations have since been constructed in support of the main scheme, notably on the River Erne near Ballyshannon.

In Great Britain most of the developed water power resources are in the mountains of Scotland and north Wales. Some of the developments are for the reduction of aluminium, but by far the greater number are for the public supply of electricity. In 1962 the total installed capacity of hydro-electric plant in Great Britain was 1,231 Mw. with an average annual output of 3,720 million Kwh., whilst plant with a capacity of 160 Mw. and an average annual output of 473 million Kwh. was under construction in Scotland. In a recent estimate the North of Scotland Hydro-Electric Board put the potential annual output of undeveloped water power resources in its area at 4,587 million Kwh. The development of hydro-electric power in Scotland has largely taken place in the post-war years, significant pre-war schemes being mainly confined to those at Foyers, Kinlochleven, Lochaber, Rannoch, and Tummel Bridge. In 1943, however, there came the Hydro-Electric Development (Scotland) Act which set up a public authority for the development of H.E.P. in the Scottish Highlands. A large number of integrated stations were built in the post-war years from 1945 onwards, notably in Shin, Luichart, Mossford, Fasnakyle, Glenmoriston, Clunie, and Lochay. Outside the Highlands of Scotland H.E.P. stations are confined to the Southern Uplands of Scotland and the mountainous districts of north Wales: but both potential and output are relatively small. These H.E.P. schemes, although important water-users, fortunately do not add to the water-supply problems created by the increased industrial usage.

On top of the increasing industrial and domestic demand for water there are now signs of an increased agricultural need as a result of the trend towards the adoption of summer irrigation in the drier southeastern parts of England and east-central Scotland. This at first sight appears paradoxical in view of the traditional British climate. However, droughts are not infrequent. As Gregory has pointed out, an annual rainfall of 36 in. (915 mm.) is needed to offset moisture loss by evaporation—yet here rainfall is often under 30 in. (760 mm.). The deficiency can be made up by irrigation. The knowledge gained by irrigation experts in the semi-arid and arid regions of the world is now being applied to Britain with pronounced success. Careful water management will increase a potato yield by two tons an acre whilst irrigated grass pastures enable a maximum head of stock to be carried. Rotary sprinkling devices are becoming a familiar sight in southeast England for hay crops, root crops, fruit and sugar beet, whilst it has even been found advantageous to irrigate higher-value crops in parts of Pembrokeshire, Cornwall and the Tees estuary.

With short-term and long-term weather forecasts of increasing reliability, the farmer of the future can, with electrical pumps and piped water supplies, really farm scientifically. At present farmers have sufficient equipment to irrigate about 150,000 acres (100,000 ha.) of crops in a season and this is increasing at about 15,000 acres (10,000 ha.) a year. The potential acreage which could theoretically benefit is of the order of $1\frac{1}{2}$ million acres (1m. ha.). The prospective demand on the water supply is enormous—one farmer could consume a quarter of a million gallons a day (enough for a small town) and it has been calculated that in a really dry year up to 10,000 million gallons (45,000 million l.) a day could be usefully applied. This is about four times as much as the total quantity now being supplied daily by all the public water undertakings in England and Wales. With these figures we are clearly passing beyond the bounds of practical possibilities: the pressure for irrigation water however mounts and it is obviously a need which it is in the interests of the community to satisfy as far as possible.

Whilst the remaining water users are not heavy water consumers we must not in our preoccupation with the domestic, industrial and agricultural needs overlook the importance of water in the sphere of inland transport and also recreation. Although river and canal transport has declined in the British Isles it is often a surprise to many to learn that British Waterways have a total storage potential in their canals and reservoirs of 10,000 million gallons (45,000 million l.) of water and that they must have at their disposal 100 million gallons (450 million l.) a day to keep the system in being.

The use of water for recreational purposes is also important:

there are few outdoor leisure activities that do not involve water and we have to bear in mind that over fifty million people will feel the need to swim, boat, fish, skate, ski, or picnic from time to time. There are for instance over $2\frac{1}{4}$ million regular anglers in Great Britain and from many of our larger cities special anglers' trains run regularly at week-ends. Water must be conserved for all these needs or the needs must be integrated with other water uses, e.g. recreational facilities combined with water supply reservoirs.

In our natural concern with the increasing *quantity* of water needed by an increasing population with a rising standard of living, we must also not overlook the importance of the *quality* of different water resources and of the different qualities needed by the users. Problems of incrustation of pipes and boilers, scale forming con-crete dissolving, turbidity, colour, purity, saltness, hardness, soft-ness, lead poisoning, pollution and epidemics all arise from time to time to trouble the water engineers.

The quality of water from upland sources approaches that of rainwater, and the majority of upland waters are soft and slightly acid. Nearly all the streams of Ireland, Scotland, Wales and the Lake District and to a lesser extent Lancashire, Yorkshire, Derby-shire and Cornwall contain soft peaty acidified water. Those streams of the Midlands and the eastern and southern counties with gather-ing grounds of limestone, chalk and chalky boulder clay however often contain water as hard as some of the underground sources.

The quality of water from underground sources may in contrast vary considerably both chemically and bacteriologically because rainwater in its passage through the rock takes up many of the rock ingredients. The acidified character of much percolating water facilitates this attack upon the rock through which it passes. Thus soft water as it passes through chalk or limestone invariably becomes hard: on the other hand hard water passing through sandy beds may become soft. Water may become saline, contaminated or polluted and any of these conditions in excess will have repercussions on the water use.

The movement towards the concept of water conservation.

The need for the conservation and wider integration of the available water resources in the British Isles and more especially Great Britain has but recently received public recognition and is only now gaining a more rapid acceptance. In the past a smaller population on a lower standard of living found little difficulty in obtaining its water needs from the available precipitation. As a

consequence domestic water supplies were organised in relationship to established administrative units. Other water users ranging
from industrial abstractors to navigational and fishing interests
have been either unorganised or made responsible to quite different bodies, varying in Great Britain from the River Boards of
the Ministry of Agriculture and Fisheries to Port and Harbour
Authorities. In the past the land drainage engineers similarly often
worked independently and without reference to the water supply
engineers.

The collection of hydrological data has also been undertaken by
a number of different bodies and has not been co-ordinated. Great
Britain, through some 5,000 rainfall recording stations, has one of
the longest and most detailed precipitation pictures available in the
world; but, unlike the U.S.A., the rainfall data collected by the
Meteorological Office remained unsupported by any widespread
knowledge of surface run-off until the establishment of the Inland
Water Survey in 1935—and this appeared as a department of the
Ministry of Housing and Local Government. The responsibility for
collecting data on underground water resources falls to the Geological Survey and that on pollution to the Water Pollution Research
Board: both being responsible to the Department of Scientific
and Industrial Research.

Increasingly frequent water shortages and a growing realisation
of the consequences implicit in the steady and inexorable rise in
consumption have, however, combined to produce a different
climate of opinion in the last decade. The new phase dates from
1955, a year which was marked by a very dry summer and serious
water deficiencies. Renewed efforts were made to reduce the large
number of small water undertakings by amalgamation, and there
followed the reconstitution by the Minister of Housing and Local
Government of the Central Advisory Water Committee and the
Surface Water Survey both of which had been suspended as
economy measures in 1952. Since 1955 the Central Advisory Water
Committee has published a series of reports dealing with information
on water resources and the growing demand for water, whilst the
Surface Water Survey has supplemented its annual reports by a
notable series of river basin reports.

Additional impetus to the rethinking that was in progress
followed from the events of 1959-60. In the summer of 1959, the
driest for nearly 250 years in Britain, some ten million people
(nearly a quarter of the population of England and Wales) were
affected by drought orders or restrictions on their water supply.

88

This state of affairs was immediately followed in 1960 by the third wettest year for 250 years which led to serious and prolonged flooding in the autumn. Even the normally disinterested layman now began to take notice and could see the need for an integrated national policy of flood control and water conservation. Further discussion and examination of proposals took place in 1961, and early in 1962 the Central Advisory Water Committee published what might well prove to be its most significant report. The Committee's report was rapidly followed in April 1962 by a white paper to Parliament outlining proposals for an integrated policy of water conservation in England and Wales. The white paper recognised that there was little or no co-ordination between the multifarious bodies concerned with hydrological interests and that a major re-organisation was necessary to meet the anticipated changed situation of the second half of the twentieth century.

As the river basin is the natural hydrological unit the proposal was made that new authorities based on the river basin and to be called ' River Authorities ' should be set up charged with the positive duty of water conservation. This was defined as 'the preservation, control and development of water resources (both surface and ground) by storage and other methods, and the prevention of pollution to ensure that the largest possible amount of water is made available for all purposes in the most suitable and economical way whilst safeguarding legitimate interests'. It was envisaged that the River Authorities would construct and operate river regulating and other reservoirs according to need and where appropriate transfer water from one basin to another. The hydrologists in Britain who had consistently stressed the importance of the river basin as the natural physical and hence administrative unit welcomed the recognition at long last of this fundamental starting point for re-organisation. The main recommendations of the Central Advisory Water Committee and the subsequent White Paper were incorporated in the Water Resources Bill presented to Parliament in the autumn of 1962.

Along with this new approach to administrative organisation there has also been the realisation that increasing attention must be paid in future to the investigation of conservation measures such as the recharge of underground supplies (which might be especially applicable in the London Basin and in the Bunter sandstone of the Midlands), the reduction of evaporation losses, the multi-purpose approach to river basin development, the industrial re-use of water, and the adoption of integrated schemes such as those that combine the production of electric power with the desalinisation of salt or brackish water.

With the mean yield of water theoretically obtainable from the rainfall on England and Wales as a whole amounting to 40,800 million gallons (180,000 million l.) a day there would at first sight appear to be ample reserves: Nature, however, rarely distributes the water at the right time, in the right amount, and in the right place! Conservation by positive measures of flood control, water storage and regulated use alone enables the maximum value to be derived from the ample resources available.

References

BALCHIN, W. G. V., 1957. The Nation's water supply. *Geography*, **42**, 149-59.
— 1958. A water use survey. *Geogr. J.*, **124**, 476-93.
— 1961. Conservation of water in Great Britain. *Nature*, **191**, 421-23.
COLLIERY GUARDIAN COMPANY LTD. *Water Engineer's Handbook*. Annual volumes. London.
BRITISH NATIONAL COMMITTEE FOR GEODESY AND GEOPHYSICS, 1960. *Report on Hydrological Activity in the United Kingdom*. Royal Society. London.
— —1961. *Selected Bibliography of Hydrology in the United Kingdom for the years 1955-59 inclusive*. Royal Society. London.
CENTRAL ADVISORY WATER COMMITTEE, 1959. *Sub-Committee on Information on Water Resources*. H.M.S.O. London.
CENTRAL ADVISORY WATER COMMITTEE, *Sub-Committee on the Growing Demand for Water*, 1959. *First Report*. H.M.S.O. London.
— 1960. *Second Report*. H.M.S.O. London.
— 1962. *Final Report*. H.M.S.O. London.
GREGORY, S., 1957. Water supply maps of England and Wales. *Town Plann. Rev.*, **28.**
— 1958. Contributions of the uplands to the public water supply of England and Wales. *Trans. Inst. Brit. Geogr.*, **25.**
MINISTRY OF HOUSING AND LOCAL GOVERNMENT, AND SCOTTISH OFFICE. *The Surface Water Year Book of Great Britain*. Annual volumes of hydrometric statistics for British rivers, together with related rainfalls. H.M.S.O. London.
MINISTRY OF HOUSING AND LOCAL GOVERNMENT. *Hydrological Surveys of Selected River Basins*. H.M.S.O. London. (Hydrometric areas available include Wear, Tees, Great Ouse, Essex Rivers and Stour, Lee, Severn.)
NATURAL RESOURCES (TECHNICAL) COMMITTEE, Office of Ministry for Science, 1962. *Irrigation in Great Britain*. H.M.S.O. London.
PARLIAMENTARY WHITE PAPER, 1944. *A National Water Policy*. Cmnd. 6515. H.M.S.O. London.
— 1962. *Water Conservation in England and Wales*. Cmnd. 1693. H.M.S.O. London.
PLANNING, 1958. Policy for Water. *Pol. Econ. Plann.*, **24.**
RESEARCH COMMITTEE INSTITUTION OF CIVIL ENGINEERS, 1956. Recent developments in hydraulics. *Proc. Inst. Civ. Engrs.* **4,** 990-1049.
SYMPOSIUM ON CONSERVATION OF WATER RESOURCES, INSTITUTION OF CIVIL ENGINEERS. 30th October-1st November 1962. Sixteen papers with numerous references.
WALTERS, R. C. S., 1936. *The Nation's Water Supply*. London.

6

RELIEF AND STRUCTURE

Relief

THE British Isles are a detached portion of Europe rising from the western edge of a broad continental shelf, but though similar to, they are also independent of, their mainland counterparts. The two main islands exhibit considerable differences of relief, though their tectonic patterns have much in common. In Great Britain the highest land lies in the north and west in contrast to the central belt of lowland with higher land to the north and south in Ireland. Again the British main watersheds lie nearer to the west coast than the east with easterly flowing streams being commonest between the Thames and Scottish Dee. In Ireland north-south streams are more common except in the southwest and in the northern uplands.

Altitudes are low by Alpine standards, the highest point, Ben Nevis, being only 4,406 ft. (1,343 m.) above sea level, and even the more mountainous regions have smooth sky-lines indicating the presence of former plateau surfaces, though isolated peaks and greater dissection characterise the Irish uplands. The distribution of the main relief types is shown on Figure 12. Upland is considered to begin at 700 ft. (210 m.) since in southern England this altitude lies close to the limit of the Calabrian sea, which had such a significant effect upon the subsequent landscape evolution. Above 2,000 ft. (600 m.) is considered to be mountainous. Lowland is further subdivided at 350-400 ft. (105-120 m.) since in that height range there is frequently a sharp change in the general slope. Plateau surfaces have also been indicated where a considerable area of gently sloping land occurs on the summits. A simplified grouping of these units in Figure 13 reveals the basic relief pattern. There is no officially-accepted classification, though Unstead (1935) has produced the most detailed scheme to date, and many authors have used a combination of structural and relief regions.

Scotland is divisible into three major relief groupings, the Highlands and associated marginal lowlands, the Central Lowlands and the Southern Uplands. The Highlands have been blocked out of a high plateau of 2,000-3,000 ft. (600-900 m.), with occasional monadnocks above. The Highland glens are cut deeply into the

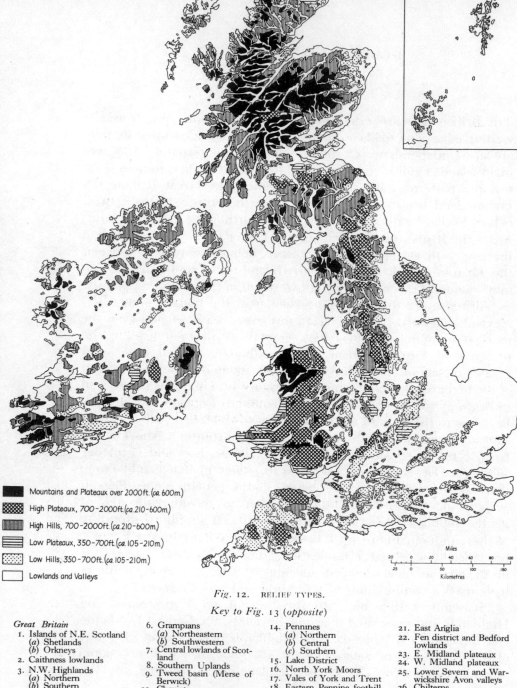

Mountains and Plateaux over 2000ft.(*ca*.600m.)

High Plateaux, 700-2000ft.(*ca*.210-600m.)

High Hills, 700-2000ft.(*ca*.210-600m.)

Low Plateaux, 350-700ft.(*ca*.105-210m.)

Low Hills, 350-700ft.(*ca*.105-210m.)

Lowlands and Valleys

Fig. 12. RELIEF TYPES.

Key to Fig. 13 (*opposite*)

92

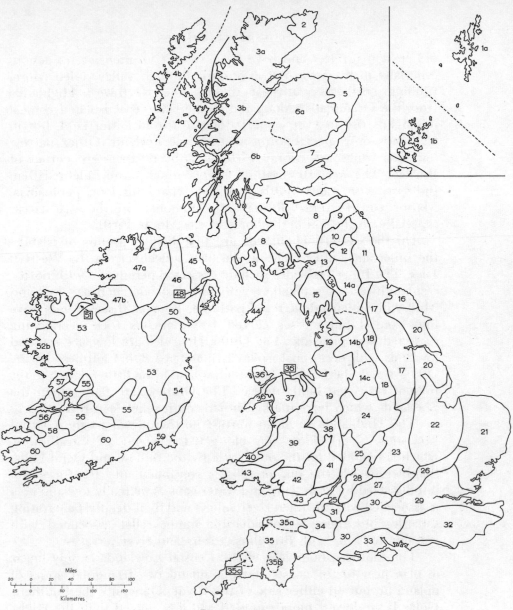

Fig. 13. RELIEF REGIONS.

29. London basin
30. Wessex Downs (including Salisbury Plain and White Horse Hills)
31. Mendip Hills
32. Weald
33. Hampshire basin
34. Somerset plain
35. Southwestern England
   (a) Exmoor
   (b) Dartmoor
   (c) Bodmin Moor
36. N. Wales coastal lowlands and Anglesey

37. Mountains of N. Wales
38. Welsh border hills
39. Dissected plateau of central Wales
40. W. Wales coastal lowlands
41. Lower Wye basin
42. Dissected plateau and mountains of S. Wales
43. S. Wales coastal lowlands
44. Isle of Man

Ireland
45. Antrim 'plateau'
46. Bann valley
47. N.W. 'Highland'
   (a) Northern
   (b) Southwestern
48. Lagan valley
49. Co. Down lowland
50. Northeastern Hills (including the Mourne Mountains)
51. Ox Mountains
52. Western uplands
   (a) Northern

   (b) Southern
53. Central lowland
54. Leinster Hills (including the Wicklow Mountains)
55. South-central hills
56. Lower Shannon lowlands
57. North Clare hills
58. Feale Hills (or Mullarghareirks)
59. Southeastern lowland
60. Southwestern ranges and valleys

old erosion surfaces and have been subject to intensive ice action, especially in the west. An important through valley, Glen More, running northeast-southwest divides the Northwest Highlands from the Grampians. Along the Sutherland coast isolated conical mountains rise to over 2,000 ft (600 m.) from flatter land, but in Caithness only glacial forms disturb the lowland. Other narrow lowlands fringe the Moray Firth and the northeastern corner of Buchan. The western coastline is very much more indented than the east, with many fjords and rias separating long peninsulas. Marine constructional forms are commoner on the east coast, especially on the southern shores of the Moray Firth.

Off the western Highlands are two distinct groups of islands, the Inner and Outer Hebrides, known collectively as the Western Isles. The Inner Hebrides include dissected peninsulas with northeast-southwest axes together with large islands such as Skye and Mull with independent relief patterns. Both of these islands have high conical hill masses carved from igneous rock overlooking dissected lava plateaux. The Outer Hebrides are low, ice-scoured lowlands with occasional isolated mountains. Off Caithness lie the Orkneys and Shetlands, whose higher land bears little relation to the present restricted land surface. The Orkneys are flatter than the Shetlands which have marked north-south relief features.

The Highlands form an abrupt northern wall to the Central Lowlands, overlooking the elongated lowland of Strathmore, which is bounded on the other side by the Sidlaw and Ochil Hills. Southwestwards the line of hills is continued into Renfrewshire, but dissected by both wind and water gaps. The really lowland area is associated with the main river valleys and their deeply-penetrating estuaries but there is considerable minor relief associated with volcanic hills, or with drumlins, eskers and river terraces.

The southern boundary of the Central Lowlands is only linear in plan near to the coasts; farther inland two triangular spurs of upland jut out on either side of the Clyde. Generally the Southern Uplands are lower, more rounded and less rugged than the Highlands, and more of the old erosion surfaces are preserved. Glaciation was again more intense in the west, especially around Loch Doon, where there is a small system of radial troughs with ribbon lakes dissecting a granite mass. The Cheviots form a spur of the Southern Uplands south of the Tweed valley, rising in The Cheviot to 2,676 ft. (816 m.).

Broadly the relief pattern of England and Wales consists of two north-south masses of upland arranged *en échelon*, formed of the

Pennines, and Wales with the Southwest Peninsula. Lowland, diversified by plateaux and cuestas makes up the remaining area. There is much more lowland than in Scotland, and the uplands are also lower.

The Pennines traditionally stop at the Tyne Gap, but the Northumbrian Fells to the north are equally typical of much of th' Pennine high plateaux, rising to over 1,000 ft. (300 m.) with occasional residuals reaching 2,000 ft. (600 m.) and dissected by deeply-entrenched rivers, whose valleys, only slightly modified by glaciation, are referred to as the Dales. The Pennines may be divided into three distinct relief regions. In the north, Cross Fell (2,930 ft., 893 m.) rises above the plateaux and overlooks the steep descent to the Vale of Eden. Only the head of the Greta (Stainmore Gap) and Ure valleys notch the western edge to provide easy transverse routes. South of the Ure watershed the Central Pennines are more dissected, with smaller expanses of plateau but more high residuals. Its northwestern part is noted for well-developed karstic phenomena. Farther south, a horseshoe-shaped ring of sandstone cuestas surrounds a central limestone plateau and much of this forms the Peak District with southeasterly-flowing rivers.

Around the Solway Firth is a strip of lowland, extended towards the southeast along the Vale of Eden, though the river only occupies an inner trench cut into rock benches modified by drumlins and many glacial drainage channels. Westwards rises the Lake District with a distinct radial pattern of glaciated troughs, many of them occupied by ribbon lakes. A through valley provides easy access from north to south but the other valleys terminate in steep heads leading to high passes in the central highland section which attains 3,210 ft. (978 m.) at Scafell.

On the eastern side of the Pennines the lowlands north of the Tees consist of a wide fringe of low hills, passing northwards into a ring of cuestas surrounding the Cheviots and succeeded eastwards by lower land covered by varying thickness of till. In eastern Durham this is largely replaced by a plateau of dolomitic limestone with a cliffed coastline. South of the Tees the surface is much lower and flatter, with large areas covered by alluvium drained by straight artificial channels. Near York two low end moraines give a slight variation and drier land. East of these low-lying areas is a region of flat-topped ridges separated by clay-vales, and flanked on the eastern side by till plains. The inner ridge, of chalk, is cut in several places by water gaps, notably by the Humber, but the outer ridge fades out in the centre and is replaced northwards by the North

York Moors, a wide expanse of steep-edged plateau, which is really a detached part of the Pennines from the point of view of relief.

The rivers flowing across the Lancastrian Lowlands are unimpeded by higher land before reaching the coast which is very low, with dunes protecting coastal marshes giving way inland to gently-rising ground with an irregular veneer of drift. The southern part is divided by a discontinuous line of low sandstone hills in Cheshire.

Low plateaux of 400-500 ft. (120-150 m.) occupy much of the Midlands with occasional residuals such as Charnwood Forest. The lower Severn and Warwickshire Avon have cut wide valleys into these plateaux which have well-developed flights of gravel terraces. The Cotswold scarp rises abruptly above these valleys to 1,134 ft. (346 m.) in the north. The top is bevelled, and forms a remnant of the western upland surfaces, sloping gradually down to the valleys of the upper Bristol Avon and upper Thames. The latter is divided longitudinally by a discontinuous line of low hills and overshadowed by the chalk cuesta on the southeastern edge. The Fen District is the northeastern continuation of this vale, though much lower and covered by peat and alluvium. Drainage and wind erosion have lowered the surface, accentuating old channel and levée deposits which rise a few feet above the lower peaty land. Seaward the land rises slightly and clay replaces peat.

East of the Fens the chalk cuesta is very low, only 150 ft. (45 m.) in the north, but it rises gradually to over 800 ft. (240 m.) in the Chilterns. This ridge is dissected by a large number of dry gaps but only the Thames cuts through it today. Continuing beyond the Thames the chalk ridge joins the dissected plateau of Salisbury Plain, much of it lying between 350 and 500 ft. (105-150 m.) but enlivened by ridges rising to 800 ft. (240 m.). Only the main valleys contain rivers, most of the tributaries being dry.

Relatively little of the Thames lowland consists of floodplain, being mainly occupied by gravel terraces and valley-side benches. On the north, dissected till sheets give added diversity, passing imperceptibly into East Anglia where most of the surface is drift-covered. The Thames estuary is the largest on the east coast, and farther north many of the smaller estuaries are blocked by spits and have silted up. In Norfolk many of the rivers are flanked by shallow lakes, called Broads, but these are not natural features, being flooded medieval peat workings. In northern Norfolk the Cromer Ridge, an end moraine, provides some local relief.

South of the London Basin the Weald is rather more complex, with the bounding chalk ridges of the North and South Downs facing inwards over a concentric series of clay vales and sandstone ridges. The Lower Greensand ridge is somewhat discontinuous but in Leith Hill (965 ft., 294 m.) it locally rises higher than the chalk downs. All of the hills are breached by northward or southward flowing streams. Farther west the Hampshire Basin is also cradled by chalk hills but the southern rim is broken by the sea, forming the Isle of Wight. The southwestern edge of the Basin is more complex, with compound ridges, extending westwards into dissected low plateaux that fall steeply towards the north into the Somerset Plain, which is very similar to the Fen District, though more divided by low ridges into separate peaty basins drained by artificial channels. On the northern edge rise the Mendips, a flat-topped limestone plateau, almost devoid of surface water and again forming an upland outlier. Farther north there is a complex series of low plateaux rising abruptly from low, former marshlands.

Southwest England, especially Devon, is part of upland Britain. On the north coast the high plateau of Exmoor plunges quickly to the sea. In the south Dartmoor shows many of the classic features of granite landscapes, most hilltops being crowned by fantastically-shaped tors. To the west of Dartmoor the land is much lower, Bodmin Moor, another large granite mass, being the main upland. Much of the rest is dissected low plateaux interrupted by smaller granite masses and steep-sided valleys whose lower courses are drowned. Most of the rivers rise very close to the northern coast which in consequence has fewer estuaries.

Wales, like Scotland, consists largely of high plateaux, but the surfaces are better preserved and the valleys have suffered less intensive glaciation. The highest and most glaciated area occurs in the north, especially around Snowdon (3,561 ft., 1,085 m.) and often the mountains approach close to the sea though embayments of lowland occupy the Clwyd and Conway valleys, and Anglesey is a very low plateau. The north coast is relatively smooth, with but one estuary at the Conway mouth, but south of the Lleyn Peninsula rias are well developed with straight stretches of spit-defended marshland fronting the high mountains.

The upland plains of central Wales are characterised by three erosion surfaces (described in chapter 7), and by a few monadnocks. The Wye drains most of this area, flowing through a well-defined interior plain near Builth. In its lower course, dissection is more complete and interior lowlands interrupted by discontinuous lines of low hill, are the typical landforms. The eastern edge of this area is more complex, including the stark, jagged ridge of the Malverns.

On the southern edge the Wye has cut a magnificent series of incised meanders into the Forest of Dean, an outlier of the lowest Welsh erosion surface. Towards the northeast, the plateau surfaces become broken up into isolated hill ranges around the Teme valley, and so these Welsh Border hills have been separated off from central Wales. The Severn valley cuts through a spur of these hills at Ironbridge as far as Bewdley.

The high plateaux continue into the eastern part of south Wales, and their northern rim reaches over 2,000 ft. (600 m.) in the Brecon Beacons and in their continuation in the Black Hills, cut off by the Usk valley. Farther south the surface is strongly dissected by two sets of parallel valleys at right angles to each other. The plateau surface drops quickly to the low coastal plateau of Glamorgan and west of the river Lougher similar coastal plateaux prevail in Carmarthenshire and Pembroke. The coast of south Wales is largely cliffed with very well-developed estuaries and occasional low constructional coasts facing southwest.

As in Scotland, so in England and Wales the west coast is more irregular than the east. Estuaries are commoner and longer on the west, but fjords are absent. Cliffed coasts predominate except off the lowlands of Lancashire and Somerset. The smoother east coast is much lower and constructional forms commoner. The south coast is intermediate between the other two with fine rias in the southwest, but low cliffs are more frequent than spits and marshes. Good examples of constructional forms do occur, notably at Chesil Bank and Dungeness Foreland. Small islands are commonest on the west coast, but Anglesey and the Isle of Man are the only large ones. This last is an extension of the Lake District mountains, rising to 2,034 ft. (620 m.) in Snaefell though the northern and southern tips of the island are quite low and a through valley bisects the mountain core.

Ireland has much more lowland than Britain, much of it between 200-300 ft. (60-90 m.) above the sea, though little of it lies below 100 ft. (30 m.) The highland is concentrated in the north and south with a little in the west and it is much more dissected than in Britain with a general absence of high plateaux.

The northern upland region is divided by lowlands into three parts, of which the largest, the Northwest Highlands of Ramsey, is fairly complex, being mainly arranged around the river Foyle. Tributary valleys have a marked northeast-southwest trend, and in Donegal some of these are occupied by ribbon lakes. Near to the coast is a low coastal platform except in the southwest where

Slieve League (1,972 ft., 601 m.) falls straight into the sea, making the highest cliff in the British Isles. A southwestern extension of the uplands is cut by various streams, including the Erne which expands into island-studded lakes. An extension of the Central Lowlands reaches into the heart of northeast Ireland and continues northwards as the Bann Valley, much of which is occupied by Lough Neagh. Eastwards the lowland continues down the Lagan valley into northern Co. Down. Much of the local relief of this belt is produced by drumlins which occur in large numbers. In the northeast the lowlands cut off the Antrim 'Plateau', which is really a dissected upland with parallel valleys modified by glacial action. South of the Ulster lowlands is another complex hill mass at its greatest altitude in the Mourne Mountains.

In the Central Lowland, apart from isolated hills, glacial drift forms the major relief. Most of this area is drained by the Shannon and much is very flat and boggy. To the west the western uplands are bisected by Clew Bay and both halves are heavily glaciated, Connemara in the southern half having a radiating system of lake-filled troughs. Off to the northeast, the Ox Mountains form an elongated outlier of these hills.

The southern upland region is less homogeneous than the northern hills. The Leinster Hills are largely composed of the granite-cored Wicklow Mountains and there are few through valleys. The Wexford Lowlands lie to the southeast. In the south-west is a parallel series of west-east streams and ridges, turning towards the southwest in the far west where the relief is much higher and reaches 3,414 ft. (1,041 m.) in Macgillycuddy's Reeks. Around the mouth of the Shannon is an extension of the Central Lowlands relieved in northern Clare by limestone plateaux capped by residual hills and southwards by an anomalous hill mass with no general name around the river Feale.

The Irish coasts are more like those of England than Scotland. The west coast is more indented with long rias and peninsulas, while the south coast conforms more with the general run of the relief though cutting obliquely across it. The east is relatively smooth with a few major estuaries in the north but it is only in the southeast that lowland coasts with spits and bars blocking the estuaries are found. Cliffed coasts predominate, and some are of outstanding beauty.

Geological structure

The geology of the British Isles is extremely varied due to

rapid alternations of lithology and distinct tectonic patterns. A table of strata is given below and for distributional details geological maps should be consulted, the most suitable being the 25 miles : 1 inch of the British Isles and the 1 : 625,000 map of Great Britain.

Outcrops of sedimentary rocks occupy much greater areas than either igneous or metamorphic rocks, though locally igneous rocks are important for their resistance to weathering which usually makes them stand out. The main occurrences are shown in Figure 14.

The tectonic patterns of the British Isles correspond closely with the general age of the rocks and in Figure 14 four major groups of rocks are shown, Pre-Cambrian, Lower Palaeozoic, Upper Palaeozoic (less Permian) and post-Carboniferous (Permian, Mesozoic and Cainozoic). These rocks were subject to deformation mainly at the end of their era, giving rise to particular trend lines of folding and faulting, though sometimes depositional conditions and deep structures interfered with the general pattern. Four major alignments are usually recognised, named after typical localities, i.e. Malvernian (north-south) and Charnian (northwest-southeast) of Pre-Cambrian age; Caledonian (northeast-southwest) of Lower Palaeozoic age; and Variscan (east-west) of Upper Palaeozoic age (also termed Altaid, Armorican and Hercynian). The last tectonic episode, the Alpine, also produced east-west lineaments. (Structures that parallel older structures are usually distinguished by the suffix -oid.) The groups have been subdivided on the basis of the intensity of the folding.

There is a close general relationship between the Pre-Cambrian rocks and the Scottish Highlands, though northeast Buchan and the Outer Hebrides are exceptional in being lowland. The summit planes cut indifferently across the most complicated structures in the British Isles. The general structural lineaments are Caledonian but at least five different periods of deformation are known, some resulting in great nappe structures, the largest causing Moine schists to be pushed at least 10 miles (16 km.) over gently-dipping Cambrian rocks in Sutherland. The associated Moine Thrust Plane outcrops along a line running from Loch Eriboll in Sutherland towards southeast Skye. Several later faults on Caledonoid lines have been etched out by rivers and ice, including Glen Spey and Glen More. This last is on the line of a sinistral wrench fault with a horizontal displacement of 65 miles (105 km.). The existence has been claimed of another sinistral wrench fault with a displacement of 75 miles (120 km.) under the Minch.

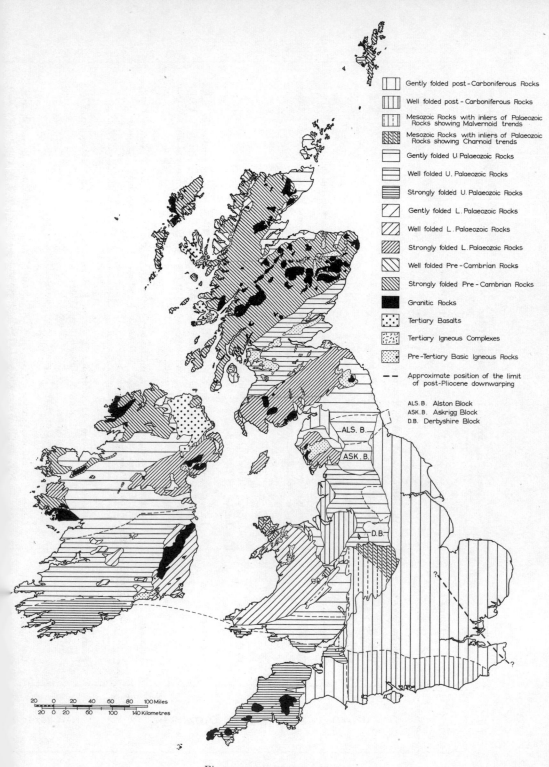

Gently folded post-Carboniferous Rocks

Well folded post-Carboniferous Rocks

Mesozoic Rocks with inliers of Palaeozoic Rocks showing Malvernoid trends

Mesozoic Rocks with inliers of Palaeozoic Rocks showing Charnoid trends

Gently folded U. Palaeozoic Rocks

Well folded U. Palaeozoic Rocks

Strongly folded U. Palaeozoic Rocks

Gently folded L. Palaeozoic Rocks

Well folded L. Palaeozoic Rocks

Strongly folded L. Palaeozoic Rocks

Well folded Pre-Cambrian Rocks

Strongly folded Pre-Cambrian Rocks

Granitic Rocks

Tertiary Basalts

Tertiary Igneous Complexes

Pre-Tertiary Basic Igneous Rocks

Approximate position of the limit of post-Pliocene downwarping

ALS.B.   Alston Block
ASK.B.   Askrigg Block
D.B.   Derbyshire Block

ALS. B.

ASK. B.

D.B.

20   0   20   40   60   80   100 Miles
20   0   20   60   100   140 Kilometres

Fig. 14.   STRUCTURAL REGIONS.

Table 4. Strata of the British Isles

Era	Period	General Lithology
CAINOZOIC	**Pleistocene**	Alluvium, gravel, till, and minor littoral deposits.
	Pliocene	Thin littoral deposits in S.E. England.
	Miocene	Absent—Alpine folding in S. England.
	Oligocene	Largely lacustrine clays, sandstones and limestone in Hampshire Basin and Devon.
	Eocene	Predominantly clay, with sands and flint gravels in the London and Hampshire Basins. Clays in N. Ireland with basalt lavas, extending into the W. Isles.
MESOZOIC	**Cretaceous**	*Upper* Chalk mainly in S.E. and E. England and N.E. Ireland. *Lower* Clays and sandstone in S.E. England.
	Jurassic	Limestones and clays in S., S.E. and E. England, and S. Wales. Much sandier in N.E. Yorkshire and subsidiary ironstones in L. and M. Jurassic of E. Midlands and N.E. Yorkshire. Patches of sands, shales, limestones and thin coals on E. and W. coasts of the Scottish Highlands. Clays in N.E. Ireland.
	Triassic	Sandstones, conglomerates and mudstones in the Midlands, Pennine flanks, Solway Firth, S.W. England, N. and S. Wales, N.E. Ireland and scattered patches in W. Scotland.
PALÆOZOIC	**Permian**	Dolomitic limestone and sandstones E. of the Pennines; sandstones and breccias in N.W. and S.W. England. Dolomitic limestone in Ulster. Main Variscan folding. Granitic intrusions in S.W. England and Scottish Highlands.
	Carboniferous	*Upper* Sandstones, shales and coals in C. Scotland, N. England, Midlands, Bristol district, N.E. and S. Wales and C. Ireland. Shales and sandstones in S.W. Peninsula (Culm

		Description
UPPER	Devonian	*Lower* Massive limestone in C. and S. Pennines, N.E. and S. Wales, Mendips, C. Ireland, Isle of Man. Replaced in part by shales, sandstone and coals in N. England and Scotland. Shales and thin limestones in S.W. England (Culm) and S.W. Ireland (plus sandstones). Basic lavas in Scotland and Derbyshire. Mainly sandstones in Scotland, Cheviots, Welsh borders and S. Wales (with marls) and Ireland. Transition to marine sandstones, shales and limestones between N. and S. Devon and Cornwall. Main Caledonian folding in L. Devonian. Lavas in Scotland, granitic intrusions in S.W. Highlands, S. Uplands, Cheviots and Leinster.
LOWER PALAEOZOIC	Silurian	Shales, sandstones and greywackes in S. Uplands, Lake District, N. and C. Wales, C. and N.E. Ireland. Some argillaceous limestones in Welsh Borders and Midlands.
	Ordovician	Shales and sandstones in S. Uplands, Lake District, N. and S.W. Wales, Leinster mountains and N.E. Ireland. Lavas and ash in Lake District, N. Wales and Ireland.
	Cambrian	Shales, sandstones and quartzite in N. and S.W. Wales, Shropshire, and Midlands. Slates and flagstones in I. of Man, Dolomitic limestone over sandstones in N.W. Scotland.
	Pre-Cambrian	Chiefly schists, gneisses, with quartzites, marmorised limestones and igneous rocks. Exposed in isolated inliers except in Scottish Highlands and N.W. Ireland. In Scotland the following sequence is recognised:
	Torridonian	Sandstones with shales, arkoses and conglomerates in Sutherland, Lewis and Skye.
	Dalradian	Schists, with slates, quartzites, arkoses and conglomerates in S.E. Grampians and Shetlands.
	Moinian	Schists and granulites mainly, in N.W. Highlands and N.W. Grampians.
	Lewisian	Gneisses in two groups, the younger Laxfordian and older Scourian separated by dolerite dykes, in Sutherland and Outer Hebrides.

In Sutherland, gently-dipping Torridonian sandstone rests unconformably upon Lewisian gneiss and the residuals of the coastal area are composed of the former rocks. The Scourian rocks were folded on Caledonoid lines, the Laxfordian on Charnian. In the Moine series east of the Moine thrust, north-northeast-south-southwest trends are commonest, but systems with other trends were superimposed upon these. In the southwest Grampians around Glen Coe, Bailey (1950) has detected a complicated series of nappes and overfolds which have been caught up in later movements and injected by granites. Also in Buchan a nappe has been postulated on stratigraphical grounds, but the shear planes have been destroyed by five later periods of metamorphism. Here again Caledonian trends prevail, but there are also fold-axes at right angles to these. Nearer the Highland Boundary fault which forms the edge of the Central Lowlands, the degree of metamorphism decreases and some of the recumbent structures overturn southeastwards.

Much of the northwestern and western uplands of Ireland form part of the same structural province as the Highlands, and many of the smaller valleys pick out the dominant Caledonian trend. In the Shetlands there are more Dalradian rocks but with a Malvernian trend and further nappe structures. The lack of fossils and intense metamorphism makes correlation difficult over wide areas though absolute measurements using radio-active minerals are beginning to help (Giletti, 1961).

The Lower Palaeozoic rocks are much less metamorphosed and deformed than their predecessors and show general northeast-southwest strike lines and fold axes. In Sutherland a thin strip of unfolded Cambrian rocks does not fit in with the general pattern which is of decreasing intensity of folding from north to south. The Southern Uplands are the most complicated, structurally speaking. Lapworth deciphered a northern anticlinorium and southern synclinorium made up of tight, isoclinal folds. Recent work suggests the presence of asymmetric anticlines separated by strike faults and often complicated by thrusting. The northern boundary consists of successive normal faults hading northwards, but in the southwest Ordovician rocks also occur on the downthrow side around Girvan, where nine different periods of folding have occurred. Most of the valleys run in the direction of the regional dip —southeastwards—and some run along lines of post-Caledonian folding on Charnoid lines marked by Carboniferous and Permian inliers.

The Lake District Lower Palaeozoic rocks form the southern

limb of an anticlinorium creased by short Caledonian folds and cut by north-south faulting. (The Isle of Man belongs to the same structure.) The central mountainous area coincides with the very resistant Borrowdale volcanics, but the drainage pattern shows little adjustment to the structure. In north Wales deformation was accompanied by low-grade metamorphism and some cleavage, with strongly-asymmetric folding more Variscoid in direction, but westwards and southwards the folding becomes less intense and more normal in direction. In the Welsh Border hills the folding is very shallow and open, being affected by the underlying basement which is not far below, and even appears at the surface occasionally. Some of the faults of this zone appear to have been rejuvenated by later movements.

The Lower Palaeozoic rocks of Ireland are more dispersed in their outcrops, the largest being in northeast Ireland and the Leinster Hills. The former continues the Scottish Southern Uplands, but without the boundary faults, and the second has a more north-northeast-south-southwest trend. Both of these areas have granitic intrusions, the latter, in the Wicklows, being the largest batholith in the British Isles and continuing southwestwards for some considerable distance beneath its sedimentary cover. Many of the isolated hills of central Ireland contain cores of Lower Palaeozoic rocks, with Caledonian structures.

The Upper Palaeozoic rocks were laid down in less continuous basins than the earlier deposits and so they show less uniformity, but in general there is a tendency towards greater simplicity of structure northwards, especially in Ireland and southern England. Trend lines are also more varied, being only markedly Variscan in the southern parts of these islands. In northeast Scotland and the Orkneys there are detached fragments of a former greater expanse of Devonian sandstones which have been more easily eroded than the metamorphic rocks and have been largely reduced to lowland. Quite detached is the central graben, lying between the Highland and Southern Boundary faults and forming a synclinorium with a general Caledonoid axis, but individual basins have more independent axes inherited from their depositional phase. Thick masses of lava further complicate the tectonic pattern.

In northernmost England the granite core of the Cheviots forms the centre of a dome that successively exposes Devonian lavas and Lower Carboniferous rocks of Scottish facies, including sandstones, shales and limestone, the first making bold cuestas. South of the Tyne, Carboniferous rocks cover stable blocks which are probably composed largely of Pre-Cambrian rocks, though a small mass of granite has been proved under the northernmost or Alston Block. These massifs with sharp, faulted boundaries have protected the overlying rocks from deformation. Another block underlies the Derbyshire Dome, though it has a greater thickness of rocks over it. Between the blocks greater thicknesses of more argillaceous rocks with some sandstones and limestones have been folded along Caledonoid lines, especially in south Lancashire, where the uplands of Bowland and Rossendale coincide with folded structures. Stress was also relieved by normal faulting running northwest-southeast. Other folds wrap around the Derbyshire Dome and some cross its main north-south anticlinal structure in Variscan lines that turn eastwards along Charnoid trends. The blocks underlie the present high plateaux; the westward-flowing rivers such as the Ribble have eaten into the softer rocks of the Central Pennines, though the southern part is high due to a very great increase in sandstones. In northeast Wales there are narrow strips of Carboniferous rocks with Charnoid strikes and fold axes.

In South Wales and the Bristol District, the general outcrop of Upper Palaeozoic rocks is triangular in shape, the apex of the triangle being an area of very gentle structures, though the eastern boundary is complicated by the Malverns. Farther south, after open folds under the South Wales Coalfield, folds of short wavelength occur under the coastal plateaux, and in the Mendips thrusting occurs at Vobster. Even greater disturbances are found in the southwest peninsula, where there is evidence to suggest widescale thrusting of Devonian over Carboniferous rocks under Exmoor. Devon and Cornwall form a synclinorium, disturbed by a great granite batholith which is exposed in Dartmoor, Bodmin Moor, etc. Folding and thrusting increase in intensity southwards and the southern tips of Devon and Cornwall consist of metamorphosed Devonian rocks associated with major thrusts. It has been suggested recently that in Tertiary times Variscan dextral wrench faults were reactivated, resulting in lateral displacements up to 22 miles (35 km.).

The Irish Upper Palaeozoic rocks form a compact mass making up most of the island. In the north and centre the trend lines are Caledonoid, but markedly Variscan in the south. In the extreme north there is little folding of these rocks, only block faulting. In central Ireland the folds are still very gentle and dips are low. In the southwest from Galway Bay to Waterford, there is a thrust zone, to the south of which folding is much stronger and also associated with a facies change in the Carboniferous rocks, and a close adjustment of the relief to the geological structure.

The largest area of post-Carboniferous rocks is in southern and eastern England where a mantle of Jurassic and later rocks covers a more complicated pattern of older rocks, in part exposed in the Midlands. The newer sediments consist of alternating argillaceous and calcareous rocks, the latter forming well-developed cuestas. North of the Thames the basement is relatively near to the surface, and so has prevented the overlying strata from being seriously folded. In the Weald where the Jurassic and Cretaceous rocks were much thicker, an anticlinorium with tight east-west folds and strike faults resulted from Alpine compressional movements. Somewhat fewer east-west folds cross the Hampshire basin, the southern limb of which is exceptionally steep. There is also simple folding and parallel faulting along Variscoid lines in northeast Yorkshire. Although subject to considerable denudation the anticlines still correspond broadly with upland areas and the basins with lowlands.

Subsidence in independent basins was more prevalent in Triassic times, reaching a depth of 6,500 ft. (2,000 m.) in Cheshire in an oval basin with a Caledonoid axis. Remnants of a similar basin but probably with a Charnoid axis are to be found in Lancashire and west Cumberland with the remainder under the Irish Sea. In the Midlands fault-bounded basins were developed between horsts of Pre-Cambrian rocks covered with thin deposits of Palaeozoic age. In the west these were orientated on Malvernoid lines and eastwards on Charnoid lines, and these are distinguished in Figure 14. On the eastern flank of the Pennines, Permo-Triassic rocks exhibit the same simple structures as the later rocks and have been included in the same structural region. In the Bristol District, Somerset, Devon and South Wales, Triassic rocks wrap unconformably around older structures, and subsequent differential weathering has removed much of the softer Triassic material (and Permian in Devon). It is probable that Permo-Triassic rocks underlie the entrance to the English Channel and parts of the Irish Sea.

Solway Firth is in part carved out of more Permo-Carboniferous deposits, which also outcrop in the Vale of Eden. In Scotland and Ireland, post-Carboniferous strata are rarely preserved. Many of those that do exist owe their preservation to burial beneath the Eocene lavas of Northern Ireland and the Western Isles. Up to 6,000 ft. (1,800 m.) were poured out on Mull, but later subsidence caused warping and collapse. The Cuillins of Skye are formed from one

of the igneous complexes associated with these outpourings. There
is also a great dyke swarm injected along Charnoid lines in the Inner
Hebrides, and a few of the dykes penetrate as far as northern England.

Gravels associated with the Calabrian shoreline occur above
650 ft. (185 m.) around the London Basin, but in East Anglia
contemporary deposits are at sea level. This is probably due to
downwarping associated with the Rhine delta area, and there is
some morphological evidence to support this. A 'hinge line' for this
movement has been tentatively suggested on Figure 14.

Since the last war much geophysical information has been
published, though the data are still incomplete. De Bruyn (1955)
has summarised the gravity anomaly information and the Geological
Survey is publishing a series of overlays on the scale of 1 : 253,440
of Bouguer anomalies, whilst Murphy is producing a similar series
of maps for Ireland. The results to date indicate that the highland
areas of Wales, the southern Pennines and the northwestern and
western uplands of Ireland have strong positive gravity anomalies,
whereas the Mesozoic basins of Cheshire, the Midlands and
southern England have marked negative values. The northern
Pennines are nearly perfectly adjusted. The data concerning Scotland is very meagre, but a strong series of anomalies is known to
occur over the Outer Hebrides, and the Highlands probably have
negative values. The occurrence of such marked variations in
close proximity indicates a rigid crust beneath these islands without
close isostatic adjustment locally. Perhaps the Highlands may be
more sensitive to change since raised beaches indicate a post-
glacial upwarping in that area.

Conclusion

It is evident from a comparison of Figures 12 and 14 that there is
great deal of broad adjustment between the geological structure and
the relief. The Lower Palaeozoic blocks and the Pre-Cambrian mass
of the Highlands stand out clearly. Within these masses many of the
rivers do not conform to the structural lines, though others show
marked adjustment, especially those flowing into the sea to the west
of Great Britain. The correlation in Ireland is much less perfect,
because planation has proceeded further there. In detail the effect
of differences of lithology is most marked, often quite rapid changes
in rocks produce an immediate response in valley width and degree
of slope. Where the contrasts in rock type are great and the struc-

ture simple as in southeast England there is very strong adjustment of the landscape to the structure. Where planation has proceeded far over complicated tectonic patterns, these last are not so clearly detectable as in the Midlands.

References

ARKELL, W. J., 1936. Analysis of the Mesozoic and Cainozoic Folding in England. *Rept. 16th Int. Geol. Congr.*, **1**, 937-52.

BAILEY, E. B., 1950. The Structural History of Scotland. *Rept. 18th Int. Geol. Congr.*, **1**, 230-55.

DE BRUYN, J. W., 1955. Isogam Maps of Europe and North Africa. *Geophysical Prospecting*, **3**, 1-14.

CHARLESWORTH, J. K., 1963. *The Historical Geology of Ireland.*

COE, K. (ed.), 1962. *Some Aspects of the Variscan Fold Belt.*

EVANS, J. W., and STUBBLEFIELD, C. J., 1929. *Handbook of the Geology of Great Britain.*

FALCON, N. L., and KENT, P. E., 1960. *Geological results of Petroleum Exploration in Britain* 1945-1957.

GILETTI, B. J., *et al.*, 1961. A geochronological study of the metamorphic complexes of the Scottish Highlands. *Quart. J. Geol. Soc.*, **117**, 180-90.

KENT, P. E., 1949. A structure contour map of the surface of the buried Pre-Permian rocks of England and Wales. *Proc. Geol. Assoc.*, **60**, 87-104.

READ, H. H., 1961. Aspects of Caledonian magmatism in Britain. *Liverpool and Manch. Geol. J.*, **2**, 653-93.

STEERS, J. A., 1946. *The Coastline of England and Wales.*

— 1952. The Coastline of Scotland. *Geogr. J.*, **118**, 180-90.

TRUEMAN, A. E., 1938. *The Scenery of England and Wales.*

UNSTEAD, J. F., 1935. *The British Isles.*

WILLS, L. J., 1951. *A Palaeogeographical Atlas of the British Isles.*

7

TERTIARY LANDSCAPE EVOLUTION

GREAT BRITAIN is a large island of strikingly irregular shape and diversity of relief forms. Ireland has a diversity of its own, and only occasionally duplicates features of the larger island. Much of this diversity in both islands reflects the nature and disposition of the underlying rocks, and one of the characteristic traits of British physiography is the generally high degree of adjustment of surface to structure in both islands. This was brilliantly set forth by Archibald Geikie in his *Scenery of Scotland* (1865), it was the main concern of Lord Avebury's *Scenery of England* (1902), and it is still the essential basis for any understanding of the pattern of British relief.

Yet, although the concordant relation of surface to structure is widespread it is by no means universal. Discordance of streams to structures is common both in detail and at a large scale, and in such cases as the rivers of the Weald, of south Wales, or of southern Ireland has excited attention for at least a century. Hardly less conspicuous are the remnants of base-levelled surfaces, that, especially at higher altitudes, pass with a high degree of indifference across outcrops of contrasted rocks. Such discordances between streams and structures, or between structure and surface, can only be explained in terms of hypotheses of drainage evolution or denudation chronology. Such hypotheses, in the present state of knowledge, are not infrequently mutually inconsistent and consequently our prime concern must be, not so much to give a plausible account of what may have been the course of Tertiary landscape evolution, as to indicate the principal forms of evidence that have been brought forward and the conclusions toward which they tend.

Our aim is to reconstruct in outline the history of landscape evolution in our region before the impact of the glacial episodes. Part of the story will probably remain a matter of surmise only, for, almost certainly, the later stages destroyed the work of the early periods. And even the work of later Tertiary times has been everywhere profoundly modified by the multifarious changes brought about by Quaternary events, especially the cutting of the low-level valleys we now see, in relation to a generally falling base-level.

Landscape evolution in the English plain

The first significant step in evolving a denudation chronology for the English Plain was made in 1875 when Topley claimed that present valleys and lowlands were carved from a former widespread surface now represented only by the accordant summits of the uplands. Southeast of a line drawn from east Yorkshire, past the southern Pennines, the Malverns and Quantocks to the southeast corner of Dartmoor, he found that 'the summits of the various hills and escarpments rise to 700, 800 and in a very few cases to 900 feet. They evidently point to the former existence of a great plain of marine denudation over this area. This plain is far older than the glacial period; for the escarpments around which the Boulder Clay and other deposits of that period have accumulated, have been carved out of it. It is later than the Eocene period; for outliers of that formation lie scattered over the plateaux'. Moreover, he recognised that such a view facilitated the explanation of 'the present system of longitudinal and transverse valleys', for, he wrote, 'to achieve this result it is necessary that the strata should be *planed across* so that successive rocks in turn should crop up to the surface'.

Other workers gave greater precision to the concept over more restricted areas. Jukes-Browne (1895) recognised that the flat interfluvial uplands of the Dorset Downs are cut indifferently across several stages of the Chalk and attributed both the flats and 'a reddish, sandy loam or clay, full of flints' that he found upon them, to marine action. Andrews (1891) had interpreted the ridges on either side of the Vale of Wardour as relics of a former plane of marine erosion uplifted and tilted to the east. Since it bevelled the mid-Tertiary folds he suggested a Pliocene date for the planation.

In 1895 Davis put forward the alternative interpretation of these upland surfaces as remnants of a fluviatile peneplain. In his view the present rivers are the 'revived and matured successors of a well adjusted system . . . inherited from an earlier and far advanced cycle of denudation', but for some areas this assumption leads to insurmountable difficulties. In 1910 Bury showed for a part of the western Weald that at the beginning of the present cycle of erosion certain subsequent streams, now well established, had no existence, and that cherty sandstone from the outcrops of the Lower Greensand (Aptian) had been transported across their present courses to be incorporated in flint gravels on the crest of the North Downs. Clearly the drainage of this area has arisen in one cycle, not two as Davis's hypothesis demands. The same conclusion was advanced for the Wessex rivers in 1932 by Linton, for here the major streams are so out of accord with the structures that they cannot be regarded as derivatives of the drainage initiated by the mid-Tertiary folding. To explain this regional discordance superposition must be invoked; this, it was thought, might have been from a cover of fluviatile deposits resulting from widespread aggradation consequent upon a rise of base-level. This hypothesis still finds favour with Pinchemel (1954). However, the evidence of superposition of streams in Wessex, Sussex, and the western Weald overlaps with the area in which marine transgression had already been demonstrated by Wooldridge in 1927. After re-examination of the Wessex area in the light of the evidence from the London Basin, Wooldridge and Linton concluded in 1938 that marine transgression had occurred throughout the area in which epigenesis could be established, and tentatively drew a coastline limiting the submerged area. From this result certain conclusions follow.

(*a*) The coastline reveals a large unsubmerged tract in the Wealden area and some smaller islands, implying a true transgression submerging ground already eroded to a lower level and sparing areas less thoroughly degraded.

(*b*) The unsubmerged tracts differ from those submerged in one or all of three ways: they possess residual elevations that have local relief 100-150 ft. (30-50 m.) in contrast to the uniformity of level of those portions of the wave-cut bench that survive in the North Downs and Chilterns; they possess a 'revived and adjusted' drainage of generally longitudinal and accordant character; and they commonly carry deposits, mapped as 'Clay with Flints' or 'Clay with Chert', that are certainly polygenetic but include materials most satisfactorily regarded as residues of the regolith developed *in situ* on a former land surface. In a word they can be identified as parts of the later Tertiary peneplain postulated by Davis.

(*c*) Where the shoreline can be traced most definitely, in the North Downs, Chilterns, and Marlborough Downs, it shows no significant or systematic variations in altitude, and may be represented by the generalised contour of 650 ft. (c. 200 m.). Thus, over the area just specified, later changes of base-level have presumably been eustatic. Two qualifications, however, should be added. First, there may have been a measure of differential upwarping of the margins compared with the axial portion of the London Basin.

Second, while uniformity of altitude characterises the strandline from Marlborough to Luton or from Andover to Maidstone and Lenham, marked relative downwarping must ensue farther to the northeastward, for the main outcrops of the Red Crag are at low levels on the Essex-Suffolk border, and the equivalent horizon is far below sea level near Lowestoft. Differential subsidence has been shown by Coleman (1952) to have occurred in northeast Kent and we may conclude that the whole of East Anglia and the Thames estuary region belong to the margin of the subsiding North Sea depression.

(d) The date at which the sea stood along this strandline must be presumed to be that of the fossiliferous Red Crag (Scaldisian) sandstone that was found in 1926 in sands resting on the associated wave-cut bench at Netley Heath on the North Downs near Guildford. This is now correlated with the lowest or Calabrian division of the Italian marine Pleistocene. It should be noted that in solution subsidences or 'pipes' in the chalk near Lenham in Kent at heights exceeding 600 ft. (200 m.) sandstone blocks have yielded a fauna of earlier Pliocene (Diestian) age, regarded by Reid as having lived in water 40 fathoms (70 m.) deep. Shotton takes this to imply a Pliocene sea level 900 ft. (275 m.) above present—a conclusion difficult to reconcile with the morphological evidence already noted.

Topley's conception of a planation of the English plain anterior to the cutting of the present valleys can now be given some precision. During Miocene and Pliocene times the relief created by the mid-Tertiary foldings had been virtually destroyed, and by late Pliocene times a land surface of low relief existed, to be later partly submerged by the transgressive Calabrian sea. Marine modification of the surface on submergence, together with slight warping during regression, gave rise in the emerged areas to a new and simple pattern of drainage that has since been superimposed on the underlying structures. During Pleistocene times the existing valleys and lowlands have all been opened up and there has been extensive adjustment of surface to structure.

Evidence exists to show that valley excavation has been related to a spasmodically-falling, eustatically-controlled base-level. Sparks finds both along the seaward face of the South Downs (1949) and in the Weymouth lowland (1952) nine benches between 475 and 130 ft. (145 and 40 m.). These benches have been recognised by purely morphological evidence, but the lowest of them has long been known by its associated deposits. It is, in fact, the 'Hundred Foot' raised beach of west Sussex. In the Hampshire Basin Everard (1956) finds evidence for benching of the chalk dipslopes of the northeast and northwest margins at heights virtually identical with those mapped by Sparks. Here, however, the concept of marine excavation of the soft-rock infilling of an almost completely enclosed basin is not easy of acceptance.

During the process of valley excavation that produced the main outlines of the topography of Lowland England an important structural plane was widely uncovered—namely, the uppermost surface of the Chalk on which the Eocene formations rest. This surface is of importance for two reasons. On the one hand enough of it has been revealed—perhaps 400-500 square miles (1,500 sq. km.) in the aggregate—for it to form a significant element in the present landscape. On the other hand it proves an earlier period of erosion of particular importance since it is the period in which the late Cretaceous sea-floor was upraised throughout the British region, never again, in the view of many, to be generally submerged. There is good reason to think that the period of erosion involved— which comprises the Maastrichtian, Danian, and Montian stages of European stratigraphy—saw the reduction of relief to a peneplain. There is no basis in England for the view of Pinchemel that the sub-Eocene surface is an irregular one of karstic erosion, with fossilised lapiés and dolines. Where it has been made irregular, as beneath the Blackheath Beds south of London, this is the result of later and sub-surface solution. The base of the lowest Eocene beds when seen in section is very regular, and its exhumed representative is a very regular surface. The oldest bed resting upon it—unworn flints at the base of the Thanetian—is rightly described by Pinchemel as a pre-Tertiary clay-with-flints divested of its fine constituents by wave-winnowing during the advance of the sea. The thickness of the Senonian Chalk that was eroded before Thanetian times and could have contributed the unworn flints amounts to roughly 1,000 ft. (300 m.) in the London area. As this district is approached from either Hampshire or Norfolk where the Senonian is most complete, the lowest Eocene beds overstep the palaeontological zones one by one. Detailed study of the zonal distribution by Wooldridge and Linton (1938) shows that the initial relief in the lower Thames region was already marked by east-west folding, and strongly suggests that both in the Weald and the south Midlands rocks older than the Chalk were already exposed.

Important, however, as is the sub-Eocene surface of southeast England, the evidence does not favour the conclusion reached by

Pinchemel that it is 'the fundamental surface' of this region and the nearer parts of France, or that, in his own words, 'elle n'a été retouchée que faiblement par les niveaux d'érosion localisés de la fin du Pliocène et du Quaternaire'. His belief that the Clay-with-Flints of the higher crests reflects the recent proximity of the Eocene base is readily disproved by the fact that these crests fall much lower in the Senonian zonal sequence than the zone that outcropped locally on the sub-Eocene plane. In fact the true sub-Eocene surface is commonly stripped remarkably clean. As was clearly recognised by White (1923), the sub-Eocene surface rises from the main Eocene outcrops with visible inclination and is bevelled with angular discordance by the late-Tertiary peneplain. It is the latter surface that carries the main spreads of Clay-with-Flints, and, though Eocene materials are known to enter significantly into its composition, this surely demonstrates the post-Eocene character of both the deposit and the surface on which it rests.

In the uplands of west Dorset and east Devon a very interesting relationship has been described by Waters (1960). Their very flat surfaces bevel the Upper Greensand (Albian) and the restricted outcrops of Chalk, and were recognised by Green (1936) as planation surfaces, believed to be marine. Waters does not favour the latter contention though beach-battered cobbles of flint, chert, and Eocene silicified sandstone ('Sarsen') occur in fluviatile gravels with Palaeozoic rocks on the northeasterly parts of the upland. Since the altitude of these gravel patches shows sympathetic variation with that of the underlying solid rocks Waters interprets this part of the upland surface as having been deformed by the mid-Tertiary earth movements and as bearing the remains of an Eocene formation, probably the lateral equivalent of the Bagshot Beds. In contrast to this, the western part of the upland shows no such sympathetic relations with structure, is not affected by the faults that dislocate the underlying Cretaceous rocks, and carries only an angular drift of sub-aerial origin. Waters concludes that it is part of the late Tertiary peneplain rising northward from 750 to 920 ft. (230 to 280 m.) in 17 miles (25 km.).

This same peneplain is also recognised by Waters on the western side of the Exe valley, developed again on the Upper Greensand formation in the Haldon Hills. But from here it passes northwards on to the Culm Measures near Exeter and round the northern and northwestern flanks of Dartmoor, and, still on the same formation, on both sides of the narrowly-incised middle course of the Exe. West of the middle Teign the peneplain extends on to the Dartmoor granite, and round the southeastern, southern, and southwestern flanks of the Dartmoor upland it is developed on Devonian rocks. At this point a link is forged between lowland England and the most southerly of the massifs of upland Britain, and it is clear that, as the late-Tertiary surface passes from the one to the other, its character changes. On the soft rocks of the English plain it seems nowhere to have possessed local relief greater than a few tens of metres and truly to have deserved the name peneplain; on the hard rocks of Devonshire it passes completely round the unsubdued upland of Dartmoor whose higher summits dominate it by fully 1,000 ft. (300 m.). This is a clue of inestimable value that will be recalled later in the discussion.

The development of the late-Tertiary peneplain round Dartmoor is clearly correlative with the surface named the Bodmin Moor surface by Barrow in 1908, but Waters would not agree with Barrow's view that the surface is marine. Barrow's claim was a natural extension of the early recognition along the north Cornish coast of a well-marked platform about 400 ft. (120 m.) backed by an old cliff feature whose base is often masked by sands or by pottery clays that locally rest on beach shingle. Reid in 1890 had associated with this platform the very fossiliferous St Erth clays that occur at a low level (30 m.) near Penzance, since he believed that their fauna indicated accumulation in fifty fathoms (c. 90 m.) of water. This ascription of the platform, which Dewey (1910) showed to have a strandline at 430 ft. (130 m.), to the Older Pliocene may well stand in need of revision, but of the marine origin of the feature there seems little question. Much later Gullick (1936) and Balchin (1937) claimed evidence of a '600-foot' (180 m.) marine surface in west and north Cornwall, and in a detailed study of Exmoor, Balchin (1952) finds morphological evidence for a stairway of platforms between 280 and 1,225 ft. (85 and 370 m.), all of which he believes to be marine. Wooldridge, in reviewing the matter (1954), has accepted Balchin's interpretation of the marine fashioning of the upland at heights up to and over 300 metres and has drawn a map (1952) showing the 200-metre 'Pliocene' coastline that puts virtually all Cornwall beneath the sea and submerges a large embayment, open to the Atlantic, between Dartmoor and Exmoor. This interpretation is hard to reconcile with the evidence of the drainage pattern, as was noted by Linton (1957), and indeed, with the reconstruction of the early drainage made by Wooldridge himself in 1954. On his map the early rivers of the peninsula are shown rising in a former water-parting close to or even beyond the present Atlantic coast, a view that still has everything to commend it. Everard (1960) accepts Wooldridge's drawing of the 200-metre shoreline and the marine origin of all platforms below this level, but has confessed difficulty in reconciling these views with his own on the close adjustment of drainage to structure. Again Weller (1960), although believing the 1,000 ft. (300 m.) surface of David-stow Moor to be marine, concludes that the '750-800 foot partial peneplain' is sub-aerial. It therefore seems best to accept Waters's careful reading of the east Devon (1960) and Dartmoor (1960) evidence and return to the view, put forward by Davis in 1909 and supported by Reid in 1912, that the uplands of Dartmoor and Ex-moor are residual masses rising from a platform or partial pene-plain produced by sub-aerial weathering and erosion in coastal situations or on softer rocks. Only locally, as in the lowest part of the Tamar valley, does it appear that any shoreline earlier than that at 430 ft. (130 m.) can be recognised as having transgressed notably within the present coastline.

Returning to the English lowland, the relationships in the region between the chalk cuesta and the lower Severn are obviously im-portant, for here the uplands of Mendip and the southern Cotswolds offer a partial bridge to Wales. Wooldridge and Linton (1939) sug-gested that the late Tertiary peneplain passed from the uplands of Wiltshire on to the Mendip hills without significant change of altitude. This suggestion receives some support from Frey (1961) who has observed that at the western end of the Mendips remnants of a later and lower surface are separated from the late Tertiary peneplain by a rise approximating to the 200-metre shoreline. He traces this feature round Barrow and Dundry hills and south of Bristol towards the Cotswold scarp. To the west of this line the streams, apparently initiated on the emergent sea floor, flow west-northwestwards, and notable among them is the Bristol Avon, with its superimposed gorges. East of the supposed strandline the drain-age is of quite another character and a series of streams from the Chew to the Frome drains northeastwards with a grand disregard for structure. They look like nothing so much as the right-hand tributaries of some former eastward-flowing headstream of the Kennet that received the present upper Avon as a left-hand tribut-ary from the Cotswolds.

In the Cotswolds themselves recent work by J. Davis has con-vincingly demonstrated the planation of a wide summit area that we may identify with the late-Tertiary peneplain. Below it on the dip-slope is a broad bench with an aspect and an altitude similar to that cut by the Calabrian sea in the Chilterns, but the evidence of the drainage pattern and of such gravels as occur on its surface gives only equivocal support to the suggestion that the sea entered the Cotswold region. It is inherently probable, however, that the sea spread across what is now the Fenland on to the Jurassic uplands of Northamptonshire and Rutland, and the complete transection of these uplands from the Lower Lias to the Oxford Clay by the river Welland in a fairly direct northeasterly course may present evidence of this. Farther north the uplands are lower and carry no evidence. However, on the Permian limestone cuesta that flanks the southern Pennines, Humphries (1958) has described a series of marine benches of which the highest is at 640 ft. (195 m.). Strike valleys separate this development from the higher ground of the Pennines, but there is a notable change in the pattern of the drainage from the adjusted, 'disadjusted' and variously discordant streams of the older rocks, to a simple series of widely-spaced and sub-parallel streams flowing east-northeast from the Coal Measures across the Permian and Bunter outcrops. The latter are surely first-cycle streams in contrast to the older and more adjusted streams of the Pennines, and they were most probably superimposed from the emergent floor of the 640 ft. (195 m.) sea. The waters of a sea at this level would submerge the whole of the Lincolnshire Wolds, some 45 miles (70 km.) to the east, but no seabed could slope from the 640 ft. (195 m.) shoreline on the Pennine flanks continuously to the North Sea across their summits (550 ft., 167 metres), and it seems likely that here, as farther south (Kidson, 1962), transgression occurred after the soft rock outcrops had been eroded to levels possibly as low as 450 ft. (140 m.).

Denudation chronology in the uplands

The essential fact about the morphology of the British uplands is that when one climbs out of the dissecting valleys the view opens up widely and reveals a multitude of accordant ridge-tops seen as a formerly continuous surface of gentle gradients, small relief and high discordance to the underlying, and usually complex, geological structures. It is impossible not to associate these surfaces—whether as 'planes of marine denudation', as peneplains, or as pediplains—with ancient base-levels, but there is still no agreement as to the number, nature or dating of the surfaces concerned. Even the notion that they are geologically ancient surfaces buried and re-exhumed in a latter day, is not wholly dead. Fearnsides ascribed the conspicuous 'thousand-foot' surface of the southern Pennines to stripping of a Triassic cover, and O. T. Jones has more than once put forward a similar view of the Welsh tableland. But it has been pointed out by Clayton (1954) for the southern Pennines and by George (1955) for the Southern Uplands, that where portions of the upland plains and the sub-Triassic surface exist in close proximity they are, in George's words, 'completely at variance'. Guilcher (1949) has attempted to trace a post-Hercynian surface from beneath the New Red rocks into Palaeozoic Devon, and Godard (1957) has sought a sub-Torridonian surface in the landscapes of Sutherland and Wester Ross, but these attempts merely show that such features are of importance only locally, marginally, and at low altitudes. Indeed, we may say that the conspicuous high level surfaces of upland Britain as a whole, and doubtless of Ireland also, owe nothing to exhumation from beneath a former sedimentary cover.

There is positive evidence in some areas that they are later in origin than the Tertiary dykes across which they are cut indifferently. Such dykes extend from the Mull volcanic centre across Argyllshire, Renfrewshire, and the Southern Uplands into Northumberland, and from the Mourne mountains in Ireland northwestwards to Tyrone and Donegal, and southeastwards into Anglesey and Snowdonia. Many are younger than the Antrim lavas. and presumably older than the Lough Neagh clays that overlie the lavas to a depth of more than 1,100 ft. (340 m.) and yield shells that suggest an Eocene and plants that suggest an upper Oligocene age. A radioactive dating (Dubarry and Holmes, 1929) suggested an age of 26 million years for the Cleveland dyke which belongs here but the determination may be an under-estimate. (See *note*, p. 130.) Yet despite these uncertainties it is clear that on both sides of the Irish Sea the upland surfaces we are concerned with are wholly the products of Tertiary erosion. If the intrusive phase of vulcanicity were no later than Eocene some of these surfaces might antedate the mid-Tertiary folding of southern England and any contemporaneous uplift or warping that affected Highland Britain or Ireland. It is, indeed, possible that our higher upland plains are of earlier Tertiary formation, but it is unthinkable that they should be older.

Yet, even if it be conceded that no important part of the plateau surfaces of the British uplands is an exhumed fossil plain, and that even the oldest of them is not greatly older than the mid-Tertiary movements, that is unfortunately the limit of present agreement about them among British geomorphologists. For some believe them to be of marine origin and some believe them to be sub-aerial and in the complete absence to date of any associated deposits above the 670-ft. (200-m.) level, only the morphological and drainage characteristics are available to decide this question; but present methods of analysis yield conflicting results.

Much work has been done mapping flats on interfluves and spurs. Correspondences in altitude between neighbouring flats lead rather naturally to correlation, and in some cases groups of correlated flats have been claimed to be backed at a constant altitude by rising ground marking a former strandline. Particularly important are the investigations of Balchin on Exmoor (1952) and Sissons on the Yorkshire Pennines (1954) which have suggested strandlines at 1,225, 925, 825, 675 and 425 ft. (373, 282, 252, 206 and 130 m.) in the first case, and at 1,800, 1,380, 1,070, 710, 530 and 500 ft. (550, 420, 325, 216, 161 and 152 m.) in the second. Less rigorous investigations, not relying on mapping of flats in the field, have led George to postulate 'bench levels' of 2,600, 2,300, 1,670, 1,070 and 600 ft. (800, 700, 510, 325 and 180 m.) in the Southern Uplands and 2,300, 1,670, 1,070 and 650 ft. (700, 510, 325 and 200 m.) in Northern Ireland. A purely statistical analysis of the relative frequency of summits of different altitudes in some six different parts of upland Britain made Hollingworth (1938) claim particular significance for the levels 2,000, 1,000 to 1,070, 730 to 800, and 430 ft. (610, 305-325, 220-240, and 130 m.) with levels of subsidiary importance at 1,130 to 1,170, 900 to 920, and 550 to 570 ft. (345-355, 275-280, and c. 170 m.). Finally an application of a similar method to Ireland led Davies (1958) to conclude that while eight frequency maxima could be observed below 510 ft. (155 m.) with fair consistency between the results for a southern and a northern group of counties, the frequency maxima between 500 and 1,000 ft. (150 and 300 m.) though numerous showed little discernible relationship when the figures for the southern and northern groups of counties were compared. Moreover, as Davies himself observes 'there is little similarity between the statistical results for County Down and the surfaces mapped in the Mourne mountains by Proudfoot' (1954).

In a review of some of this work in 1952 Balchin postulated eustatic changes of sea level, but the findings do not possess the internal consistency that this particular hypothesis entitles one to expect, nor are they strengthened by more recent work. Moseley (1961) in a study that related more than 26,000 individual slope determinations over an area of some 140 sq. miles (360 sq. km.) in the Forest of Bowland to both situation and altitude finds that a frequency curve of 'flats' with altitude is apparently in contradiction to the main conclusion of his work. He states categorically that 'these maxima are . . . therefore thought to be accidents of [geographical] distribution'. There are, moreover, difficulties of other kinds that the hypothesis has yet to meet. As envisaged by George, it suggests the addition of marginal strips of land to each upland area as 'the core grew by progressive emergence from beneath a widespread sea'. Those words were written about Wales, but Balchin has given cartographic expression to the same concept for Exmoor, while in a discussion of the Southern Uplands George speaks of the [high] 'platform residuals as centres of stream deployment'. The hypothesis thus implies a process of drainage evolution by progressive extension from a number of upland centres that is both locally and regionally difficult to apply to what appear to be the better established facts of British stream development. Moreover, the assumption of eustasy means that the sea could not have withdrawn into growing down-warps but only into pre-existing depressions, and since the work on both Exmoor and the Yorkshire Pennines has suggested that the sea withdrew into neighbouring soft-rock lowlands, it is implied that these were already in existence. The hypothesis is thus really one of the deep submergence (locally to more than 2,000 ft. or 600 m.) of a strongly diversified pre-existing landscape, a view explicitly stated in these terms by T. N. George (1965) but still unsupported by any evidence of sedimentary accumulations in the areas where the sea presumably remained longest. The concept of the submergence of a strongly-accidented surface is again somewhat inconsistent with George's postulation for Wales of 'a post-Miocene emergence of a uniform surface' (1961, p. 262) to provide the constructional slopes that guided the radially-disposed initial rivers. Sissons (1960), in discussing the nature of the surface that underwent submergence, has concluded that 'a peneplain or pediplain . . . has been developed across southern Scotland and northern England prior to the final submergence,' and further that 'this peneplain or pediplain must have been warped and faulted before, and possibly during, the final emergence'. This would appear to introduce new complications without in any way disposing of the difficulties presented by the benches that are claimed to fringe such soft-rock lowlands as the Vale of York or mid-Devonshire.

If equivalence of altitude of platform-remnants be not accepted as sufficient for establishing both the former extent of a base-levelled surface and correlations between surfaces in different areas, there are two alternative criteria that may still be employed, namely, apparent continuation in the field and comparability of development. The first permits discontinuous remnants to be grouped, by possession of similar surface characteristics and visible relations to other landforms, into formerly continuous surfaces which may display uniform or changing gradients. The second permits a sequence of such surfaces in one area to be compared, if not correlated, with a sequence elsewhere. A number of field studies based on these criteria have been made in different upland areas, and by an extended use of the second criterion we may here use this material to hazard a tentative general correlation.

The most extended and important of the field studies is undoubtedly that by Brown of the whole of Wales (1957 and 1960). He recognises three surfaces of which the highest—the High Plateau—is the surface so much discussed in the literature but never before systematically mapped. The most northerly mapped remnants directly overlook Menai Straits, the southernmost Swansea Bay and the westernmost Cardigan Bay, while the most easterly are in fact in England on the Clee Hills. All these lie between 1,700 and 2,000 ft. (520 and 600 m.) above sea level, but rising definitively and sometimes dramatically above them to heights that range up to 3,561 ft. (1,085 m.) are several residual masses such as Snowdonia, the Berwyn hills and Brecon Beacons, or individual monadnocks such as Plynlimon. Two points about these residuals should be noted. First, that they are distributed through an area not much less than the High Plateau itself, ranging through nearly a hundred miles from north to south. Such a distribution is not very favourable to George's concept of a 'core area', and especially of a core area that would provide an explanation of a drainage system believed to radiate from Snowdonia. Second, that the small extent and wide distribution of the monadnock groups suggest a true sub-aerial peneplain dominated by residual reliefs of the order of 1,500 ft. (450 m.).

At levels 400 to 500 ft. (120 to 150 m.) lower than the High Plateau, Brown recognises several areas of partial planation formed at the expense of the High Plateau. Collectively these can be referred to as the Middle Surfaces. They are thought by Brown to have been developed in relation to a base level not higher than 1,200 ft. (365 m.). Below these again are marginal benches and dissected valley plains related to all the larger rivers, both consequent and subsequent. These Low Surfaces may have been graded to a base level rather below 700 ft. and their relationship to the 650-700 ft. (200 m.) coastal platform that Brown has traced from Glamorgan to Flintshire invites comparison with the transgressive relations traced by Kidson (1962) in the valley of the Exe.

The only other British upland area of comparable size of which a map of erosion surfaces has been prepared is the Grampian Highlands of Scotland (Fleet, 1938). This map is not based on field work but on the three-dimensional examination of two series of projected profiles. Its results are strikingly parallel to those announced by Brown for Wales. The most important surface recognised—called by Fleet the Grampian Main Surface—is still preserved widely, rising from 2,500 ft. (760 m.) in its most northerly and easterly remnants to over 2,900 ft. (880 m.) in western Perthshire and over 3,000 ft. (910 m.) in the Monadhliath. In the latter area it bevels the summits completely and impressively but elsewhere it is dominated by several important groups of residuals—including the large Cairngorm and Lochnagar areas—and numerous bold monadnocks. These are rather widely scattered through the high country and stand anything from 500 to 1,500 ft. (150-450 m.) above the adjacent surface which declines away from them toward certain of the main valleys. These characteristics both bespeak a sub-aerial peneplain and recall the High Plateau of Wales. Below this surface Fleet recognised a Grampian Lower Surface, widely developed as a summit surface in the northeast, where it may descend as low as 1,500 ft. (450 m.) but penetrating the higher ground in the southwest as a partial planation backed at 1,800-1,900 ft. (550-580 m.) by slopes that lead, often steeply, up to the Grampian Main Surface. A third surface is recognised on the margins of the upland and beside certain valleys in the interior. Its remnants are named the Grampian Valley Benches and are found mostly between 800 and 1,000 ft. (250 and 300 m.).

In all respects except altitude this development offers close parallels with that described for Wales. In each case a true peneplain of wide general extent and surmounted by thousand-foot monadnocks has been partially destroyed and replaced by a lower surface, and that in turn has been dissected to give valley plains below which the present fluvial or glacial valleys are trenched. The parallelism is at least worth pursuing and is here adopted as a working hypothesis.

For evidence that might support or weaken this suggested correlation it is natural to look to the uplands that lie between the Grampians and Wales. In the Ochil hills Soons (1958) has mapped two main surfaces—an Ochil Lower Surface at 800-1,000 ft. (250-300 m.) which in form and relationships (as well as altitude) invites comparison with the Grampian Valley Benches, and an Ochil Main Surface that appears to offer correlation on the same three grounds with the Grampian Lower Surface. Published accounts for the Cheviots, Southern Uplands and English Lake District appear all to be based on correlations by altitude, but in the Pennines a summit surface surmounted by monadnocks has been recognised by Trotter (1929) at heights ranging up to 2,600 ft. (800 m.) round Cross Fell, and by Hudson (1933) at heights between 1,800 and 2,300 ft. (550-700 m.) in Yorkshire. Surfaces at lower levels in the Pennines are insufficiently well correlated among themselves to afford any help in more extensive correlation, but the existence of a summit surface carrying monadnocks at altitudes intermediate between those of Wales and the Grampians is surely significant.

Looking southwards from Wales it is to be noted that the sub-aerial summit surfaces described by Balchin in Exmoor and by Waters in Dartmoor occur at altitudes rather below those of the High Plateau of Wales and that the highest residuals rise above them by only two or three hundred feet. The culminating altitude of the southwestern upland is thus only 2,028 ft. (618 m.) compared with 3,561 ft. (1,085 m.) for Wales or 4,296 ft. (1,309 m.) for the Grampians. Still farther to the south lies Brittany whose culminating ridges are not even as high as 1,300 ft. (400 m.). They rise sharply by 200-250 ft. (60-80 m.) from a senile surface which is at 720-850 ft. (220-260 m.) in the interior and locally bears continental deposits regarded as Eocene. In southern Brittany this surface has been contoured by Guilcher (1948) and falls southwards to pass below marine Eocene sediments at the coast near Lorient. Here then is a surface similar in morphological characteristics to the summit surfaces of the principal British uplands that is claimed as early Tertiary and is manifestly deformed. Moreover the deformation is decidedly local. If the upland surface of interior Brittany is truly Eocene its correlative lies beneath the Eocene limestones that are known to exist only fifty miles to the north below the waters of the Channel.

There is thus some probability that all the summit surfaces reviewed are of a single age but unequally elevated, and, in the south at least, locally deformed also. This view conflicts with Brown's that the Welsh High Plateau is undeformed, but his evidence is not so strong as to preclude our alternative. The way is thus open to regard all these summit surfaces as belonging to the same general period of formation—Early Tertiary—to which Lester

King has attributed much more extensive surfaces over a large part of the world's plainlands. Although the high surface in Brittany is regarded as Eocene it may well be that de Martonne was right in regarding it as polygenetic and that only its marginal southern portions are actually of this age. In any case the British summit surfaces must be of rather later date since, as we have already seen, they post-date the phase of dyke intrusion in the Irish and Hebridean igneous episode. Moreover the continuation of the Grampian Main Surface into western Scotland and the Hebridean area by summits developed from the plutonic complexes of Skye, Rum, and Mull, must surely post-date their emplacement by a fairly lengthy period. An early Oligocene date would not be unreasonable as the last date at which these summit surfaces stood near to their common base-level. Between that date and the Calabrian transgression there was ample time for the development of such partial peneplains as the Middle Surface in Wales or the Grampian Lower Surface in Scotland, and for the opening up of valley plains at a lower level in both areas in response to a later fall of sea level. And it is quite reasonable to think that the time available to open up the valley plains in interior Wales was also sufficient to produce the true peneplains represented by the accordant summits and bevelled cuestas of the English lowland.

The uplands of Ireland

In turning to the problems of the evolution of the uplands of Ireland a fresh approach must be made. In the first place, since geophysical and kindred evidence gives increasing reason to think that the Irish Sea occupies a tectonic downwarp, or even rift, between the upstanding massifs of Leinster and Wales, Ireland must be reckoned a tectonic unit in its own right. The second and even weightier reason arises from the importance of climate, for Ireland is uniquely wet. Its wetness resides not so much in heavy annual amount of precipitation—for nowhere does that approach the amounts received in western Inverness-shire, Snowdonia, or the English Lake District—but in the persistence of the rain and the feebleness of the evaporation.

The morphological consequences of the wetness of Ireland are far reaching. First, there is the fragmentation of the relief. There are no large upland areas comparable to those of Wales or the Pennines: the most massive upland in Ireland—the Wicklow mountains—covers barely 200 square miles (500 sq. km.). Partly this is just the result of outcrop geology, many outcrops of resistant rock being limited in area and circumscribed by notably less resistant rocks, as in the Slieve Bloom or the Galtee mountains. Yet this is not the case in either the northwest or the southeast where rocks akin to those that build continuous high land in Wales or Scotland outcrop extensively. Here fragmentation is a matter of subdivision of uplands into hill groups and the reduction of these to isolated hills. The effect is clear if we compare like outcrops on the two sides of the Irish Sea, contrasting the veritable archipelago of mountains that is Donegal and their Dalradian counterparts in Perthshire, the isolated tables of Yoredale Beds and Millstone Grit that surround Lough Allen and the continuous divides that separate the Yorkshire Dales, the eighty-two separate hills of the Slieve Felim Silurian inlier and the High Plateau in Cardiganshire, the skeletal grandeur of the Old Red Sandstone in the Caha mountains of Kerry and the solidity of the same formation in the Brecon Beacons. Fragmentation evidently proceeds by an enlargement of valleys and their branches and this leads to a consequent proliferation of cols or windgaps.

Another consequence of the prevailing wetness lies in the general lowering of the Irish uplands. It is well seen by comparing the Lower Palaeozoic outcrop that extends from the Shannon in County Longford for 110 miles (180 km.) to the shores of the North Channel without reaching an elevation of even 1,000 ft. (300 m.), with the Southern Uplands, where the same rocks surpass 1,750 ft. (530 m.) through virtually the whole of their extension across Scotland, save only in their most southwesterly and most Irish portion, namely in Wigtownshire. This lowering does not mean that the erosive processes necessarily operate differently in Ireland, they need only be faster. Every renewal of erosion in relation to a new base level advances more rapidly to maturity or even peneplanation. Consequently—unless it be locally in Wicklow or on the Galtees or Comeraghs—there is no equivalent in Ireland of the High Plateau of Wales: it has been destroyed. Innumerable summits rise to its level but they rarely imitate their Welsh counterparts by rising from a basis on the Middle Surface. Instead they rise in isolation from the lowlands like Slieve Gullion or Carlingford mountain, or are linked to neighbours, as is Caherbarnagh to the Derrynasaggart mountains, by fragments of mature high level valleys that are probably all that survive to represent such great intermediate platforms as that of the Forest of Atholl in the Grampians. In rather more cases the high summits rise from a fringing bench or belt of accordant low hills a few miles wide that is probably the representative of the Grampian Valley Benches or of the Low Surface of Wales, and especially does this appear to be true of the drier east and south. A good example is the assemblage of low hills between 700 and 900 ft. in altitude (220-280 m.) that margins the Mourne mountains on their northern side between Hilltown and Castlewellan, and indeed extends northwards to link up with Slieve Croob. More extensive and better preserved are the remarkable benches that flank the eastern and western sides of the Wicklow mountains. That on the east is obviously the late mature valley plain of the Vartry river, some 600-900 ft. (180-270 m.) above the sea. Above it rise the steep slopes of the Wicklow mountains on one side and on the other a collection of strikingly-isolated monadnocks including the Great Sugar Loaf (1,854 ft., or 565 m.); beyond them and between them there is an abrupt descent to the coastal lowland (150 m. in 4 km.). This topographic discordance leads, a little farther south, to the deep dissection of the continuation of the Vartry surface. The comparable bench on the western side drained by the headwaters of the Liffey is possibly even more striking in its relations. To the east it sends two wide tongues into the mountains, on the west the river Liffey leaves it by the gorge and falls of Polla-phuca, and on the north it overlooks the Dublin lowland by an abrupt descent of over 700 ft. (210 m.). But the most important of all the possible correlatives of the Low Surface of Wales is the South Ireland Peneplain described by Miller in 1939. This is a much more extensive surface that is found virtually throughout those parts of the counties of Cork and Waterford that lie between the generalised 800-ft. contour and the coast. Miller regarded this surface as marine, but Farrington (1961) finds evidence from his study of the drainage basin of the Lee that this essentially subsequent river was already in existence on the surface. In view of our earlier conclusion that the advanced dismemberment of ridges by gaps simulating wind-gaps is a response to climatic conditions, Miller's argument would appear not to have the force he attached to it, and we may therefore accept Farrington's view of the sub-aerial origin of the surface.

If greater rapidity of erosion has meant that in Ireland any representatives of the High Plateau of Wales have been destroyed, that those of the Middle Surface are rare and very reduced, and that even the likely correlatives of the Lower Surface and the Grampian Valley Benches are largely confined to the drier southern and eastern parts of the island, it is to be expected conversely that the same greater effectiveness of erosion should mean a greater extension of base-levelling in relation to the base-levels of the present and the recent past, and furthermore that this phenomenon should be most apparent in the north and west. This generalisation, stated here as a deductive corollary of the distribution of higher platforms, is equally valid as a summary statement of the observed field relationships as the following instances will show.

In Kerry the elongate anticlinal masses of Old Red Sandstone are all massive, and relatively undissected at their eastern ends. By contrast their western portions have been eroded to a late mature aspect, with uplands reduced to low, narrow ridges broken by gaps and cols, separating interior lowlands. In the Dingle peninsula a comparison of the Slieve Mish at the eastern end, where the form is essentially that of the sub-Carboniferous surface massively elevated to 2,796 ft. (852 m.) and little mutilated by valley cutting, and the lowlands of the west, compartmented by low mature divides dominated by Mount Eagle soaring smoothly and swiftly from sea level to 1,696 ft. (517 m.), reveals a contrast that is particularly striking.

In Connemara the greater part of the outcrops of the Galway granite and the adjoining quartz-diorite gneisses have been reduced almost to sea level, with occasional residual hills rising abruptly to heights of the order of a thousand feet. Although the lowland has been heavily ice-moulded and has been partly drowned by the sea, its existence on hard rocks and its modest but upstanding monadnocks must be accepted as evidence of the advance of the current (Quaternary) cycle of erosion to the stage of very late maturity, if not senility. The landscape recalls, and for the best of reasons, the landscapes of Uist and Benbecula in the Outer Hebrides with their even more striking monadnocks (e.g. Beinn Mhor 2,034 ft., 620 m.) rising from an exactly comparable ice-moulded and half-drowned plain. Nor is the degradation of Connemara confined to the crystalline rocks. The quartzites that do so much to uphold the summits of Maumturk and the Twelve Bens can raise nothing more than low hills in the country north of Clifden.

In Mayo and Donegal the quartzites of the Dalradian sequence are again conspicuous as summit-builders though their dominance over the granites is not so exclusive as is implied by Guilcher (1963): nor are any of them properly to be called 'horns', for though glacial erosion has been a factor in emphasising the gaps between some of these mountains it has not isolated them. The isolated mountain was, in fact, a characteristic feature of the region before the glacial episode began. Even more significant than the summits are the extensive areas of western Mayo where gneisses, granites, mica schists and quartzites alike are base-levelled and shrouded beneath a seemingly endless peat bog, out of which, at rare intervals, rise sharp little residuals of these same rocks. The question posed by Guilcher whether this lowland owes its character to lithology or to recent tectonic movements can be answered on both counts with an emphatic negative. Like the other instances we have noted its character results essentially from the rapidity with which the erosion cycle has progressed to the stage of late maturity in the basins of the small rivers that drain the remaining mountains of this wet western seaboard.

Selected references to work published since 1950

General discussions

BALCHIN, W. G. V., 1952. The evidence for late Tertiary eustatic changes of sea-level in western Europe. *Proc. XVIIth Int. Geogr. Congr.*, Washington, 296-300.
BROWN, E. H., 1960. *The relief and drainage of Wales.* Cardiff.
GEORGE, T. N., 1955. British Tertiary landscape evolution. *Sci. Progr.*, **43**, 291-307.
— 1961. The Welsh landscape. *Sci. Progr.*, **49**, 242-264.
GUILCHER, A., 1963. In *Les Iles Britanniques*, Paris, by BEAUJEU-GARNIER, J., and GUILCHER, A.
LINTON, D. L., 1951. Problems of Scottish scenery. *Scot. Geogr. Mag.*, **67**, 65-85.
— 1957. The everlasting hills. *Advanc. Sci.*, **14**, 58-67.
PINCHEMEL, Ph., 1954. *Les plaines de craie*, Paris.
SISSONS, J. B., 1960. Erosion surfaces, cyclic slopes and drainage systems in southern Scotland and northern England. *Trans. Inst. Brit. Geogr.*, **28**, 23-38.
WOOLDRIDGE, S. W., 1951. The upland plains of Britain. *Advanc. Sci.*, **7**, 162-175.
— and LINTON, D. L., 1955. *Structure, surface and drainage in south-east England.* London.

Specific contributions

BRUNSDEN, D., KIDSON, C., ORME, A.R., and WATERS, R. S., 1964. Denudation Chronology of parts of south-western England, *Field Studies*, **2**, 115–32.
CLAYTON, K. M., 1954. The denudation chronology of part of the middle Trent basin. *Trans. Inst. Brit. Geogr.*, **19**, 25-36.
DAVIS, J., 1963. *The Geomorphology of the Mid-Cotswolds.* Unpublished M.Sc. Thesis, University of Birmingham.
DURY, G. H., 1959. A contribution to the geomorphology of central Donegal. *Proc. Geol. Ass.*, **70**, 1-27.
EVERARD, C. E., 1956. Erosion platforms on the borders of the Hampshire Basin. *Trans. Inst. Brit. Geogr.*, **22**, 33-46.
FARRINGTON, A., 1961. The Lee Basin: Part 2. The drainage pattern. *Proc. R. Irish Acad.*, **61**, 233-253.
FREY, A., 1961. Lecture to Geographical Association, Bristol, April, 1961.
GEORGE, T. N., 1965. THE geological growth of Scotland in *The Geology of Scotland*, Ed. G. Y. Craig, 1-47.
GODARD, A., 1965. *Recherches de géomorphologie en Écosse de Nord-Ouest,* Paris.
JOHNSON, R. H., and RICE, R. J., 1961. Denudation chronology of the south-west Pennine upland. *Proc. Geol. Ass.*, **72**, 21-31.
KIDSON, C., 1962. The denudation chronology of the river Exe. *Trans. Inst. Brit. Geogr.*, **31**, 43-66.
LINTON, D. L., 1956. Geomorphology, pp. 24-43 of *Sheffield and its region.* Sheffield.

MOSELEY, F., 1961. Erosion Surfaces in the Forest of Bowland. *Proc. Yorks. Geol. Soc.*, **33**, 173-196.

PARRY, J. T., 1960. The erosion surfaces of the south-western Lake District. *Trans. Inst. Brit. Geogr.*, **28**, 39-54.

SOONS, JANE M., 1958. Landscape evolution in the Ochil hills. *Scot. Geogr. Mag.*, **74**, 86-97.

STRAW, A., 1961. The erosion surfaces of east Lincolnshire. *Proc. Yorks. Geol. Soc.*, **33**, 149-172.

WATERS, R. S., 1960. Erosion Surfaces on Dartmoor. *Abstracts of Proc. of 3rd Conference of Geologists and Geomorphologists,* 28-9, Bristol.

WATERS, R. S., 1960. The bearing of superficial deposits on the age and origin of the upland plain of east Devon, west Dorset and south Somerset. *Trans. Inst. Brit. Geogr.*, **28**, 89-97.

WELLER, M. R., 1960. The geomorphology of Bodmin moor. *Abstracts of Proc. of 3rd conference of geologists and geomorphologists,* Bristol, 17.

WILKINSON, H. R., and GREGORY, S., 1956. Aspects of the evolution of the drainage pattern of northeast Wales. *Lpool. and Manchr. Geol. J.*, **1**, 543-558.

Note (p. 119) Recent radiometric determinations give ages of about 54 million years, i.e. Eocene, for certain Skye granites and rocks from the complexes of Arran, Ardnamurchan and St. Kilda, though an age determined as 35 million years for a St. Kilda dyke rock is comparable to that quoted for the Cleveland dyke.

8

THE GLACIAL PERIOD

DURING the Pleistocene many of the landforms of the British Isles established during Tertiary time suffered major modifications. Valley glaciers nourished in the mountains of the west and north developed repeatedly and gouged out the U-valleys that form part of our most spectacular scenery. At times these glaciers coalesced to form piedmont glaciers and ice-sheets that covered most of the British Isles and laid down thick deposits of drift as far as East Anglia, the Midlands, and southeast Ireland. Meanwhile, frost action attacked areas not covered by ice, permafrost developed and solifluction was widespread, the effects being especially severe in the south of Britain. Between times the climate became as mild or even milder than now for long periods when glaciers disappeared completely, and there were numerous shorter intervals of climatic amelioration when widespread glacier-decay ensued. Throughout, the level of the sea in relation to the land varied widely, at times standing well above its present level, as witnessed by raised shore-lines and river terraces, at other times falling far below with the production of deep valleys now largely infilled by later deposits.

Conflicting opinions have been expressed on almost all these Pleistocene events, and quite often interpretations accepted for many years have been subsequently proved invalid. In the space available here it is quite impossible to attempt a discussion of the many controversial problems of the moment and it would, in any case, be especially unwise to do so at the present time, for studies of pollen and coleoptera along with radiocarbon dating are beginning to establish a chronology and necessitate a re-orientation of ideas such as could not be envisaged fifteen years ago.

It is certain, however, that at least four major glaciations have affected the British Isles. Each of these was itself composed of many lesser oscillations during each of which the glaciers advanced and then decayed, only to be revived once again by a renewed deterioration of climate. As yet even the oscillations of the last major glaciation, the Würm, are incompletely known. The few older radiocarbon datings at present available, and comparison with the pattern emerging on the European mainland, suggest that this glaciation occupied a period of roughly 60,000 years ending about 10,000 years ago. During this time there may have been four important interstadials, one of which possibly lasted for more than 15,000 years, as well as many shorter ameliorations of climate.

Altitude, location and a prevailing westerly air stream combined in Pleistocene times, as now, to produce the heaviest precipitation in the west of the British Isles. This resulted in more prolonged and more severe glacial conditions than elsewhere and produced the deep glacial troughs with their rock basins, steps and bars, the hanging valleys and cirques of the western mountains. The work of valley glaciers dominates the scenery nowhere better than in the western Highlands and adjacent islands of Scotland. Here are located all the large rock-basin lakes of that country, including Loch Morar, deepest of all British lakes (1,017 ft., 310 m.), most of the major glacial troughs, most of the glacial breaches in watersheds and by far the larger proportion of the cirques. Here too are the fjord coastline and many deep rock basins on the adjacent ocean floor (Linton, 1959). In northern Scotland at the height of the glaciations the ice-shed lay east of the mountain back-bone and powerful westward-flowing ice-streams scooped out the thirty or more troughs, up to 2,000 ft. (600 m.) deep, that now breach the mountain line. In the western Grampians the Rannoch basin formed part of a major centre of ice dispersal. The heart of the western Southern Uplands has many cirques and some U-valleys and in the Lake District the U-valleys with their rock-basin lakes point out radially from the mountain core. In Wales the northwest, dominated by the Snowdon group, the Arenig mountains and Cader Idris, suffered most from the erosive action of ice, and in the south glaciers flowed from the cirque-fretted, north-facing, sandstone scarp of the Brecon Beacons. Killarney's famous lakes reflect the ice-gouged slopes that bound them and the high precipitation that made the uplands of Kerry and western Cork a major glacial centre, while the mountains of Donegal have been deeply eroded by the glaciers that radiated from this important source area in northwest Ireland.

Eastwards and southwards the scene changes. In Scotland the eastern Grampians have none of the large rock basin lakes and only a small proportion of the lesser ones, while extensive tracts of Tertiary plateau often separate the glaciated valleys. Here, too, survive in places the marine deposits of Pliocene or early Pleistocene age and deeply-weathered granites. The contrast between east and west is great yet must not be pressed too far; thus the heads of the glens of Isla, Prosen, Clova, and Esk are major ice-gouged troughs, while in the Cairngorms numerous cirques fret the plateau edge and deep glacial breaches lead from one side to the other. Rather is the contrast between intense glaciation in the west and locally severe glaciation in the east, with much land in the latter area showing only slight evidence of glacial erosion.

In the Southern Uplands the contrast between parts of the east and west is equally striking, although assisted by geological factors. While the ice-scraped rocky surfaces of the Loch Doon granite and metamorphic region resemble parts of the western Highlands, the smooth rounded slopes of the sedimentary Moorfoots and Lammermuirs bear little sign of glacial erosion even though they were ice-covered on several occasions. Farther south the U-valleys of the northern and central Pennines with their stepped sides in limestone or grit and shale testify to the work of ice, but they lack rock bars and basins, while the extensive plateaux between owe their form essentially to Tertiary base-levelling and periglacial processes. In Wales also wide plateaux dominate the scene away from the strongly-glaciated northwest, and the over-steepened valley slopes comprise the main evidence of glacial erosion. Still farther south Exmoor and Dartmoor failed to nourish glaciers but may well have carried permanent snow-caps. In Ireland the pattern is complicated by the presence of numerous isolated mountain areas such as the Mournes, Comeraghs, Knockmealdowns, Galtees, and those of western Connacht, all of which at times nourished their own glaciers and are now deeply bitten by cirques. Nevertheless, even the Wicklow Mountains, the principal ice centre of the east, do not equal the mountains of Kerry, western Cork, and Donegal in their glacial erosion forms.

Where glaciers escaped from the bounding valleys of their mountain-source regions they coalesced to form thick sheets of ice that often spread widely over the surrounding territory, sometimes overwhelming other upland areas completely. Erratics, striae, and ice-moulding show that mountains as high as 3,000 ft. (900 m.) in the west of Scotland were overwhelmed and Highland erratics are found on the summits of the various uplands of central Scotland. The ice-streams often remodelled the ground over which they flowed, in some places plucking and abrading the rock, in others depositing their debris as distinctive linear features. The erosional effects are especially marked in the coastlands of northwest Scotland, much of the Outer Hebrides and parts of west Donegal. Here rock hills and knolls, either plucked by the ice or smoothed and polished by its contained debris, dominate the landscape and, along the coast, often descend beneath the sea almost unmodified by marine action. Innumerable lines of weakness in the rocks have been exploited by the ice, as is clearly seen in the drainage patterns and in the angular outlines of lakes and coastlines. In the east of Scotland the country on either side of the Firth of Forth has been moulded into ridges that are part rock and part drift, best seen in the crag-and-tail features associated with isolated igneous hills. In the Southern Uplands a northeastward movement, with the strike of the rocks, produced between the Tweed and Teviot a parallel graining of the hills and plateaux that grades into the drumlins of the lower Tweed basin. Drumlins splay out eastwards and southeastwards from the Glasgow area and in southwest Scotland they characterise much of the low ground. In the Vale of Eden, the Solway plain, and the Tyne gap other large groups occur, while around Morecambe Bay piedmont glaciers from the Lake District hills spread out on the low ground to produce their drumlin fields.

Nowhere in the British Isles, however, are drumlins better displayed than in Ireland where, over some 4,000 square miles (10,000 sq. km.) of the northwestern half of the island, they form a striking feature of the landscape. Numbering tens of thousands they sweep in gently-curving systems across the plains and even over some of the lesser uplands. Often they provide fertile ground rising above the bogs and lakes, and in coastal areas, such as Galway Bay and Strangford Lough they continue into the sea, where they stand out of the water as elongated oval islands.

In contrast, in the less-recently glaciated parts of the British Isles, including almost all East Anglia and most of the Midlands, the landscape is quite different. These areas were not occupied by ice during the Würm and here sheets of till that have lost their original constructional forms cover wide areas. Most of East Anglia is characterised by flat or gently-undulating till plains partly dissected by shallow valleys. In the Midlands, where bedrock relief is greater, the oldest drifts are restricted to the interfluves and are absent from the valley floors and lower valley sides. The later glacial deposits, however, often mantle the oldest drifts and descend the valley slopes to lower levels, showing that the valley excavation occurred partly in interglacial times. In these areas the Würm glaciation is represented by solifluction deposits and, in the Severn valley and some of its Welsh tributaries, by outwash terraces laid down by streams draining from the glaciers of Wales and from the lobe of Irish Sea ice that pushed into the Cheshire-Shropshire lowland.

In these peripheral parts of the glaciated area, where deposition often prevailed over erosion, the broad pattern of Pleistocene climatic oscillations has been deciphered. In East Anglia the upper part of the Crag reveals two cold periods during the lower Pleistocene and is succeeded by the drift sequence, which indicates four more major cold periods. The East Anglian drifts comprise several beds of till that mostly include a high proportion of chalk, along with series of stratified sands and gravels and occasional beds with organic remains. The earliest established interglacial deposit is represented by the Cromer Forest Bed, a second interglacial by deposits at Hoxne and other sites, and a third and last by deposits at Ipswich and elsewhere (West, 1958). In the preceding and intervening glaciations the glaciers of the west and north spread outwards to extend eventually over East Anglia and the northern part of the Thames basin, laying down their various till sheets. The innumerable oscillations that must have accompanied each glaciation remain almost unknown and only the broad patterns of the main movements have been provisionally identified: for example, during the last glaciation of the area (the penultimate of the British Isles as a whole) the ice is believed to have fanned out southeastwards, southwards, and southwestwards from the Fenland region (West and Donner, 1956).

In the Midlands remains of only the two last interglacials have been discovered as yet and the main mass of the glacial deposits was accumulated during the penultimate glaciation of the British Isles. At this time a mass of ice moving down the eastern side of England, another coming from the Irish Sea basin, and a third supplied by the uplands of Wales, came together in the central belt and produced a complex series of drifts. In Ireland only doubtful evidence of the earliest glaciations has been discovered and only in the southeast has the pattern of the later ice-movements been elucidated in some detail. Here ice from the Irish Sea (derived originally from Scotland) penetrated some distance inland, meeting local glaciers from the Wicklow mountains and an ice-sheet that had moved over the central plain in a southeastward direction. The ice at this time is believed to have covered the whole of Ireland apart from a few small mountain summits. At a later date ice once again moved southeastwards across the central plain and reached the Irish Sea, but this time much of the southeast remained ice-free, although local glaciers developed on the Wicklow Mountains and a large mass of ice accumulated in the mountains of the southwest (Farrington, 1944, 1949; Synge and Stephens, 1960).

Over the large area comprising the northern half of Ireland, most of northern England, and the whole of Scotland, the existence of definite interglacial deposits has not yet been proved. Furthermore, although many accounts refer to ice-movement at the time of 'maximum glaciation' it is clear that often these ice-movements relate to the various readvances that interrupted the decay of the last ice-sheet. Almost the whole of the evidence pertaining to the earlier glacial events has been destroyed or obscured. True, a westward movement of Scottish ice into Ulster is said to have occurred during the penultimate glaciation (Synge and Stephens, 1960), an ancient till and loess have been found in Durham (Trechmann, 1919), and a sequence of drifts in northeast Scotland is considered to include elements pre-dating the Würm (Synge, 1956). Yet within this large area as a whole the organic remains interbedded with the glacial deposits point to cool conditions (mammoth and woolly rhinoceros have been frequently discovered), while in recent years radiocarbon dating, pollen and beetle studies have shown that certain deposits formerly regarded as possibly interglacial belong to late-glacial times or to Würm interstadia. A radiocarbon date of plant remains in the Lancashire-Cheshire plain indicates an age of 57,000 years, thus assigning the climatic amelioration represented by the plant-bearing deposits to an early Würm interstadial (Simpson and West, 1958). Pollen analysis of a supposed interglacial deposit in Strathmore suggests a late-glacial (Allerød) age (Donner, 1960), while study of beetle remains in peat inter-bedded with till in Lanarkshire points to a cool climate probably associated with one of the late Würm ameliorations (Coope, 1962). Thus the complexity of the Würm is being increasingly revealed.

Within this extensive northern zone there is, at the time of writing, a big gap in the dated events of the last glaciation. Radiocarbon dating of plant remains contained in the valleys of the Avon and Salwarpe, tributaries of the Severn, has given figures of 38,000 and 42,000 years respectively. These plant remains are said to post-date the Main Terrace of the Severn whose upper part, at least, is composed of outwash laid down by meltwaters issuing from a lobe of ice that covered the Cheshire-Shropshire lowland (Coope et al., 1961). The next established date in the glacial sequence is the Allerød recession that began about 12,000 years ago and was followed by the Loch Lomond Readvance (Fig. 15) between about

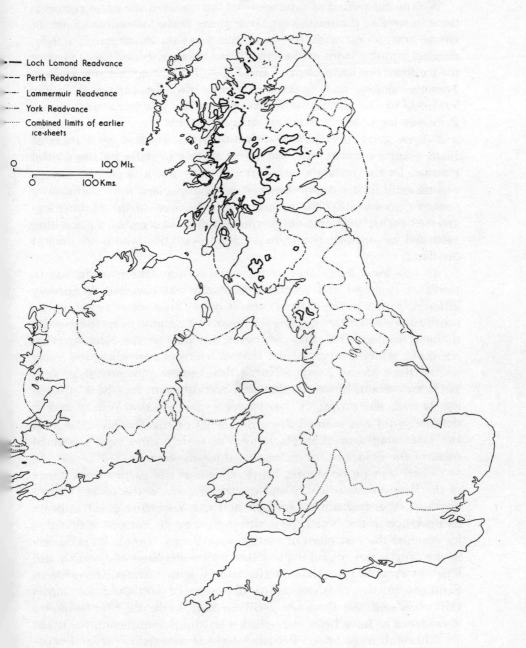

Loch Lomond Readvance
Perth Readvance
Lammermuir Readvance
York Readvance
Combined limits of earlier
ice-sheets

0   100 Mls.
0   100 Kms.

Fig. 15., SOME IMPORTANT GLACIAL LIMITS.

10,800 and 10,300 years ago. There is thus at present a gap of some 30,000 years in the glacial chronology.

Within this period of time some of the ice from the great accumulation centre of the southwest Grampians flowed down the Firth of Clyde and, along with ice from the western Southern Uplands, flooded into the basin of the Irish Sea. This combined mass pushed the ice from the Lake District and Howgill Fells against the western Pennine slopes and extended across the Lancashire-Cheshire lowlands to the northwest Midlands. In the northern and central Pennines ice from the west streamed through the Aire, Stainmoor and Tyne gaps, the Stainmoor route being marked by a train of Shap granite erratics, and the Tyne route especially by the Criffel granite. In the uplands between the gaps the absence of foreign constituents in the drifts shows that local glaciers were sufficiently powerful to ward off the invading ice. Farther north erratics, ice-grooved rocks, crag-and-tail forms and drumlins reveal a prevailing eastward or northeastward movement over the whole of eastern Scotland.

It has long been accepted that this eastward-moving ice in northern England and southern Scotland was diverted to entirely different routes in the eastern coastal areas. Thus ice at times moved southwards down the whole east coast of England from the Border to East Anglia. That this diversion was due to the Scandinavian ice-sheet, which prevented the British ice from spreading out freely on the floor of the present North Sea, seems very probable. It is far from certain, however, that the Scandinavian ice-sheet affected the British ice during a considerable part of the Würm and it definitely did not control the movements of the British ice during the later stages of that glaciation, at which time was produced most of the evidence for an eastward ice-movement.

There can be no doubt, however, about the earlier importance of the Scandinavian ice. Scandinavian erratics in the oldest known drifts of Aberdeenshire, Durham and the Yorkshire coast indicate its presence in the North Sea, although they do not prove that this ice reached the east coast of Britain (e.g. Penny, 1959). Its influence in the North Sea region is indicated by the carriage of Scottish and Cheviot erratics into East Anglia and is demonstrated in northern Scotland by the northwestward diversion of Highland ice across Caithness and the Orkneys. Still farther north the Shetlands are considered to have been over-ridden by the Scandinavian ice itself.

Although most of the British Isles was covered on several occasions by ice-sheets, which in the western Grampians may well have had a surface level exceeding 4,000 ft. (1,200 m.) above present sea level, certain parts of the country escaped glaciation. In addition to the unglaciated area of southern England it seems likely that the highest summits in the peripheral west and south such as those of the Outer Hebrides, southwest Ireland and the Brecon Beacons remained ice-free. As the last ice-sheet decayed, interrupted by occasional readvances, the domain of periglacial activity followed in its wake, extending northwards and westwards and at the same time operating at lower and lower levels on the uplands as they emerged from the ice. This extension continued until the final (post-Allerød) readvance, at which time modest solifluction still operated even in southeast England. Thereafter occurred the rapid post-glacial increase in temperature that forced the cold climate phenomena up to high levels on the mountains. Consequently, within the limits of the last readvance solifluction deposits are thin and frost-wedges as yet unknown, but eastwards and upwards and especially southwards the fossil periglacial evidence increases in abundance to reach its optimum development in southern Britain.

Whereas in the glaciated area the ice redistributed or buried the solifluction deposits of earlier cold phases, in favourable locations in the unglaciated south, the successive layers accumulated one above the other, occasionally reaching thicknesses as great as 100 ft. (30 m.). In the dry valleys of the chalk country and especially at the foot of long chalk slopes the soliflucted waste is represented by the pasty mass of chalk and flints known as coombe rock. These deposits are sometimes associated with loess and in places it can be seen that they formerly extended beyond the present coastline, having partly accumulated when the sea level was lower than at present. The dry valleys of the chalk areas have been ascribed to various origins, but at least in part they were formed at a time when the ground was frozen, while the rounded coombes are probably the result of nivation. In the granite upland of Dartmoor large accumulations of angular frost-shattered debris, stone stripes, altiplanation terraces and the numerous tors demonstrate the action of processes no longer operative (Palmer and Neilson, 1962). In southern Britain as a whole the stripping of dip-slopes, the etching out of escarpments, the cambering of competent strata, the occurrence of landslips and the spreading of debris by streams and mass-wastage were all facilitated by the cold conditions, whose repeated occurrence is shown by the relation of solifluction layers to river terraces and raised beaches.

Some of the most striking evidence of periglacial action has been described in the east Midlands (Hollingworth et al., 1944). Here valley excavation in sandstones and sandy limestones underlain by clays resulted in the flowage of the clays towards the valleys with consequent cambering of the overlying more competent beds, which have been bent down as much as 100 ft. (30 m.) below their original level. At the same time the competent beds often fractured along lines parallel with the valley sides. Clay strata have been forced up into valley floors, sometimes as much as 100 ft. (30 m.) above their level beneath neighbouring higher ground, with resultant disruption of the adjacent, overlying, more competent rocks. Although there is reason to believe that some of these processes are operating on a small scale at the present time, there is good evidence to show that the superficial structures were essentially produced during various past cold periods when frost action operated to depths up to at least 150 ft. (45 m.) below the ground surface.

Within the Flamborough-Shropshire ice limit (Fig. 15) the effects of periglacial processes are less striking but nonetheless evident. Although large-scale patterned ground such as occurs just outside the limit near Scarborough (Dimbleby, 1952), and large solifluction deposits, such as lie near the limit in the southern Pennines and extreme western Ireland, are exceptional, modest accumulations of solifluction material are widespread|and fossil frost wedges, especially in unconsolidated deposits, are quite common. Slopes are often covered with a layer of frost-shattered material and minor valley-heads are often infilled with it, while wide plateaux such as occur on the Pennines and Southern Uplands may carry several feet of earthy angular debris covered by later accumulations of peat. On the higher parts of the Scottish Highlands the severe climates of the past are demonstrated by sheets of solifluction material, lobes and terraces of coarse angular debris, block fields, and the isolated upstanding tors especially characteristic of granite areas. Even at the present time periglacial processes operate on a modest scale in northern Britain forming turf-banked lobes, stone stripes and small stone polygons. An altitude of 2,000 ft. (600 m.) sets an approximate lower limit to these processes in much of the Grampians, Southern Uplands and northern England, but, owing probably to the influence of severe winds, this lower limit falls sharply towards the outer Scottish islands. Exceptionally, where vegetation is sparse, solifluction is active and patterned ground forms at altitudes as low as 1,300 ft. (390 m.) in central Scotland and near sea level in the Shetlands (Galloway, 1961).

While the fossil periglacial phenomena indicate in a general way the limits of former ice-sheets they have been rarely studied in sufficient detail as yet to permit accurate delimitation. Unfortunately such a lack of information pertains to much other evidence of ice-limits, such as the extent of till sheets, the sequence of late-glacial shorelines and the distribution of moraines and fluvioglacial deposits. Furthermore, where studied, some of the evidence has been misinterpreted. Consequently it is not possible to present an accurate map of glacial stages in the British Isles as a whole and the ice-limits shown in Figure 15 are, in common with other maps of this type, to a considerable extent speculative.

The maximum extent of the ice-sheets is largely unknown since most of the evidence lies beneath the surrounding seas. In southern England and the Midlands, however, the combined limits of several different ice-sheets are marked by th southe nmost limit of ice-deposited drift (Fig. 15). The ice extended into the northern part of the London Basin in the first three glaciations. As a result of the two earlier ones the Thames was diverted to its present course through London from a route that originally followed the Vale of St Albans and crossed central Essex (Wooldridge, 1960). In the Midlands the Avon, as we now know it, did not exist until the third glaciation, for previously much of the area now drained by this river was the basin of a river that flowed northeastwards towards the Trent. An extensive ice-dammed lake that existed in this area at this time was gradually occupied by ice advancing from the north and from Wales (Shotton, 1953). The Welsh ice on several occasions entered the basin of the lower Severn but the ice limit in the Bristol Channel is uncertain. It is often represented as having been situated in the area now occupied by this arm of the sea, but Mitchell (1960) concluded that at one time the ice reached the northern coasts of Devon and Cornwall even as far as Land's End.

During the Würm according to one view, the ice on the east coast of England failed to extend beyond Flamborough Head, near which its limits are considered to be represented by a belt of morainic mounds (Farrington and Mitchell, 1951). On the other hand, the majority opinion is that the western part of a mass of ice that terminated on the north coast of Norfolk in the vicinity of Hunstanton occupied Holderness and eastern Lincolnshire (e.g. Straw, 1960). This ice limit in eastern England is usually correlated with the well-marked morainic ridges of York or Escrick that sweep in broad arcs across the Vale of York. An inevitable consequence of this interpretation is the formation of a huge lake occupying the lowlands drained by the Humber and Trent as well as the Fenland and certain other low-lying areas. This lake, which has often figured in the literature, is presumed to have overflowed by the Little Ouse-Waveney gap in East Anglia at about 80 ft. (24 m.) above sea level, and a shoreline at 100 ft. (30 m.) on the Permian dip-slope in Yorkshire has been correlated with it. Surprisingly, the large meltwater rivers that should have flowed into the lake, as along the Calder valley from the deep gaps connecting with Lancashire at its head, and along the Trent valley from the large ice lobe in the Cheshire-Shropshire lowland, seem not to have produced the extensive deltas that might reasonably be expected. Furthermore, much evidence cited in favour of the lake is capable of different interpretation and it seems likely that some modification of current views will be required.

In southern Ireland the maximum extent of the Würm ice is generally considered to correspond with the line shown in Figure 15 (Charlesworth, 1928; Mitchell, 1960). This view is not tenable, however, if the low level marine platform and cliff that is widely developed in Ireland and southern Britain was formed during the last interglacial, since the platform is overlain by glacial deposits in south-east Ireland and south Wales. In Yorkshire, where the apparently-equivalent platform is thickly covered with glacial drift, a last interglacial age is usually favoured and the glacial deposits are attributed to the Würm (Penny, 1959). On the other hand, in much of south-east Ireland the deposits immediately overlying the platform are considered to belong to a pre-Würm glaciation. A major divergence of opinion thus exists. Perhaps the complexity of the Würm has not been always appreciated, with the possibility that some of the 'older drifts' of Wales and Ireland represent early Würm deposits.

The second line in Figure 15, based largely on the work of Charlesworth, is here considered to mark the limit of the most extensive readvance of the ice during the later Würm. In north-east Yorkshire the ice surrounded the Moors except in the south, where Lake Pickering was impounded and the Derwent caused to adopt its present peculiar course (Kendall, 1902). Arcuate moraines in the Vale of York and in the Cheshire-Shropshire lowland (Peake, 1961) define the margins of lobes of ice that attained their limit, decayed and then advanced again. In the latter area an ice-dammed lake was produced and its waters escaped mainly through the Ironbridge gorge (initiated earlier by glacial diversion) and down the Severn valley. The Irish Sea ice also reached the north coast of Wales, where it was in contact with ice from the Welsh mountains (Embleton, 1961). In Ireland the ice rose against the flanks of the Wicklow Mountains, which possessed their own independent valley glaciers, and its limit across south-central Ireland to the mouth of the Shannon is marked by a belt of moraines and fluvioglacial deposits that follows the lower slopes of many uplands and fingers into the intervening valleys and basins (Charlesworth, 1928). In western Mayo the ice limit is again clearly defined by the limit of fresh glacial forms (Synge, personal communication) and in the southwest an independent ice-mass existed. In Scotland the extent of the ice is uncertain, but the 'unglaciated' area described by Synge (1956) in the northeast may date from this period.

The decay of the ice, once well established, was probably rapid with widespread downwasting resulting finally in stagnation. Extensive systems of meltwater channels, often misinterpreted as the overflows of ice-dammed lakes, were produced by streams flowing sometimes along the ice-margin, but much more often, beneath the ice itself (Sissons, 1960, 1961). First described in detail in northeast Yorkshire by Kendall (1902), meltwater channels are of widespread occurrence, especially on the slopes of uplands, as in the western Pennines, the Rossendale and Bowland Hills, north Wales and the flanks of the Wicklow Mountains. In the central plain of Ireland the subglacial streams were engaged mainly in deposition and numerous esker systems were produced.

How far back the ice wasted is unknown, but eventually it readvanced to a limit possibly indicated by the Lammermuir line in Figure 15. This readvance is characterised by important drumlin fields, although drumlins do occur outside this limit as well as within the area covered by the later, Perth, readvance. In Ireland the Kells moraine, comprising mainly fluvioglacial debris, separates drumlins on its northern side from the esker area to the south. In north Lancashire Gresswell (1962) has described drumlin fields associated with this readvance formed by Lake District ice spreading southwards into the Morecambe Bay lowlands. Such a considerable extent of Lake District ice in this area suggests that the Vale of Eden, with its drumlin field, may have been occupied by ice at this time. The drumlins of the Tweed lowland may also be of the same age, the limit of a large lobe of ice being indicated on the south in part by the kame moraine that still almost blocks the Till valley (where an ice-dammed lake with an extensive unpitted delta was formed), and on the north by the upper limit of fluvioglacial features on the southern slopes of the Lammermuirs. On the northern side of these hills the fluvioglacial forms have a sharply-defined upper limit that falls eastwards to St Abb's Head. Farther north the Aberdeen Readvance, normally correlated with the following stage, appears to be of this age, while a large mass of ice fanned out into the Moray Firth.

Again the climate ameliorated and rapid glacier decay with abundant meltwater activity ensued. Kames, kame terraces, and meltwater channels are especially common where the ice wasted down the slopes of rising ground it had partly overrun, as on the southern side of the Moray Firth, in Strathmore, the Lothians and the Vale of Eden. In much of the eastern part of the Southern Uplands a system of englacial streams flowing north and northeast was lowered with the wasting ice on to the hills and ridges beneath, producing a pattern of meltwater channels that is often markedly discordant with the present major valley pattern. The widespread decay may well have freed many upland source areas from ice and even near the major centre of the southwest Grampians it appears that the Glasgow area and lowland Ayrshire had become ice-free, for the subsequent Perth Readvance here over-rode lacustrine and marine sediments.

The Perth Readvance, first identified by Simpson (1933), is especially characterised by remarkable displays of fresh fluvioglacial phenomena and its limit is only occasionally marked by till moraines. Large terraces of coarse outwash cross eastern Strathmore from valley glacier limits at the Highland edge. Farther southwest the Highland ice flooded into the central lowlands, surrounding the western Ochils and largely overwhelming the Campsies. Ice moved up the Clyde valley over the present site of Glasgow, forming an ice-dammed lake that was ultimately extinguished by the advancing ice. Drumlins in the Glasgow area and in Ayrshire were formed by the Highland ice, while some of the Galloway drumlins relate to tongues of Southern Upland ice debouching on the lowlands (Charlesworth, 1926). Along most or all of the west coast of Scotland the ice terminated in the sea. In the east the fluvioglacial deposits of the Beauly Firth and the Dinnet moraine in the Dee valley probably relate to the Perth Readvance.

During the Allerød period of relatively mild climate, widespread glacier wastage supervened, probably resulting in complete deglaciation. The final readvance of glaciers that followed, between approximately 10,800 and 10,300 years ago, produced a distinctive morainic topography. Numerous small cirque and valley glaciers were formed and their extent is indicated by steep-sided hummocks of angular debris, in some places disposed as lateral and terminal moraines and in others as seemingly-chaotic assemblages of hundreds of small mounds and hollows. Small glaciers existed on mountains such as Snowdon, the Wicklows and those of Kerry. In northern Britain the moraines descend to 1,250 ft. (375 m.) above sea level in the Cross Fell area, 500 ft. (150 m.) in the Lake District, 1,000 ft. (300 m.) in the central Southern Uplands, 500 ft. (150 m.) in the western Southern Uplands, and to sea level in Arran, Skye, and Mull. On the eastern side of the Cairngorms, however, the limit is as high as 1,500 ft. (450 m.) and in the Cheviots moraines are absent. The dominance of the west and the marked eastward rise of the snowline is implicit in these figures. In accord with this pattern, the valley glaciers of the western Grampians and the mountain area west of the Great Glen were of considerable size. Large moraines outline the margins of former piedmont lobes in the upper Forth valley and around the southern end of Loch Lomond, while in fjords such as Gare, Long, Fyne, Etive, Creran, Leven, and Linnhe valley glaciers terminated in the sea. In the Glen Roy area, and on a much smaller scale in the Moor of Rannoch, glaciers held up ice-dammed lakes whose former existence is now recorded by deltas and shorelines.

Although the limits of the various readvances are necessarily generalised in Figure 15, it will be apparent that the several readvances of the main ice mass would have had their counterparts in many of the uplands not overwhelmed by extraneous ice. Moraines of various ages are known from some of these uplands, as in Wales and parts of Ireland, but correlation with the main ice-mass is not usually established. When, ultimately, it becomes possible to produce a detailed map of readvance limits an intricate pattern related to the many ice-centres will be revealed.

The complexity of the glacial oscillations is matched or exceeded by that of land and sea level relationships, a subject that has produced major divergences of opinion. Most of the northwest of the British Isles was depressed by the weight of the last ice-sheet and the associated shorelines were tilted during the subsequent isostatic recovery. Much of East Anglia, however, has suffered tectonic downwarping through the Pleistocene along with the rest of the southern North Sea region: here buried valleys descend to as much as 380 ft. (115 m.) below sea level, and the Ordnance Survey geodetic levellings suggest downwarping is still in progress. On the other hand, in an area extending at least from the western part of the London Basin through south and southwest England to north Wales, a lack of warping seems to be implied by the apparent horizontality of erosion surfaces. Within the unglaciated part of this area these surfaces and the river terraces, raised beaches and buried channels might be expected to record clearly the changes of the Pleistocene sea level. Yet the pattern is far from simple. Not only have the sea and rivers tended to remove the evidence they produced in earlier stages by their own action in later times, but periglacial and interglacial weathering and mass-movement have destroyed or concealed much of the story. The broad pattern, however, suggests an intermittent eustatic lowering of sea level through the Pleistocene on which were superimposed the eustatic oscillations produced by the growth and decay of glaciers.

A falling sea level in the unwarped part of the London Basin is recorded by the shoreline at 600-700 ft. (180-210 m.) and the later Pebble Gravels at about 400 ft. (120 m.). How far sea level had dropped before the first ice-sheet reached the area is uncertain, but during the first interglacial sea level is often considered to have been about 200 ft. (60 m.) above the present level. Wooldridge and Linton (1955, p. 137) allow this possibility in discussing the Winter Hill terrace of the Thames, considered to have been formed at this time, but point out also that the matter is not yet proved. During the second interglacial a sea level between 100 ft. and 130 ft. (30-40 m.) is fairly widely accepted. On the south coast a raised beach extending up to 130 ft. (40 m.) and overlain by coombe rock contains a temperate fauna as well as archaeological evidence that correlates it with the extensive Boyn Hill terrace of the Thames, which is considered to have accumulated during the second inter-glacial. Within the glaciated area, in Norfolk, the Nar valley estuarine clay indicates a sea level of at least 75 ft. (23 m.) and quite possibly 90 ft. (27 m.), which pollen analysis shows to belong to the second interglacial (Stevens, 1959). At and near Kirmington in Lincolnshire marine deposits up to 90 or 100 ft. (27-30 m.) have also been assigned to this interglacial on the basis of their pollen content (Watts, 1959).

On the Hampshire coast pollen and mollusca show that beach deposits, which are covered by loess and coombe rock, were laid down when the sea stood approximately 25 ft. (8 m.) above its present level during the last interglacial (West and Sparks, 1960). In the Severn valley the Kidderminster Terrace, which contains a warm fauna and was shown by Wills (1938) to correlate with a sea level at about 20 ft. (6 m.), is now considered to have been formed

146

during the last interglacial (Coope et al., 1961). In Holderness and Lincolnshire, and along parts of the coasts of south and southwest England, Wales, the Isle of Man and Ireland there occurs a well-developed, wave-cut rock platform, backed by a cliff. The notch at the cliff base usually lies between 10 and 25 ft. (3-8 m.) above sea level. The altitudinal correspondence between this erosional feature and the depositional evidence referred to, as well as the manner in which the shoreline frequently follows every minor indentation of the present coastline, favours its formation in the last interglacial. In accordance with this view are the faunal remains at Sewerby, near Bridlington (King, 1955, p. 204) and archaeological evidence on the south coast of England (Wright, 1937, p. 121). As mentioned above, however, this interpretation is not in accord with recent views on the age of the platform and on the drift sequence in Ireland.

The low sea levels of glacial times are in part recorded by steep-sided valleys cut in rock to depths well below present sea level and subsequently infilled partly or completely by various deposits. To what extent the excavation of these valleys is related to the last major eustatic lowering of ocean level and how much it owes to earlier ones is uncertain, although in the Thames valley evidence of more than one period of low sea level has been identified. In Ireland the buried valleys of the Lee, Liffey, and Lagan have been traced to about 100 ft. (30 m.) below sea level and in England and Wales many valleys descend to 100-150 ft. (30-45 m.) and occasionally to even greater depths. The seaward continuations of some of these valleys, represented by depressions on the sea floor, have been tentatively identified on the beds of the English Channel and North Sea. With the final great eustatic rise of ocean level many of the valleys were converted into estuaries, of which the smaller rapidly silted up and the larger still indent the coastline.

In Scotland remains of old shorelines cut in rock exist in many places, the most remarkable being the abrasion platform backed by cliffs up to 200 ft. (60 m.) high that occurs in western Mull, Jura, Islay, and the adjacent area. Till, striae, and ice-moulding on the feature show that it pre-dates at least part of the last glaciation. Its clarity where best exposed points to a late rather than early Pleistocene age. The cliff base varies between 80 and 160 ft. (24-48 m.) above sea level, suggesting warping or faulting.

The story of the isostatically-deformed shorelines of the north-west of the British Isles is not yet fully deciphered. In part this is the result of shorelines of different ages having been correlated with each other, producing especially the so-called '100-ft.' and

'50-ft.' (30 and 15 m.) beaches (Sissons, 1962). Late-glacial marine deposits are best developed in central Scotland and are absent or at a very low level in northern England, Caithness, the Orkneys, Shetlands, and Outer Hebrides. Most of the deposits of the east of Scotland are far more arctic than those of the west and were formed before the maximum of the Perth Readvance, for outwash at the limit of this readvance overlies them. The outwash grades into shorelines that attain 120 ft. (36 m.) near Stirling and 100 ft. (30m.) near Perth.

Continuance of isostatic recovery after the Loch Lomond Readvance resulted in a period of relatively low sea level. During this time accumulated the beds of peat that are now buried beneath the highest post-glacial marine and estuarine deposits of Scotland and northern Ireland. Radiocarbon dates of the peat so far available

YEARS BEFORE PRESENT	Pollen Zones	BLYTT-SERNANDER PERIOD	VEGETATION	CLIMATE	Man	Sea Level in Stable Areas	Sea Level in Mid Forth
1000	VIII	SUB-ATLANTIC	ALDER BIRCH OAK		Norman		
					Anglo Saxon		
2000					Romano-British		
				DETERIORATION	Iron Age		
3000				↑	Bronze Age		
	VIIb	SUB-BOREAL					
4000			ALDER MIXED OAK FOREST	CLIMATIC	Neolithic		
5000							
6000	VIIa	ATLANTIC		OPTIMUM			
7000				↓ ↑			
8000	VI	BOREAL	HAZEL PINE	RAPID	Mesolithic		
9000				AMELIORATION			
	V		HAZEL PINE BIRCH				
10,000	IV	PRE-BOREAL	BIRCH	↓			
	III	UPPER DRYAS	TUNDRA	COLD			
11,000	II	ALLERØD	BIRCH	MILDER			
12,000	I	LOWER DRYAS	TUNDRA	COLD			

Table 5. CORRELATION OF SOME ASPECTS OF LATE-GLACIAL AND POST-GLACIAL TIMES. Based partly on Godwin (1956, 1961), Godwin and Willis (1961, 1962), and Fairbridge (1961).

range from 9,700 to 8,100 years before present, thus according in age with peats on the floor of the southern North Sea, which at that time was still partly land, for 8,400 years ago world sea level was still at least 90 ft. (27 m.) below present (Godwin and Willis, 1962).

The final major eustatic rise of ocean level, which ended about 5,500 years ago (Godwin and Willis, 1961, 1962), restored the North Sea to approximately its present shape and gave rise to the first post-glacial raised shoreline represented by the carse clays of central Scotland and sand and shingle beaches in more exposed areas (Table 5). The shoreline reaches its maximum altitude of 48 ft. (15 m.) in the upper Forth area and declines in altitude outwards from this vicinity. Thus it is said to be absent from the Orkneys and Shetlands, is at about 25 ft. (8 m.) in northeast Ireland, about 15 ft. (4·5 m.) around Dublin and is reported to be absent from extreme southeast Ireland. In England the transgression is represented by low-level silts and clays overlain by peat in the Morecambe Bay area, the Somerset Levels, the Fenland and the land around the head of the Humber estuary. A second post-glacial shoreline identified in parts of Scotland is at about 36 ft. (11 m.) near Stirling. Two lower shorelines have also been identified in the Forth valley. The lowest of the four may have been formed by the slight eustatic rise of sea level that produced the Romano-British transgression in the Somerset Levels and the Fenland.

Thus glaciation in the British Isles and developments in post-glacial times, greatly added to the basic variety of structure and relief, to produce surfaces many of which had the greatest influence on the geography of settlement and development.

Note: All altitudes are related to Ordnance Datum.

References

CHARLESWORTH, J. K., 1926. The glacial geology of the Southern Uplands, west of Annandale. *Trans. Roy. Soc. Edinb.*, **55**, 1-23.
—— 1928. The glacial retreat from central and southern Ireland. *Quart. J. Geol. Soc.*, **84**, 293-344.
COOPE, G. R., 1962. Coleoptera from a peat interbedded between two boulder clays at Burnhead, near Airdrie. *Trans. Geol. Soc. Glasg.*, **24**, 279-86.
COOPE, G. R., SHOTTON, F. W. and STRACHAN, I., 1961. A late Pleistocene fauna and flora from Upton Warren, Worcestershire. *Phil. Trans.*, **244**, 379-421.
DIMBLEBY, G. W., 1952. Pleistocene ice wedges in northeast Yorkshire. *J. Soil Sci.*, **3**, 1-19.
DONNER, J. J., 1960. Pollen analysis of the Burn of Benholm peat bed, Kincardinshire, Scotland. *Soc. Sci. Fenn.*, *Commentationes Biologicae*, **22**, 1-13.
EMBLETON, C., 1961. The geomorphology of the Vale of Conway, North Wales, with particular reference to its glaciation. *Trans. Inst. Brit. Geogr.* **29**, 47-70.
FAIRBRIDGE, R. W., 1961. Eustatic changes in sea-level. *Physics and Chemistry of the earth*, **4**, 99-185.

FARRINGTON, A., 1944. The glacial drifts of the district around Enniskerry, Co. Wicklow. *Proc. R. Irish Acad.*, **B, 50,** 133-57.
— 1949. The glacial drifts of the Leinster Mountains. *J. Glaciol.*, **1,** 220-25.
FARRINGTON, A., and MITCHELL, G. F., 1951. The end-moraine north of Flamborough Head. *Proc. Geol. Ass.*, **52,** 100-6.
GALLOWAY, R. W., 1961. Solifluction in Scotland. *Scot. Geogr. Mag.*, **77,** 75-87.
GODWIN, H., 1956. *History of the British Flora.* Cambridge.
— 1961. Radiocarbon dating and Quaternary history in Britain. *Proc. Roy. Soc.*, **B, 153,** 287-320.
GODWIN, H., and WILLIS, E. H., 1961, 1962. Cambridge University natural radiocarbon measurements III and V. *Radiocarbon*, **3,** 60-76; **4,** 57-70.
GRESSWELL, R. K., 1962. The glaciology of the Coniston Basin. *Lpool. Manchr. Geol. J.*, **3,** 83-96.
HOLLINGWORTH, S. E., TAYLOR, J. H., and KELLAWAY, G. A., 1944. Large-scale superficial structures in the Northampton ironstone field. *Quart. J. Geol. Soc.*, **100,** 1-44.
KENDALL, P. F., 1902. A system of glacier lakes in the Cleveland Hills. *Quart. J. Geol. Soc.*, **58,** 471-571.
KING, W. B. R., 1955. The Pleistocene epoch in England. *Quart. J. Geol. Soc.*, **111,** 187-208.
LINTON, D. L., 1959. Morphological contrasts between eastern and western Scotland. *Geographical Essays in memory of A. Ogilvie.* Edinburgh, 16-45.
MITCHELL, G. F., 1960. The Pleistocene history of the Irish Sea. *Advanc. Sci.*, **17,** 313-25.
PALMER, J., and NEILSON, R. A., 1962. The origin of granite tors on Dartmoor, Devonshire. *Proc. Yorks. Geol. Soc.*, **33,** 315-40.
PEAKE, D. S., 1961. Glacial changes in the Alyn river system and their significance in the glaciology of the North Welsh border. *Quart. J. Geol. Soc.*, **117,** 335-66.
PENNY, L. F., 1959. The last glaciation in East Yorkshire. *Trans. Leeds. Geol. Ass.*, **7,** 65-77.
PRICE, R. J., 1960. Glacial meltwater channels in the upper Tweed drainage basin. *Geogr. J.*, **126,** 483-9.
SHOTTON, F. W., 1953. The Pleistocene deposits of the area between Coventry, Rugby and Leamington. *Phil. Trans.*, **B, 237,** 209-60.
SIMPSON, I. M., and WEST, R. G., 1958. On the stratigraphy and palaeobotany of a late-Pleistocene organic deposit at Chelford, Cheshire. *New Phytol.*, **57,** 239-50.
SIMPSON, J. B., 1933. The late-glacial readvance moraines of the Highland border west of the river Tay. *Trans. Roy. Soc. Edinb.*, **57,** 633-45.
SISSONS, J. B., 1960, 1961. Some aspects of glacial drainage channels in Britain. *Scot. Geogr. Mag.*, **76,** 131-46; **77,** 15-36.
— 1962. A re-interpretation of the literature on late-glacial shorelines in Scotland with particular reference to the Forth area. *Trans. Edinb. Geol. Soc.*, **19,** 83-99.
STEVENS, L. A., 1959. The interglacial of the Nar valley, Norfolk. *Quart. J. Geol. Soc.*, **115,** 291-315.
STRAW, A., 1960. The limit of the last glaciation in north Norfolk. *Proc. Geol. Ass.*, **71,** 379-90.
SYNGE, F. M., 1956. The glaciation of northeast Scotland. *Scot. Geog. Mag.*, **72,** 129-43.
SYNGE, F. M., and STEPHENS, N., 1960. The Quaternary period in Ireland—an assessment, 1960. *Irish Geogr.*, **4,** 121-30.
TRECHMANN, C. T., 1919. On a deposit of interglacial loess, and some transported preglacial freshwater clays on the Durham coast. *Quart. J. Geol. Soc.*, **75,** 173-203.

WATTS, W. A., 1959. Pollen spectra from the interglacial deposit at Kirmington, Lincolnshire. *Proc. Yorks. Geol. Soc.*, **32**, 145-51.

WEST, R. G., 1958. The Pleistocene epoch in East Anglia. *J. Glaciol.*, **3**, 211-6.

WEST, R. G., and DONNER, J. J., 1956. The glaciations of East Anglia and the East Midlands: a differentiation based on stone-orientation measurements of the tills. *Quart. J. Geol. Soc.*, **112**, 69-91.

WEST, R. G., and SPARKS, W. B., 1960. Coastal interglacial deposits of the English channel. *Phil. Trans.*, **B, 243**, 95-133.

WILLS, L. J., 1938. The Pleistocene development of the Severn from Bridgnorth to the sea. *Quart. J. Geol. Soc.*, **94**, 161-242.

WOOLDRIDGE, S. W., 1960. The Pleistocene succession in the London Basin. *Proc. Geol. Ass.*, **71**, 113-129.

WOOLDRIDGE, S. W., and LINTON, D. L., 1955. *Structure, surface and drainage in South-east England*. 2nd ed., London.

WRIGHT, W. B., 1937. *The Quaternary Ice Age*. 2nd ed., London.

9

THE EVOLUTION OF THE CLIMATIC ENVIRONMENT

THE British Isles lie upon a margin, where it is for the geographer to be forever conscious of the subtle effects arising from location between continent and ocean, between subtropical languor and Arctic bite, between mobile Atlantic and rigid Russia, between Mediterranean and Nordic. Within, the diversity of the climatic environment is manifest; and, in particular, the effects of altitude and exposure, of widely varying rainfall, of evaporation through the summer months, of local variations in the incidence of frost, snow, and fog. Small changes in the average pattern of the general circulation of the atmosphere, with the resultant climatic fluctuations, may thus be very effective in one part of the British Isles, while in another they have little significance. To the stresses imposed by this changing environment the native plants, the wild and domestic animals, and the successive waves of immigrant man have become adapted. At a critical stage in history, the attraction of the milder Atlantic winters for northern European peoples prevailed. The English language itself epitomises the story of the climatic fluctuations; for, in that thirteenth century which saw the adoption of so many Romance words, the summers were warm enough to allow the cultivation of vineyards in favourable parts of southern England. Came the Reformation, and the further advance of the mountain glaciers; the vine was driven back south of Paris.

This essay reviews the present state of knowledge of the evolution of our climate since the last great phase of the Ice Age; the period, indeed, within which *homo sapiens* came to northern Europe, and under which the British have evolved. At the maximum of the Ice Age the climate was such that the British Isles were virtually uninhabitable. Over four-fifths of the land resembled not so much the Greenland ice cap as the more unpleasant and stormy Vatnajökull of Iceland. At the present day, by contrast, the climatic environment can be described as exceptionally favourable. It encourages human activity, provides a stimulus to a wide variety of stock-rearing pursuits, and permits the cultivation, with care and on a small scale, of an astonishingly wide range and diversity of plants. Within eight degrees of latitude and eight hundred metres of altitude can be found the pomegranate and the cloudberry. The beech occurs beyond Inverness, the saxifrage in Surrey. Mediterranean heaths are present in Cornwall, rare Greenland relics on the mountains of Argyllshire. To Continental visitors, the treeline even in Wales is exceptionally low, and yet in western Scotland the eucalyptus has been introduced with success. To the general climatic factors must be added the effects of aspect, exposure, and in particular the qualities of the soil. Within the English Midlands the average length of the frost-free season is known to range from about ten weeks to upwards of seven months, even at the lower altitudes (Fig. 16).

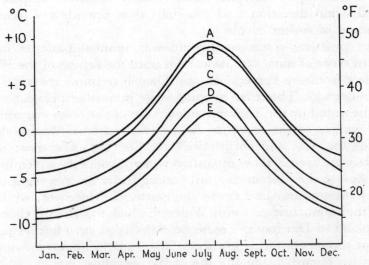

Fig. 16. ESTIMATED TREND OF THE AVERAGE EXTREME MONTHLY MINIMA IN THE ENGLISH MIDLANDS (based on officially-accepted stations). Approximate interval between damaging frosts (screen min. below freezing) for different types of exposure: A, enclosed urban site, large city, April 5-Nov. 5; B. favourable hill slope, April 15-Nov. 1; C. Normal Midland, lowlying, May 15-Oct. 1; D, frost hollow (average), June 5-Sept. 12; E, extensive sandy lowland, June 20-Aug. 25 (after Manley, 1944).

Throughout northwestern Europe the evidence for Quaternary climatic evolution comes from a very wide range of field scientists; most notably the geologists, botanists and archaeologists. Recognition of the effects of glaciation was followed by mapping and then by the historic Swedish varve-chronology. C. E. P. Brooks in his *Evolution of Climate* (1922) did much to provide a meteorological interpretation of the course of events in Britain. But, in the absence of a satisfactory varve-sequence, until the further development of pollen-analytical studies, and the advent of radiocarbon dating, the correlation of events in the British Isles with those in Scandinavia could not be confirmed, however much such a correlation might, on meteorological reasoning, be surmised. During the past four decades much research has been directed to putting the quantities in, and to giving greater precision to the earlier estimates, in order to relate the amplitude and character of past fluctuations to those of today for which we have instrumental evidence.

Of recent years it has become possible to invoke the geologists' principle of uniformitarianism in the field of climatology. Almost 300 years of continuous daily instrumental-meteorological records has enabled us to evaluate the characteristics of the minor fluctuations of several climatic elements, notably those of temperature, rainfall, wind direction, and snowfall; thus providing a basis for discussion of earlier events.

For practical purposes, Britain was uninhabitable as far as modern types of man were concerned until the retreat of the Würm ice-sheet from the Pomeranian and Danish terminal moraines was well under way. The corresponding stage in northern England may be represented by the York moraines. Each of the phases of advance bears witness to the fact that the ice was fed from the highlands towards the west and north (Chap. 8, Fig. 15). The most active sources were exactly those mountain regions where the precipitation is greatest at the present day, amounting to six or even eight times that of the lowlands not far to the eastward. Moreover, while ice from the mountains of south Wales reached the Bristol Channel, the upland of Dartmoor, a mere 60 miles (100 km.) farther south, did not support any true glaciers. This leads to important conclusions with regard to the altitude of the snowline.

That a cold, but open ocean lay to the westward is evident. Klute has given estimates of the sea surface temperature west of the Outer Hebrides, ranging from 32°F (0°C) in January-February to about 43°F (6°C) in July-August. While Scottish ice crossed the Orkneys it failed to reach St Kilda 50 miles (80 km.) west of Lewis (Wager, 1953). Harrison, moreover, has shown that parts of the Outer Hebrides stood as nunataks. This all supports the picture of a remarkably raw, cold and stormy sub-arctic margin facing the North Atlantic. The prevailing estimate of conditions in the North Atlantic about the beginning of the last great glacial retreat is shown in Figure 17 (Manley, 1951). Conjectural isobars for winter and summer have been published by several authorities, for example, Willett, Poser, Büdel; and need not be redrawn here. For

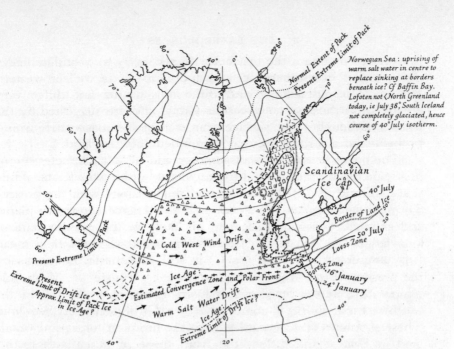

Fig. 17. THE RELATIONSHIP OF SURFACE FEATURES AND THE GLACIAL CLIMATE OF THE NORTH ATLANTIC. The Polar Front would often lie about 50°N near the convergence. An Arctic Front would probably lie through the Norwegian Sea from south of Iceland (after Manley, 1951).

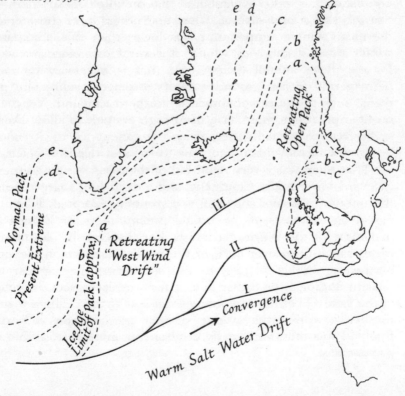

Fig. 18. REMOVAL OF AN ICE-CAP: a possible mechanism giving rise to extensive ablation by convection from a warmer sea. IIIc, a hypothetical intermediate stage corresponding roughly to the 'Perth Readvance' (after Manley, *Geogr. J.*, 1951).

in order to maintain the glaciers it is necessary to postulate heavy precipitation in southern Iceland and Norway as well as western Britain. The prevailing wind directions would not differ very greatly from those of cold seasons today, and are suggested by the isobars, although at the surface near each of the coasts there would probably be a strong thermal component off the land.

The mean temperature of summer and winter characteristic of this stage has been estimated from a variety of known effects. While there is some risk in the assumption that analogy with the present day necessarily holds in respect of the tolerance shown by plants and animals, this would seem to be likely in the present state of knowledge. To equate the tree-line in broad terms with a mean July temperature of 50°F (10°C) is still acceptable. Estimates by the present writer (1951) are illustrated by Figure 17. Mean July temperature at sea level ranges from about 47°F (8·5°C) in the southwest and south, to about 42°F (5·5°C) in northwest Scotland. These estimates are compatible with the limits of forest and woodland in France and differ little from those of other authors, for example, Poser. For January the present author's estimates range from 23°F (−5°C) on the extreme southwest coasts to 10°F (−12°C) inland; it is to be remembered that much of the southern North Sea was still a land surface. Klute and others have considered that the mean winter temperature was lower than this. Estimates for winter must depend on which of several estimates are accepted for the mean annual temperature that is necessary to maintain permanently frozen ground with its associated solifluxion phenomena, such as the coombe rock in southern England. Yet the summer temperatures must have been high enough to allow Dartmoor to be free, or virtually free, from permanent ice thick enough to be capable of movement and thus to leave evidence of glacial drift.

That there was a very rapid fall of the mean winter temperature eastward towards the Continent, and a decidedly sharp decrease in the amount of winter snowfall, is commonly accepted. Klein (1953) has given estimates of the annual precipitation for Europe at the maximum of the Würm glaciation. For the British Isles these estimates range from over 80% of the present amount in the extreme northwest, falling to 40% in the southeast; they appear to the present author to be rather low, if his surmise based on the events of the Late-Glacial is acceptable (Manley, 1959b). There is support for his view that the average annual precipitation in northwest England was then not greatly different in amount from that of the present day.

Morphological features and climate

Although the ascription of some of the coombes on the chalk downs of southern England to nivation processes is disputed, the mean summer and winter temperatures given above would just permit the survival of occasional wind-drifted snow-accumulations in the lee of hills 600-1,000 ft. (200-300 m.) high. Account must also be taken of the presence of 'exposed summit tors' in the granites of the eastern Cairngorms at altitudes above 3,000 ft. (1,000 m.). As they occur on broad, rounded uplands they can be taken as evidence that ice never moved across them. This supports the opinion that there was a very rapid eastward rise in the snowline consequent upon steadily diminishing precipitation in that direction. For the maintenance of glaciers descending into the Hebridean seas demands a snowline of the order of only 500-650 ft. (150-200 m.) above sea level. The presence of tors suggests that the eastern Cairngorm snowline, on the other hand, might well lie at 1,600-1,800 ft. (500-550 m.) (Manley, 1949). If at the same time the adjacent valleys and lowlands were full of ice, it is more than ever necessary to postulate a disturbed windy climate with a vast excess of snowfall on all the mountains farther west; providing, indeed, the source of nourishment for a broad ice-sheet lying over the greater part of the present Irish Sea.

Elucidation of events in eastern Scotland has already been provided by Sissons in Chapter 8. Many morphological features elsewhere attest the rapid southward diminution in the depth and extent of the Würm ice sheet. The existence of tors on the Pennines, the unglaciated uplands of northeast Yorkshire, the lack of defined corries in the Cheviots, and the lack of ice in the Calder valley of Yorkshire (despite its presence in the adjacent valleys to the northward), all support the view that at the maximum of the Würm glaciation the snowline in the southern Pennines was relatively high, probably at least 1,500 ft. (450 m.). There, the broad and severely windswept plateau of Kinderscout (2,088 ft., 635 m.) shows no sign of ice having accumulated upon it, although an active stream of ice, approaching 1,000 ft. (300 m.) deep, was flowing through the Cheshire Gap a few kilometres to the westward. Even the broad summit of Ingleborough (2,373 ft., 723 m.) was probably a nunatak, according to Raistrick. Such evidence points to the importance, as sources of nourishment for the glaciers, of the very limited highland areas of England and Wales that attain more than

157

2,000 ft. (600 m.), and the likelihood that the snowfall upon them was very great in order to maintain such extensive gently-sloping glaciers far down into the Midlands, not only during the Würm, but even more extensively in the earlier phases.

Northwest England and north Wales therefore offer many opportunities for investigation of the halt-stages and oscillations during the waning of the last glaciation (Embleton, 1961, Seddon, 1962). In the previous chapter Sissons has drawn attention to the evidence for several late-glacial stages, and notably the 'Scottish Readvance', together with the subsequent Bölling, and the Allerød oscillations whose effects were first recognised in Denmark.

British workers have long been tempted to correlate events in Britain with those in Scandinavia. On meteorological grounds, indeed, parallelism might be expected. Proof however was lacking until the publication of Winifred Pennington's study of the Windermere lake-sediments (1947) showed that the Allerød oscillation had left its effects in northern England, and that the subsequent climatic recession (the 'Jungere Tundrenzeit' of German workers) had resulted in the re-establishment after their previous disappearance of small glaciers in the Lake District valleys over a period, based on the count of the varves, of the order of 400 years. Radiocarbon dating gave added corroboration, and pollen-analytical evidence of this climatic oscillation (Zones II and III) has since been found by numerous workers in northern England and southern Scotland, notably Godwin's many collaborators.

These studies have shown that the amelioration of the climate by 10,000 B.C. was sufficient to allow tree-birches to grow at least as far north as central Scotland, just as they are known to have reached the coasts of southwest Norway (Faegri, 1935). The subsequent retreat of the tree-birch limit to 'somewhere in the English Midlands' corresponds very fairly with the known retreat on the Continent, to 'somewhere in Holstein'. It becomes possible to draw tentative summer isotherms between England and Denmark, and to observe not only that they are remarkably parallel to those of today, but also that the effects of this post-Allerød or Zone III climatic recession are compatible with a fall of the mean summer temperature in northwest Britain of the order of 7-9°F (4-5°C). In the wettest areas the associated lowering of the snowline should be about 2,000 ft. (600 m.).

Many accordingly have begun to hope that some similar confirmation of the occurrence, the date, and the effects of the earlier Bölling oscillation would soon follow. Establishment of the facts has however proved difficult. No satisfactory series of lake-sediments is yet known to exist towards the Midlands, wherein an earlier alternation of layers with and without tree-pollen might be determined. In a paper by Oldfield (1960) on the evolution of vegetation in the coastlands adjacent to Morecambe Bay, there is some evidence that an earlier climatic oscillation occurred, before the Allerød, but after the ice had retreated from the Windermere Basin. This earlier amelioration does not appear to have gone far enough to allow widespread growth of birches in this part of north-west England, and as yet we lack evidence for its amplitude. Some effects of earlier climatic oscillation have been found elsewhere (Suggate and West, 1959; Bartley, 1962; Kerney, 1963).

To equate the effects of the earlier 'Scottish Readvance' with the Götiglacial halt of southern Sweden might be reasonable in the light of present knowledge and, meteorologically, very acceptable. Evidence is gradually accumulating from Ireland that enables tentative correlation to be made of these several stages with events in Scotland, northern England, north Wales and Scandinavia.

The events of the post-Allerød climatic recession (Zone III)

In a paper on the location and characteristics of the latest valley-moraines in the Lake District, which undoubtedly developed as a result of the re-establishment of glaciers during this post-Allerød recession, the present author (1959b) has concluded that the mean temperature of the summer months fell by not less than 7°F (4°C) and perhaps 9°F (5°C) at the onset of the recession. The dimensions of the glaciers so formed indicate that a period of the order of 80 years of colder, wetter, and more disturbed climate was required to provide the needful accumulation.

The altitude of the snowline necessary for the establishment and maintenance of these glaciers can be estimated from the location of the lateral and end-moraines. It appears to have been lowest, about 1,600 ft. (485 m.), in that central area of the Lake District where today the rainfall is greatest, and to have risen northward and eastward to 2,450 ft. (750 m.) or more in regions where the present day precipitation is little more than half that of the central area. The rate of rise of the snowline, with the consequent decline in precipitation to which it points, compares very closely with that which would occur if not only the distribution, but also the amount of the precipitation were very much the same as today. Indeed there is some support for the view that a climatic recession of the same amount and character, had it lasted for a considerably longer time, would have been capable of again carrying the ice to the southern Midlands and the outskirts of London, as in the earlier phases of the Pleistocene glaciation.

The most reasonable meteorological explanation, compatible with the known facts, is that the Atlantic atmospheric circulation assumed a much more 'zonal' pattern, and that this became predominant throughout the majority of the summers for the greater part of a century. Accompanying such a change, at a time when pack-ice in the northwest Atlantic would be much more prominent than today, we should expect a considerable advance of the margin of the pack-ice to the region south and southwest of Iceland. With an icy Western Ocean, such a circulation change would cause the short-track maritime-polar air to be cooled to a relatively greater extent, than if a similar change were to occur with the much more open Atlantic of today (Fig. 17).

We are aware of the contrast that can exist today between such summers as 1954 and 1955, the first particularly cool and unsettled, and about 4·5°F (2·5°C) cooler, overall, than the predominantly warm-anticyclonic summer of 1955. With a more icy western Atlantic, the fall of between 7° and 9°F (4-5°C) accompanying the post-Allerød or Zone III recession might be the result of a similar change in the prevailing atmospheric circulation; in essence, the eastward displacement of the upper-level trough that is normally found in the western Atlantic.

The effects of this climatic recession are quite well documented. Pollen-analytical studies such as those quoted by Godwin (1956) for East Anglia, and by Suggate and West (1959) for Lincolnshire, suggest that in that region birches were found throughout; further confirmation comes from recent pollen-analytical studies in Surrey. According to Oldfield the head of Morecambe Bay lay near to, though probably beyond, the northern limit for tree-birches. At Windermere and other northern-England stations, such as Scaleby, they seem to have been absent; that is, wet-tundra conditions again prevailed. These facts are consistent with a mean July temperature of 50°F (10°C) across the north Midlands, with which the estimate of 45·5°-46·5°F (7·5°-8°C) at Windermere derived from consideration of the extent of glaciers is reasonably in keeping.

It may be added that the re-establishment of small glaciers in this post-Allerød recession is confirmed among the mountains of north Wales (Godwin, 1956; Seddon, 1962). The limits of their extension, when compared with the Lake District, suggest that the mean temperature in north Wales was about 1-2° (0·5-1 °C) above that in Cumberland. This is close to the present-day difference.

The winter mean temperature can be estimated from the evidence that over considerable areas the subsoil was permanently frozen. In a cloudy climate this appears to be possible with a mean annual temperature close to 30°F or −1 °C; if so, in northwest England a mean January temperature at least as low as 14°F (−10°C), and possibly lower, appears to be called for. That the range of monthly mean temperature, January-July, should attain 32°F (18°C), compared with the present 22°F (12°C), is entirely reasonable, bearing in mind that much of the area, now the North Sea and the Irish Sea, was then land. The present-day January-July range in central Holland exceeds 29°F (16°C).

Precipitation, in amount, appears to have been of the same order as that we now receive; and, during this climatic recession, snow probably covered the low ground in northern England for nearly 7 months of the year. Orientation of the corries, and distribution of precipitation, all point to the predominance of southwest to west winds in much the same fashion as today; and the summer climate must have been extremely cloudy. Some difficulties of

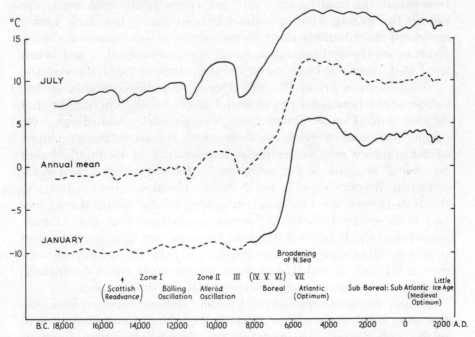

Fig. 19. ENGLISH MIDLANDS: estimated trend of the summer and winter mean temperatures during the past 20,000 years.

drawing precise conclusions with regard to this Late-Glacial period in southern England are made evident by Kerney (1963).

Post-glacial climatic evolution

The subsequent evolution of the British climate runs parallel to that on the adjacent continent. We recognise the older subdivisions of Boreal, Atlantic, Sub-Boreal and Sub-Atlantic, to which much detail has now been added. Recurrence-surfaces such as are recognised in Sweden and Germany are, however, less easy to determine in the British Isles. Studies of the marine fauna, notably the shellfish in the Scottish raised beaches occupied by Neolithic man, assist in making estimates of sea temperature; studies of the prevalence of certain land fauna, such as snails, give evidence of temperatures prevailing on land. It appears from the snails that the mean July temperature of southern England cannot have been less than 62°F (16·5°C) at the time that the last land bridge became broken. This event is commonly associated with the onset of 'Full-Atlantic' conditions, notably the mild winters that resulted from the broadening of the North and Irish Seas. Harrison indeed considered that before the final rupture, winters were already mild enough to permit the immigration of some southern plants that have now a restricted distribution, close to our mildest southwestern shores. Even in southeast England a winter mean temperature not below 43°F (6°C) seems to be required about the time of the final severance.

The location of the Atlantic Ocean and the constancy of the relationships between English and Danish vegetation suggest that English and Danish fluctuations ran parallel. Accordingly, we might make use of Iversen's deductions regarding the variations of the summer and winter mean temperature in Denmark, based on careful analysis of the occurrence of ivy, mistletoe, and holly pollen in the peat bogs. In the Atlantic period, all three appear; in the Sub-Boreal, ivy and mistletoe only; in the Sub-Atlantic, ivy and holly only. This leads Iversen to deduce that the Atlantic period was 3·5°F (2°C) warmer in summer, 0·8°F (0·5°C) warmer in winter, than now; the Sub-Boreal 3·5°F (2°C) warmer in summer, 0·8°F (0·5°C) colder in winter than now; in the Sub-Atlantic, summer and winter averages were similar to those of today.

These findings, applied to Britain, receive support from the fact that trees grew at considerably higher altitudes than today; in the Sub-Boreal, they grew on the Cairngorms up to 1,000 ft. (300 m.) above the present limit. From shellfish in the 'Neolithic' beaches of southwest Scotland it appears that the seas were about 3·5°F (2°C) warmer than today in Atlantic-Sub-Boreal time. It is not very easy to estimate what would be the effect of the broadening of the North Sea, but during the Climatic Optimum winters were prevailingly mild, and were perhaps 3·5°F (2°C) warmer than today. These departures, both in summer and winter, are not notably greater than those we occasionally experience today in individual years. In 1959, for example, all four seasons averaged about 2°F (1·3°C) above the average.

There is support from Scandinavia for the view that the climate had already become relatively mild before the breaching of the Channel land-bridge. It is necessary to postulate a eustatic rise of sea level, demonstrated by the broadening of the North Sea, and to attribute this to the melting of glaciers. The downmelting of the ice in Scandinavia has been shown by Mannerfelt to be predominantly the result of ablation resulting from the advent of warmer and moister air. With such air prevailing in Scandinavia it must fairly be presumed that in England mild winters and warm summers would predominate.

Yet the characteristics of the British climate in its 'optimum' phase appear to be attained by occasional warm years today. We may instance:

Table 6. Midlands: mean temperature contrasts

	January		July		Year	
	°F	°C	°F	°C	°F	°C
Optimum, estimated	43	6	64.5	18	52	11
Present day (1931-60)	38.2	3.4	61.2	16.2	49.3	9.6
1834	44.7	7.1	62.5	16.9	50.8	10.5
1868	39.0	3.9	64.9	18.3	50.7	10.4
1949	41.9	5.5	63.4	17.4	51.1	10.6
1959	34.9	1.6	63.1	17.3	50.9	10.5

Support for these views is also forthcoming from Holland. This leads to the belief that the characteristics of the atmospheric circulation were similar in principle to those of today, but in the 'Optimum' the northeast Atlantic was warmer, and the Arctic ice much diminished, if not almost absent. For example the mean annual temperature at Spitsbergen, during the Optimum, is known to have risen above 32°F (0°C) (Brooks, 1949).

These facts assist the prevailing meteorological opinion, that the post-glacial changes all lie within the range of behaviour shown by extreme years and extreme seasons at the present day. The main problem to be solved by the meteorologist is that of 'persistence of type' over a considerable number of years, leading to further rise, or fall, of the temperature of the ocean and variation in the extent of the Arctic sea-ice.

Precipitation

To evaluate the amount and seasonal distribution of the precipitation during the several post-glacial climatic phases is very difficult indeed. Throughout the warmer months the evaporation-precipitation balance is delicate. Small changes of temperature affect the evaporation and small variations in the seasonal incidence of the rainfall may lead to considerable rises and falls of the water-table.

There is considerable evidence, in the now dry valleys of the Chalk of southern England, that spring-lines in the past have lain at higher levels. Yet such a rise might well result from persistence of seasons only slightly wetter than the average today. On the Sussex Downs near the Channel, it appears that before extensive grazing by sheep began, scrubby woodlands with such trees as hawthorn were widespread. Whenever wind-driven low stratus cloud came in off the channel, such a cover would probably give rise to extensive fog-drip, adding appreciably to the available water for percolation.

Dury, from a study of misfit meandering streams in a number of Midland valleys, has considered that the evidence demands the occurrence of great volumes of flood water at intervals and that this points to greater precipitation, even in 'Atlantic' times. It appears however (verbal communication) that his requirements might be satisfied by an annual fall averaging something of the order of 25-50% above that of the present day, which is certainly not outside the known limits in individual wet years.

Raistrick and Blackburn, however, thought that the *Sub-Boreal* in northern England was, perhaps, rather drier than today. In southern England, the tree-rings revealed in charcoal from Neolithic sites also fall in the period commonly regarded as Sub-Boreal and appear to indicate that the summer precipitation was probably similar to that we now experience. Such a scheme of events is, however, entirely compatible with what we now know of the distribution of rainfall in time and place, as Gregory points out in Chapter

4. Glasspoole (1925) has shown that variations in the annual rainfall at Oxford, of which at least half falls in the warmer months, make virtually no correlation with the variations of annual rainfall in the western Highlands, of which a great part results from the heavy orographic falls of autumn and winter. Hence the indications of the characteristics of past rainfall from widely separated parts of Britain may differ very considerably. And whereas in many places the evidence frequently suggests a rather wet climate, we must never forget that large parts of the country on the heavy lowland soils have become subject to the effects of artificial drainage.

For these reasons the dating of the recurrence-surfaces in peat bogs might also vary very considerably. Indeed, many of our inferences with regard to the past climate of the British Isles owe more to intelligent meteorological interpretation of the evidence provided in Scandinavia, Holland, or France, than to evidence provided within the British Isles. This is because of the extraordinary number of variables operative in an area so diverse in its soils, drainage, percolation, and seasonal incidence of rain.

The advent of the Sub-Atlantic recession resulted in a fall of about 3·5°F (2°C) in the mean summer temperature, and is entirely compatible with a change to a much more unsettled westerly or 'zonal' circulation, lasting over a considerable period of years. Tree-line fell by about 1,000 ft. (300 m.), e.g. on the Cairngorms and in the northern Pennines; and our wetter uplands then began to acquire most of their very extensive peat-cover. It may be presumed that cloud amount and precipitation increased considerably on all the western and northwestern uplands, that the lowland summer temperature fell by about 3·5°F (2°C), that the upland summer temperature fell by rather more than this, and that evaporation decreased. Confirmation of the increased wetness, together with an approximate dating, comes from the discovery of prehistoric wooden trackways among the former lakes and reedy swamps of Somerset (Godwin, 1956).

In order to illustrate the comparison with present-day conditions we may instance the summers (June-July-August) of 1954 and 1955, 1959 and 1962.

Table 7. Summer mean temperature for 'Central England'

1954	1955	1959	1962
57.2°F	61.7°F	61.8°F	57.7°F
14.0°C	16.5°C	16.6°C	14.3°C

The summer of 1954 was the coolest for 32 years, whereas its immediate successor in 1955 was decidedly warm, although not the warmest. Moreover the excess of rainfall in 1954 was even more marked in the uplands, as one might expect with such persistently windy unsettled weather and short-track maritime-polar air.

Exactly how this Sub-Atlantic climatic recession was effected is not clear; there may have been more than one stage of decline, taking the form of lengthy spells of persistently disturbed weather, between 700 and 400 B.C. The flooding of the Somerset levels and the extensive construction of wooden trackways dated around 550 B.C. has already been noted. Moreover it appears that the decline of temperature was more marked in the summer than in the winter, and that, by comparison with preceding centuries, a period of the order of 50-100 years of prevailing disturbed weather occurred, accompanying the early stages of the Iron Age. There is archaeological evidence of marked impoverishment and decline of the upland Pennine population, in contrast to the relative prosperity and cultural advance of Bronze Age (Sub-Boreal) times when, at 800-1,500 ft. (250-450 m.), upland settlement was widespread. The lowland forests appear to have been damp and difficult to clear, especially on the clays. At the present day, it is still recognised that quiet anticyclonic weather favours the uplands; in the damp lowlands, fog tends to persist.

While there is some evidence for a period of wetter and more disturbed seasons about 100 B.C., the impression is gained that at the time of arrival of the Romans, the climate differed little from that of today. It is possible that in the fourth century A.D. it became wetter, if the increased use of corn-drying kilns in the Midlands can be so interpreted; but this may not be the sole reason. In Somersetshire there is evidence of increased flooding in the fifth century and of renewed construction of wooden trackways (Godwin, 1956); but again, allowance must be made for possible effects of local changes of sea level such as are known to have affected the Fens and East Anglia. That vegetation in Scandinavia is known from the peat-bogs to have responded to increased moisture about A.D. 400 leads many to think that the British Isles would at least to some extent be affected.

With the Anglo-Saxons there is some limited evidence that the climate again tended at intervals in the direction of warmth and dryness. The arguments have been largely summarised by Brooks, and little has been added, but it is tempting to see an association with Butzer's periods of drought in the Near East (Butzer, 1958). After a slight ninth-century setback, it appears that the climate then again improved in the direction of 'continentality', that is with increased warmth and dryness through the growing season, up to the late eleventh century. Again, a tendency for wetter years for two decades or so about A.D. 1100 was followed by improvement to a 'minor optimum' which prevailed through the later twelfth and early thirteenth century during which winters also tended to be relatively mild and we may reasonably conjecture that springs were 'forward'. H. H. Lamb (1959) has recently assembled the evidence for the cultivation of vineyards, and in conjunction with what is known about the climate of Iceland and that of south Germany, based on the cultivation of grain in the one, and of wine in the other, all goes to support the view that medieval times were for upwards of 200 years more often warm and relatively dry than otherwise; sometime in the thirteenth century short groups of unsettled seasons began to be noticeable, but in England their effects did not begin to predominate until the early fourteenth century.

English chronicles, and even the harvest prices, are difficult to interpret as the impression left by any given season is prone to vary considerably from one part of the country to another. Compare for example the unusual wetness of 1949 in the West Highlands, whereas in southeast England the year was generally dry, and remarkably warm almost throughout. In 1958, on the other hand, drought in northwest Scotland accompanied one of the wettest years southern England has ever known. Before 1700 many of our ideas regarding the minor fluctuations—twenty or thirty years prevailingly unsettled and wet, then a similar period with a preponderance of more favourable seasons, though never uninterrupted —derive considerably from the studies made in Germany, Belgium, Holland and France. The evidence favours a cool maritime phase about 1430-1460; the relatively favourable first half of the sixteenth century; the gradual onset of considerably cooler, unsettled weather after 1550, associated with the great advance of all the European glaciers. There are, moreover, significant associations with the well-recognised climatic vicissitudes in Iceland as well as in Scandinavia; and the noteworthy increase in the amount of sea-ice borne southward in the East Greenland current after 1600. We may also note the evidence for a marked decrease in the summer temperature in Lapland after 1586, based on recent Finnish studies.

Among other recent studies that of Ladurie (1960) should be cited, for he demonstrates a relationship between the fluctuations

of the date of the vintage in France and the fluctuations of the
mean temperature of the six months of spring and summer (March
to August inclusive) in England, derived from the present author's
data. This is sufficient to enable a tentative estimate to be made of
the prevailing characteristics of the sixteenth and seventeenth
centuries in England. In the diagram below (Fig. 20) the curve

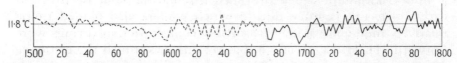

Fig. 20. ENGLISH SUMMERS: THE PROBABLE CHARACTERISTICS OF THE SIXTEENTH, SEVEN-
TEENTH, AND EIGHTEENTH CENTURIES. Fluctuations of the mean temperature of spring and
summer (March-August inclusive): successive two-year means, 1671-1800. Dashed line:
estimated trend based on dates of the vintage in France and Luxemburg, reports of
Swiss glacier behaviour and miscellaneous comments from English sources.
1901-1960, 11·8°C (53·2°F). Highest and lowest values above, 12·9 and 10·1.

representing the warmth of the growing season (spring and summer)
has been extended backwards in time from the beginnings of the
period of instrumental observation, taking into account the French
vintage data, the reported behaviour of the Swiss glaciers which
appears to provide some indication of the mean annual temperature,
and the historical notes on the character of the English seasons.

It is not easy to make use of reports of the freezing of rivers
such as the Thames at London because, when the river was not
embanked, the flow must have been less rapid. In addition, the
narrow arches of old London Bridge impeded both the flow of the
river and the scour of the tide, and the waters easily froze over the
wide stretch of marshland on the south side. Occasional notes exist
of ice in our harbours, for example the Tyne below Newcastle in
1740 and in the Mersey at Liverpool in 1838. There are accounts of
phenomena such as the freezing-over of deep lakes, for example
Windermere, notably in 1740. Such an event is very rare, and goes
to confirm the extreme severity of that winter. But in earlier times
such information with regard to the deep lakes in northern England
and Scotland is scarely to be found. It therefore becomes very
difficult to establish the character of the winters with any precision.

*The instrumental period: daily meteorological observations, and
their results*

From the later sixteenth century onward there is an increasing
number of diaries, and in 1663 under the aegis of the Royal Society
daily instrumental observations were initiated by Robert Hooke.

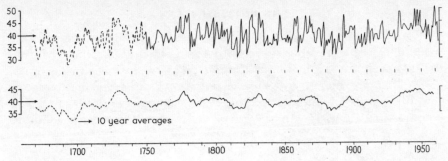

Fig. 21. NORTHERN ENGLAND: VARIATIONS OF THE ACCUMULATED WARMTH OF THE GROW-
ING SEASON AT THE 600 FT. (180 M.) LEVEL, 1671-1962. Units: month-degrees C above
5·5 (42°F). 600 ft. (180 m.) is 'generally representative' of the arable-pasture limit in
northern England. Range of variation above, 28 to 51. In the drier parts of upland Scotland the limit for occasional ploughed fields shows an average of 25, for hay 21, and for
the tree-line 17.

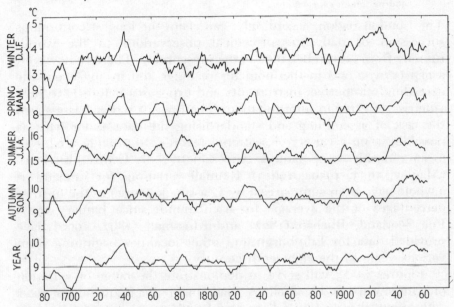

Fig. 22. DECADAL RUNNING MEANS OF SEASONAL AND ANNUAL MEAN TEMPERATURES IN
CENTRAL ENGLAND, 1671-1962.

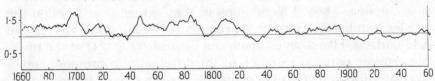

Fig. 23. VARIATIONS IN THE LONDON REGION OF THE FREQUENCY OF OCCURRENCE OF DAYS
WITH SNOW OR SLEET OBSERVED: decadal running means of the winter totals as a proportion
of 'normal today' (i.e. 1921-1960, represented by the horizontal line). Winters with more
than twice the average number: 1665, 1684, 1692, 1695, 1697, 1698, 1701, 1709, 1716,
1729, 1740, 1741, 1748, 1755, 1757, 1770, 1771, 1784, 1785, 1789, 1799, 1814, 1830,
1847, 1860, 1879, 1888, 1917, (1942), (1947), (1951). Less than one-quarter of average:
1662, 1676, 1686, 1734, 1750, 1761, 1779, 1794, 1819, 1834, 1863, 1913, 1923, 1943,
1957, 1961.

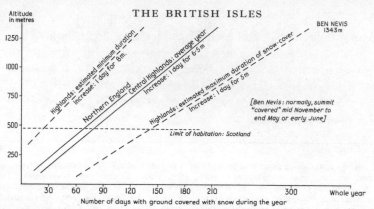

Fig. 24.   ESTIMATED RANGE OF BEHAVIOUR OF THE SNOW-COVER: maximum and minimum expectation.

The London region, accordingly, can claim the longest continuous succession of daily meteorological observations in the world, running from November 1668 to the present day. There is, however, a gap (1707-1722) in thermometer readings and in any event the exceedingly imperfect instruments and exposures before 1750 provide risk of error in interpretation. The present writer has essayed the task of assembling and standardising the data as far back as possible, using a variety of scattered records, to provide a table of mean monthly temperatures representative of 'Central England' (Manley, 1953, 1959a, 1961a). Rainfall variations for England as a whole have been summarised by Glasspoole (1931) in the form of percentages of the average, for each month since January 1727. For Scotland, Buchan (1892) and Mossman (1897, 1900) have provided data for Edinburgh and other localities beginning from various years in the eighteenth century.

Figures 21-23 will serve to demonstrate the range of variation of temperature and rainfall. A diagram of the frequency of days with snow observed to fall in the London area, standardised as far as possible, is included since it shows the considerable range of variation since 1668. Fluctuations in the frequency at London, by decades, can be shown to be representative of the north of England and Scotland. Hence an estimate can be made (Fig. 24) of the probable extreme range of variation of the duration of continuous snow-cover at various levels, based on the known rate of increase with height in exceptional years. On the mountains the normal rate of increase in the annual total of days with snow-cover is about 1 day per 20-25 ft. (7-8 m.).

Fluctuations in the mean temperature of the warmer months, by decades, bear a decided relationship with the known periods of advance and retreat of the glaciers in Iceland, Scandinavia, and the Alps. This suggests that the principal common element in the weather of northwest and west Europe must be the temperature of the maritime-polar air, which in turn is a function of the frequency of arrival and route of travel, the surface temperature of the ocean, and the mean position of the upper ridges and troughs that appear on the 500 mb. charts. Throughout northwest Europe the notable climatic amelioration since 1925 or so has attracted much attention. Glaciers have retreated as never before in their recorded history. It is a matter of some interest to Scotland that the small snow accumulations in the north-facing gullies of Ben Nevis and the Cairngorms, which until 1933 had been thought, based on accounts for upwards of 100 years, to be permanent, have since then melted away for a short period at the very end of summer on several occasions. Scotland has now no glaciers; the climatic snowline on Ben Nevis (4,406 ft., 1,343 m.) probably lies at about 5,300 ft. (1,620 m.) (Manley, 1949) but the semi-permanent snowbeds have responded to the climatic amelioration in similar fashion. It is noteworthy that, following the cool spring and summer of 1962, the surviving snowdrifts in September were considerably larger and more numerous than for many years past. In Figure 17 the upward tendency 1925-1950, characteristic of the spring, summer and autumn which include all the growing months from March to November, is very noteworthy.

Table 8, giving the average dates of first and last snow observed at and around London (below 200 ft. (60 m.)), in successive

Table 8. First and last observation of snow falling in the London area

Average dates

Period	Autumn	Spring
1811–1840	18 Nov.	22 April
1841–1870	21 Nov.	17 April
1871–1900	23 Nov.	12 April
1901–1930	25 Nov.	15 April
1931–1960	8 Dec.	1 April

Extreme dates

Since 1811	25 Sept.	27 May

30-year periods, is also noteworthy. Corresponding demonstration can be made of the decrease in the average yearly frequency of minima below 32 °F (0 °C), and the increase in the 'accumulated temperature' of the growing season (Fig. 24).

The average total of the 'accumulated temperature' during the growing season can be effectively related to the possibilities of land utilisation. Broadly, in the drier parts of the British Isles, plough-land and crops (potatoes, roots, occasionally oats) can be found up to altitudes where the mean 'accumulated temperature' is about 45 month-degrees F (25 month-degrees C). Hayfields can be found to the altitude where 36 month-degrees F (20 month-degrees C) prevails; trees under our windy conditions appear to be limited by the line of 28 month-degrees F (16 month-degrees C). In the north of England these conditions are found at about 1,600 ft. (500 m.), 1,800 ft. (550 m.) and 2,000 ft. (600 m.); in Aberdeenshire, about 150 ft. (50 m.) lower.

The approximate range of variation can be taken out from the long 'central England' table to be about 21 month-degrees F (12 month-degrees C) on either side of the mean. It can be shown that in a year such as 1879 virtually complete failure of most crops would be expected at altitudes above about 900 ft. (280 m.) in northern England, while between 1692 and 1702 at least eight of the years in eastern Scotland were so adverse that the majority of crops must have virtually failed at 650 ft. (200 m.). The 'Seven Ill Years' (1692-98) are a feature of Scottish history; and while 1699 was sufficiently favourable for a general thanksgiving, 1701 and 1702 were marked by cold springs and delayed ripening of grain.

It thus becomes evident how narrow is the margin between success and failure at higher altitudes. In the British Isles the variability of the upland climate, and the rate of decrease of the growing season with altitude, is exceptional. Hence the variability in *time* is also more significant for the uplands. Variations in the amount and seasonal incidence of rainfall since 1727 have been discussed by Glasspoole (1931) and additional illustrations have been given (Manley, 1952) and discussed (Crowe, 1940). They are becoming of increasing importance in view of the steady increase in the demand for water, and are discussed further by W. G. V. Balchin in Chapter 5. Water is required for domestic use; for sanitation; and in rapidly increasing amount for many industries; for cooling water in power stations, and, not least, for irrigation. This last will prove a surprise to many who conventionally regard the British Isles as wet. Throughout eastern England, and especially on the best-yielding arable lands, rainfall may occur frequently enough but is not heavy. From April to October the evaporation-loss normally exceeds the rainfall, which, over wide areas, scarcely surpasses 20 in. (550 mm.) yearly. Hence rootcrops in particular gain from irrigation, and, as in Holland, the practice is already increasing. Penman's studies of evaporation should be emphasised; more recently, much attention has been devoted to possible local variations resulting from changes in cropping and in the consequent roughness of the surface. In contrast with the work of many European and American scientists, relatively few hydrological studies of the regime of catchment-basins involving stream-flow, evaporation, and run-off, have yet been made. This is partly because of the great complexity of the problem in an island of small scale, but great variety. In many river basins, especially in the south, percolation and underground storage are of great importance, as Balchin shows in Chapter 5; elsewhere, catastrophic flooding has occurred but although this has caused local alarm the areas affected have in general been very small.

Summary

Britain is therefore increasingly interested in the small but appreciable climatic trends that can be recognised, and that appear to be common to much of west and northwest Europe, as the behaviour of glaciers has shown. The attribution of these fluctuations to variations in the prevailing pattern of the atmospheric circulation, in those latitudes in which the dominance of the upper westerlies must be recognised, merely begs the question why the upper-westerly flow should thus be affected. This is a matter for the meteorologists; and must be left for them to discuss (cf. Lamb and Johnson, 1959, 1961; Manley, 1961b). In particular, the very interesting suggestions made by Lamb with regard to displacements of the mean location of the upper ridges and troughs over lengthy periods are attractive; but we have still to decide why they arise. For, as this essay has tried to show, all the late- and post-glacial climatic variations can be shown to be of the same order of magnitude; but they have sometimes taken place with a cold Atlantic, and sometimes when, as at present, the northeastern Atlantic has become relatively warm. It therefore appears that further studies are required of the extent to which variations in the heat transfer in the oceans can take place independently, or at least out-of-phase, with those resulting from changes in the atmospheric circulation.

Ahlmann's dictum is indeed noteworthy; 'the present climatic fluctuation is the first that we have been able to measure and which accordingly we may perhaps explain' (Ahlmann, 1948). Suffice it to recall that in Britain, while annual rainfall has tended to increase and January in particular is wetter, judging by the averages for 1916-50 published by the Meteorological Office, the additional 4% or thereabouts has commonly been offset by the greater evaporation consequent on the higher temperatures of spring, summer, and autumn. Wind direction, when averaged for 1931-60, has backed a little from that of 1901-30. Snowfalls have become more concentrated in the three winter months, December-February. With warmer springs, vegetation has been more forward; but although frosts have quite clearly been less frequent, they tend in months such as May to be quite as severe in individual years as those we know of in the past. Moreover, in June 1962, over the sandy soils of the Breckland in west Norfolk the screen minimum temperature fell to 22°F (5·6°C), which for England is lower than any June minimum hitherto recorded. Taken as a whole, the spring season (March-June) of 1962 was the coolest for many years.

Yet, in a densely-populated island in which nevertheless 35% is for climatic reasons virtually unusable, these small but appreciable

Table 9.   England: the Range of the Monthly and Yearly Means

(Based on the 'central England' series of means, 1671–1962. From 1671 to 1723 the means are considerably less reliable.)

	Mean		Warmest			Coldest		
	1931–1960							
	°F	°C		°F	°C		°F	°C
January	38.2	3.4	1916	45.5	7.5	(1684) 1795	26.4	−3.1
February	39.0	3.9	1779	46.2	7.9	1947	28.6	−1.9
March	42.6	5.9	1957	48.6	9.2	(1674) 1785	34.2	+1.2
April	47.1	8.4	1865	51.1	10.6	1837	40.5	4.7
May	52.5	11.4	1833	59.2	15.1	1698, 1740	47.5	8.6
June	58.2	14.6	1846	64.8	18.2	1909, 1916	53.2	11.8
July	61.2	16.2	1783	65.8	18.8	(1695) 1816	56.1	13.4
August	60.8	16.0	1947	65.5	18.6 ·	1912	55.2	12.9
September	56.7	13.7	1729	61.9	16.6	1807	50.9	10.5
October	50.2	10.1	1921	55.0	12.8	1740	41.5	5.3
November	44.1	6.7	1818	49.1	9.5	1782	36.1	2.3
December	40.4	4.7	1934	46.6	8.1	1890	30.6	−0.8
Year	49.3	9.6	1949	51.1	10.6	1740	44.2	6.8

Warmest summer, 1826   Coldest winter, 1684

climatic trends are increasingly significant. Were it to become colder, the agricultural and pastoral yield would decline. The demand for fuel for heating purposes in a long cold winter can rise to 40% above the average, and as we are now barely self-sufficient in a normal year, the potential economic burden is serious (Manley, 1957). Lying on the Atlantic margin of Europe, the oceanic air is not always kindly. The wet Celtic fringe, the low treeline, the stern display of glaciation not far past that even our little mountains show, remind even the southern Englishman that he must not forsake the readiness to adapt to changing circumstances that his climate will forever demand; while of the North, and even more of Scotland, the eternal presence of the mountains and the sea sets the more uncompromising frame within which, as in Norway, man must live.

References

AHLMANN, H. W., 1948. The present climatic fluctuation. *Geogr. J.*, **112**, 165-95.
BARTLEY, D. D., 1962. The stratigraphy and pollen-analysis of lake deposits near Tadcaster, Yorkshire. *New Phytol.*, **61**, 277-87.
BROOKS, C. E. P., 1949. *Climate through the Ages*. London.
BUCHAN, A., 1892. The monthly and annual rainfall of Scotland, 1866-90. *J. Scot. Met. Soc.*, **10**, 3-24. (See also **9** and **11**.)
BUTZER, K., 1958. The Near East during the last glaciation: a palaeographical sketch. *Geogr. J.*, **124**, 367-9.
CHARLESWORTH, J. K., 1957. *The Quaternary Era*. London.
CROWE, P. R., 1940. A new approach to the study of the seasonal incidence of British rainfall. *Quart. J.R. Met. Soc.*, **66**, 285-316.
EMBLETON, C., 1961. The geomorphology of the Vale of Conway, north Wales, with particular reference to its deglaciation. *Trans. Inst. Brit. Geogrs.*, **29**, 47-70.
FAEGRI, K., 1935. Uber zwei präboreale Klimaschwaukungen in Sudwestlichen teil Norwegens. *Bergens Museums Aarbok*.
GLASSPOOLE, J., 1925, 1931. *British Rainfall*.
GODWIN, H., 1956. *History of the British Flora*. Cambridge.
KERNEY, M. P., 1963. Late-Glacial deposits on the chalk of southeast England. *Phil. Trans.*, **246B**, 203-54.
KLEIN, A., 1953. Die Niederschläge in Europa im Maximum der letzten Eiszeit. *Petermanns Mitteilungen*, 98-104.
KLUTE, F., 1951. Das Klima Europas während-Eiszeit. *Erdkunde*, **5**, 273.
LADURIE, E. le Roy, 1960. Climat et récoltes aux XVIIe et XVIIIe siècles. *Ann. Econ., Soc., Civ.*, **15**, 434-65.
LAMB, H., 1959. Our changing climate, past and present. *Weather*, **14**, 299-318.
LAMB, H. H., and JOHNSON, A. I., 1959, 1961. Climatic variation and observed changes in the general circulation. *Geogr. Ann.*, **41**, 94-134; **43**, 363-400.
MANLEY, G., 1949. The snowline in Britain. *Geogr. Ann.*, **31**, 179-93.
— 1951. The range and variation of the British climate. *Geogr. J.*, **117**, 43-68.
— 1952. *Climate and the British Scene*. Glasgow.
— 1953. The mean temperature of central England, 1698-1952. *Quart. J.R. Met. Soc.*, **79**, 242-61.
— 1957. Climatic fluctuations and fuel requirements. *Scot. Geog. Mag.*, **73**, 19-28.

— 1959a. Temperature trends in England, 1698-1957. *Arch. Met., Wien,* **9B,** 413-33.
— 1959b. The Late-Glacial climate of northwest England. *Lpool. Manchr. Geol. J.,* **2,** 188-215.
— 1961a. A preliminary note on early meteorological observations in the London region, 1680-1717, with estimates of the monthly mean temperatures, 1680-1706. *Met. Mag.,* **90,** 303-10. Also *Weather,* **18,** 98-105 (1963).
— 1961b. Late and postglacial climatic fluctuations and their relationship to those shown by the instrumental record of the past 300 years. *Ann. N.Y. Acad. Sci.,* **95,** 162-72.
MOSSMAN, R. C., 1897, 1900. The meteorology of Edinburgh, parts II & III. *Trans. Roy. Soc. Edinb.,* **39,** 63-207; **40,** 469-509.
OLDFIELD, F., 1960. Late Quaternary changes in climate, vegetation and sea-level in lowland Lonsdale. *Trans. Inst. Brit. Geogrs.,* **38,** 99-117.
PENNINGTON, W., 1962. Late-Glacial moss records from the English Lake District. *New Phytol.,* **61,** 28-31.
SEDDON, B., 1962. Late-glacial deposits in Caernarvonshire. *Phil. Trans.,* **244B,** 459-81.
SUGGATE, R. P., and WEST, R. G., 1959. On the extent of the last glaciation in eastern England. *Proc. Roy. Soc.,* **150B,** 263-83.
WAGER, L. R., 1953. The extent of glaciation in the island of St Kilda. *Geol. Mag.,* **90,** 177-81.

*Gives many further references.

Two more recent works can also be referred to:
LAMB, H. H., 1966. *The Changing Climate : Selected Papers.* Methuen.
World Climate from 8000–0 B.C. Proceedings of a Symposium, *R. Met., Soc.,* 1966.

10

PREHISTORIC GEOGRAPHY

Introduction

As prehistoric archaeology has been transformed from an exercise in the collection and classification of artifacts into a scientific source of human history, so prehistoric geography has taken its rightful place in the study of ancient man and his societies. Increasingly, therefore, geographers have concerned themselves with early man's environments and his use of them. In the British Isles Crawford and Fleure were pioneers in this field, and their work has influenced archaeologists such as Clark and Fox as well as those geographers who have turned their attention to prehistory. Just over fifty years ago Crawford (1912) published a paper on the distribution of Early Bronze Age settlements in the British Isles which, following Lissauer in Germany, used the distribution map as a guide to the interpretation of prehistory; and this tool has since been extensively used, notably by Sir Cyril Fox in his *Personality of Britain* (1932). The simple distribution map is giving way to more detailed maps illustrating various environmental factors relevant to human activities in the different periods of prehistory; and novel methods of dating the past enable these periods to be defined chronologically. It must be admitted however that we do not have more than a fraction of the information necessary for a full understanding of the interactions of man and environment in prehistoric times and there has been much circular argument. It was formerly held, for example, that Neolithic man was incapable of clearing the forest and therefore that areas known to have been occupied at that period must have been naturally forest-free. Palynological studies have shown both the very wide extent of the forests and the considerable changes in their composition that occurred during the Neolithic. It is now realised that man may have been responsible for many of the environmental modifications which were once confidently attributed to climatic change.

Palaeolithic

The British Isles came into being late in the prehistory of *homo sapiens*, for they were part of the European mainland before the re-establishment of the Dover Straits in Boreal-Atlantic times. In the Pleistocene the effect of the oceanic climate was to feed the ice sheets with copious snowfalls during glacial periods but to bring mild winters during interglacials, thus allowing the early *hominids*, whose distribution was confined to the warmer parts of the Old World, to reach their poleward limits in what is now Lowland England. The oldest unambiguous human tools are the pear-shaped flint hand-axes known as Abbevillian, found for example at Clacton in East Anglia and dating from the Great Interglacial. They were supplemented by flake tools adapted, it is thought, to conditions of life on the thinning margins of the forest. In time, improved flaking techniques produced the handsome hand-axes called Acheulian. These various tools are found in secondary positions in the gravels of rivers that flowed with greater force and at higher levels than they do today. The broad valley of the Thames provided favourable hunting grounds through most of the Middle Pleistocene, and, thanks to a long English tradition of archaeological investigation, it occupies an important place in the literature of the Lower Palaeolithic. But the complex problems involved in correlating the archaeological material with the sequence of glacial and interglacial deposits are far from being solved.

During the Upper Palaeolithic, following the emergence of *homo sapiens* somewhere on the northern fringe of the Lower Palaeolithic world, Britain again occupied a marginal position in the *oekumene*, but habitation was extended into the limestones from Devon to Derbyshire, where nearly twenty caves testify to seasonal occupation during the later phases of the Würm glaciation. If the Aurignacian hunters have bequeathed to us no spectacular cave art, their occupational débris has given us a full inventory of their less perishable equipment and of the animals they hunted: mammoth, bison, horse, reindeer, great elk, cave bear, hyaena, and woolly rhinoceros; and though nearly all had become extinct by the end of the Palaeolithic (c. 8,000 B.C.) the survival of the wild reindeer in the Highlands of Scotland into the Dark Ages is both an interesting faunal link between remote prehistory and the dawn of history, and a reminder of the variety of habitats contained in the British Isles (Ritchie, 1920, p. 342).

Mesolithic

Following the final melting of the Würm ice sheets some 10,000 years ago the whole of Great Britain and Ireland was opened up for

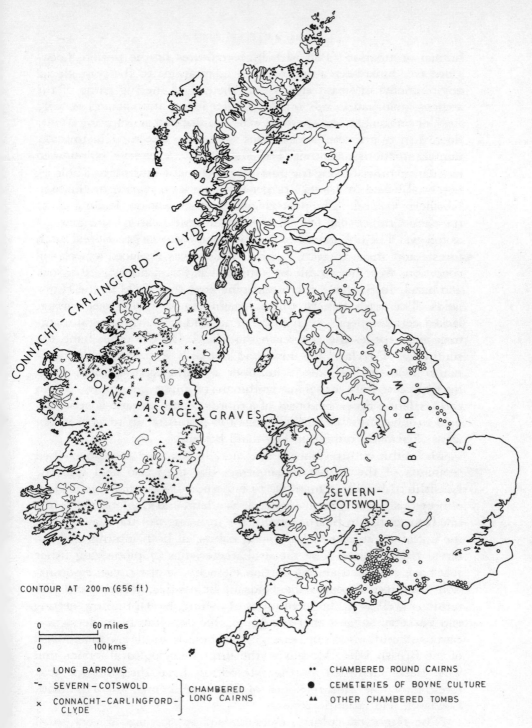

CONTOUR AT 200 m (656 ft)

0   60 miles

0   100 kms

○ LONG BARROWS	•• CHAMBERED ROUND CAIRNS
- SEVERN – COTSWOLD ⎫ CHAMBERED	● CEMETERIES OF BOYNE CULTURE
✕ CONNACHT–CARLINGFORD– ⎬ LONG CAIRNS CLYDE ⎭	▲▲ OTHER CHAMBERED TOMBS

Fig. 25.   SOME NEOLITHIC FIELD MONUMENTS AND CULTURE AREAS.

179

human occupation. The Mesolithic cultures of the period 8,000-3,000 B.C. have been interpreted as adaptations to the post-glacial environments of forest and water. Instead of the big game of the steppes, man had to rely on the smaller forest animals and on wild fowl, or on the fish and shellfish which multiplied as warming waters flooded in to give the British Isles something like their historically familiar tortuous coastlines. The eustatic rise of sea level culminated in Atlantic times during the post-glacial climatic optimum (Table 5), first established by Lloyd Praeger from work on marine mollusca in Northern Ireland. The post-glacial plant succession, leading up to the climax mixed-oak forests of Atlantic times, can be summarised as follows. The late-glacial park tundra gave way to pre-Boreal birch forests and these in turn to pine, which was replaced where soil conditions were favourable by a mixed oak forest dominated by oak and hazel. In Scotland birch and pine kept their hold in the Highlands. The Irish forests, thanks mainly to an earlier sea barrier, lacked certain species such as the lime, and similarly several mammals and reptiles did not reach the island. On the other hand the southwest of Ireland has long had not only a considerable Lusitanian element but also a number of American species; these distributions raise unsolved problems of plant geography. From early Atlantic times the onset of a more oceanic climate is generally held to have initiated blanket bogs (on slopes of up to 15°) in the areas of heaviest rainfall in Highland Britain.

Mesolithic cultures have been generally regarded as impoverished remnants of the Upper Palaeolithic, but they also lead into the Neolithic. Mesolithic man has to his credit the partial colonisation of previously empty areas (Ireland, Scotland and England north of a line from Settle to Scarborough), the utilisation of the seaways and the initiation, thanks to his roving habits, of both internal and external trade routes. The racial characteristics of pioneering fisher folk have persisted among certain elements of the present population; and researches in the fields of linguistics, folklore and folk music as well as in the techniques of fishing, boat-building, netting and basketry suggest that the Mesolithic substratum made significant contributions to our heritage, particularly in the north and west of the British Isles. Moreover, the three main cultural strains that have been identified in the Mesolithic have distributions that foreshadow the culture zones of later prehistory: the Highland, Lowland, and Atlantic zones.

The Highland culture, characterised by the use of very small flint artifacts (microliths), is best represented in the Pennines, and is properly regarded as the dying end of the Upper Palaeolithic. The ancient hunters sought refuge in hill areas free of heavy forest— their physical characteristics have been recognised, for example, in some of the present population of the Welsh moorlands—and also on sandy or exposed sites in the lowlands, using microliths that were mounted in wooden hafts to form composite barbed spears. The native population is believed to have been reinforced from France, where a related industry is known as the Sauveterrian.

More typical of the lowlands, however, are sites, usually on river banks and lake shores from the Tees to Southampton Water, which have been classified as Maglemösian and represent an immigrant movement of hunter-fishers from the Baltic. This was a forest-culture, using flint-axes for felling trees and wood-working and making extensive use of bone and antler. Pollen evidence shows that by the end of the Mesolithic considerable changes in the vegetation had been effected locally. During most of the Boreal period much of the bed of the southern North Sea was still above water, so that the Maglemöse culture reached Britain overland, though dug-out boats and probably skin boats were known.

Along the Atlantic coasts, finally, immigrant groups moving northwards from western France were navigators by force of circum-stance. An ultimately Azilian origin offers the most satisfactory explanation of the Larnian-Obanian culture established on coasts on both sides of the North Channel, at its narrowest only twelve miles wide. This channel tended to be the focus of a culture area through-out prehistory (cf. Fig. 25), and in historic times the area has played a critical part in relations between Great Britain and Ireland. Already in the Mesolithic clear cultural links with the Maglemöse of northeast England can be detected in northeast Ireland. County Antrim had the unusual attraction, in the Atlantic zone, of possess-ing abundant flints, and the teeming fish of the Irish lakes and rivers also provided a lure. This culture is closely associated with water. Along the coast, thanks to the presence of raised beaches and fossil bog-layers, successive stages of the Larnian culture through the Boreal and Atlantic periods can be correlated with eustatic and isostatic changes in sea level and with forest history.

Neolithic

By late Atlantic times brown forest earths had been widely developed in the lowlands and far up the mountain slopes from the immature soils of the glacial period, and the stage was set for the revolutionary cultural changes that accompanied the diffusion of food production. Until recently it was believed that cereal and animal husbandry were not introduced into the British Isles until towards the end of the third millennium B.C., but radio-carbon dating now places the beginnings *before* this millennium and the Neolithic period thus gains considerably in length and importance. At the same time it should not be forgotten that all the major regions of the British Isles were already peopled, however thinly, so that we must think in terms of acculturation as well as colonisation. Immigration, however, is more conspicuous in the archaeological record because novelties such as pottery, funerary monuments and earthworks can often be traced to their continental sources. Thus it can be shown that immigrant groups reached Britain along three main routes: from the North European Plain across the southern North Sea, from France across the narrow seas, and from Iberia and Brittany along the Atlantic route.

Although in later prehistoric times the chief invasion coasts were those of the Lowland zone in the south and east, in Neolithic times the western seaways were among the first to carry immigrants and ideas from Europe to the Atlantic zone of these islands. Before the recent lengthening of the Neolithic period made it more than a mere prelude to the metal age it was claimed that the metalliferous rocks and streams of the west were the main attraction for prospectors who in their search for precious metals introduced Neolithic ways of life. For an economy, however, that depended on polished stone axes for forest clearance, the Atlantic zone was no less well endowed with raw materials in the form of hard fine-grained igneous and metamorphic rocks. By the Middle Neolithic a vigorous trade in axes had developed from 'axe-factories' in Ireland, Cornwall, Wales, the Lake District and Atlantic Scotland, and much of this trade was with the English Lowlands.

As to forest clearance, in many parts of the British Isles Neolithic occupation levels revealed by archaeological excavation have been correlated by means of pollen analysis with changes in forest history and notably with the decline of the elm and an increase of weeds such as plantain as well as of light-loving trees such as the ash (Godwin, 1956; Mitchell, 1956). Some of these changes were due to a considerable extent to human interference. Thus many archaeologists and palaeobotanists would see in the remarkable fall in the ratio of elm-pollen at the beginning of the Neolithic, evidence of forest clearance and of the use of leaf and bark fodder for stock-raising. Such historic heathlands as the East Anglian Brecklands

and many Irish and Scottish moorlands are believed to have originated during Neolithic settlement. An explanation of the wide
distribution of forest clearance is sought in the practice of shifting
cultivation. Damp heavy soils were avoided, but lighter well-
drained ones were apparently utilised both in the lowlands and up
to heights of 1,000 ft. (300 m.). It is pointed out that with clearance,
cultivation and grazing, followed by soil erosion and podsolisation,
spiny and unpalatable shrubs made their first substantial contribution to the pollen record: gorse and blackthorn, hawthorn and
wild rose, rowan, bramble, box and holly have followed in the foot-
steps of man and his grazing stock. These shrubs are old companions
of man, and as such tend to be steeped in folklore and legend.
Collectively still covering hundreds of square miles of the countryside, the heathlands have been maintained by heavy grazing and
periodic firing. Much later, as Darby shows in the next chapter,
some of them were to be reclaimed for agricultural use.

It is now clear that apart from steep rock faces and areas of bog
and marsh only the highest mountains were free of forest in pre-
Neolithic times. The Neolithic farmers grew barley and emmer and
had cattle, sheep, pigs, and goats. It is mainly from their domestic
pottery that cultural distributions have been defined, but the major
Neolithic regions are also characterised by field monuments of
distinctive forms and not infrequently of imposing dimensions.
Among them those that have attracted most attention are the chambered tombs and other megalithic monuments, which not only
demonstrate the cultural links between the western and northern
parts of our islands and Brittany and Iberia, but conspicuously display regional characteristics of architecture and ritual within the
British Isles and assume, in certain critical areas, strikingly original
forms. Megalithic geography thus illustrates, and has made its contribution to, the regional diversities that have been a source of
tension and of vigour throughout our history.

Figure 25 shows the distribution of certain types of megalithic
monument, together with earthen long barrows. We may begin by
reference to the passage-graves of the Boyne culture, best represented near the Irish river but found also, usually in hill-top cemeteries,
around the central plain. Related tombs occur in Scilly, at Land's
End, in Anglesey, in the Scottish islands and in the Moray Firth
area. The passage-graves, so-called because the chamber is approached through a passage, are collective tombs covered by round
cairns, and their orthostats are frequently decorated, notably in the
Boyne group, with elaborate ornament in the form of spirals and

lozenges. Morphology and distribution alike point to their derivation from Iberia and Brittany.

Chambered tombs of the gallery type, under long cairns, lack an expanded terminal chamber. They are more widely distributed and fall into several regional groups. Most clearly derived from western France is the type of tomb found around the Severn estuary, extending into the Cotswolds and the Black Mountains of Brecon. Another area rich in gallery-graves, here segmented and usually provided with semi-circular forecourts, lies around the estuary of the Clyde and extends southwestwards across Northern Ireland to counties Donegal and Mayo, where the most elaborate of these 'court cairns' are found. This culture is of obscure origin but many of its features can be paralleled in southwest France, and it may be significant that the Mesolithic cultures of the North Channel area had earlier contacts with that region. Another extensive series of gallery-graves, tending to be wedge-shaped in plan and slab-roofed, is well represented in Ireland, where County Clare alone has about 100 examples. These wedge-tombs belong to the late Neolithic and may represent a tardy colonising movement from western France into southern Ireland.

The long barrows of the English Lowlands, or more correctly of the Chalk uplands, are non-megalithic, but in them, at their eastern ends, excavations have revealed the remains of timber mortuary chambers. It has been assumed from their distribution that long barrows must have been an introduction from the continent, but no precise parallels are forthcoming and the view has been expressed that they represent the impact of megalithic practices in an area where large stones are rare. The size of many of the Neolithic communal tombs and their continuing use show that communities were of some size and that they remained within fairly circumscribed areas for considerable lengths of time. Traces of their dwelling places, however, are extremely rare, and the large enclosures known as causewayed camps—found in the Thames valley as well as on the southern chalk uplands—which were formerly thought to be village sites, are now believed to have been stock-folds where seasonal gatherings or fairs were held.

The Bronze Age

Metal tools, at first restricted to thin hammered blades of copper, made their appearance in the British Isles early in the second millennium B.C., but it was not before the seventeenth century B.C., on present evidence, that the Age of Bronze began. The Copper Age is better known as the Beaker period, from the characteristic decorated pottery vessel that was buried with the dead and whose liquid contents, in the words of Professor Gordon Childe (1950, p. 130), may have contributed to the Beaker folks' spirituous authority. Barley was in fact their main crop, and the concentration of their burial sites in the English and Scottish Lowlands is related to the distribution of loamy brown earths suitable for its cultivation. All the evidence points to invasive movements in which two main groups penetrated from various landing places on the south and east coasts between Dorset and Aberdeenshire. The emergence of such restless warrior cultures in Central Europe at the end of the Neolithic period has been attributed to soil exhaustion following many centuries of shifting cultivation. The Beaker folk introduced a new ethnic type, brachycephalic and beetle-browed in contrast to the earlier smooth-boned dolichocephalic stocks, and they brought with them a novel social structure symbolised by individual burials of warrior bowmen, frequently placed under round barrows or cairns, a custom that persisted into the full Bronze Age. These shapely tumuli, of which some 18,000 are known in the British Isles, are the most conspicuous contribution of the Bronze Age to the landscape, for they tend to occur on hill-tops and crest lines and have therefore served as landmarks ever since. In north Britain and Ireland the Bronze Age hill-top cairns are usually found to contain 'food-vessels' which may equally well have been drinking-vessels and which seem to represent stylistically the influence of beaker ware on native Neolithic types of pottery. Such an explanation, at any rate, would fit in with Sir Cyril Fox's definition of his Highland zone as one of cultural absorption in contrast to the cultural replacement which took place in the Lowlands (Fox, 1943, p. 88). But it would be wrong to see the north and west of the British Isles as passive recipients of lowland culture-elements. For well over a thousand years, during which the demand for bronze necessitated the bringing together of supplies of copper and tin from various scattered sources in the west, the three zones of the British Isles were freely interacting. Wealthy lowland chieftains, eager for supplies of copper, tin, and gold, secured them from the Atlantic zone, especially from Ireland; and the Highlands profited from the trade that passed through them from the western harbours. The result of this cross-fertilisation can be seen not only in several novel types of field monuments, but in a series of bronze implements and weapons displaying an inventive genius that has been not unfairly compared with that shown in the centuries leading up to the Industrial Revolution. The parallel can be taken further, for the most striking manifestations in both periods are found along the junction of Highland and Lowland. Wessex and the Yorkshire Wolds were flourishing centres, receiving copper, tin, and gold from the west and serving also as foci of European trade, exporting Irish bronze and gold and importing amber and beads, which, in Wessex, include faience beads from the eastern Mediterranean. The metropolitan character of Salisbury Plain, referred to by Watson in the first chapter, is illustrated not only in the great assemblage of Bronze Age barrows and other monuments, but more obviously in the unique character of the ritual circle of Stonehenge and of the ditched sanctuary of Avebury. In the Atlantic zone also certain areas where trade-routes met or crossed, such as the Crinan district of Argyll, display marked cultural originality, while in Ireland the northeast, jutting out into the central seaways of the British Isles and long experienced in trade in flint and hard stone was, to judge by the remarkable number and quality of the bronzes found there, well populated, industrially skilled and commercially active. Here again stone circles are fairly common and assume distinctive forms. In the Scottish islands, too, there are many famous examples such as Stennis in Orkney and Callernish in Lewis, the latter site combining cairn, megalithic chamber, stone circle, and stone alignments. Nevertheless some communities that supplemented fishing and fowling by cattle raising remained little touched by the habits and rituals of food-producers. The most remarkable settlements of this kind are the excavated clusters of stone huts at Rinyo and Skara Brae in Orkney, where archaic ways of life persisted far into the age of metal. Both the stone houses and fittings and the use of peat as fuel suggest that timber in the islands was as scarce then as it is today.

Progressive changes in the amount and nature of the forest cover took place throughout the Bronze Age, which occupies the later part of the sub-Boreal climatic phase. As the name implies, this was a comparatively dry warm phase, though both its warmth and its dryness have probably been exaggerated. As Manley has shown, although its summers were warmer than today, its winters were probably colder. In Ireland the vegetational changes have been well documented, thanks to the wide distribution of peats, by analytical studies of the pollen they contain. They demonstrate a continuing shrinkage of the virgin forest, and an expansion of pasture and of secondary woodland in which hazel and birch were prominent and oak and ash increased at the expense of elm. Local studies show that population was now able to colonise many lowland areas that Neo-lithic farming had avoided, and in some areas the consequences were dramatic. Shallow cultivation and soil exhaustion are held to have been responsible for podsolisation and the development of Calluna heath. Cultivation is attested by the occurrence not only of carbon-ised cereals and of pollens of cereals and weeds of cultivation, but also of such artifacts as saddle-querns and bronze sickles. Evidence of permanent settlement, however, is rare in all parts of the British Isles before the late Bronze Age, so that the slash-and-burn methods of Neolithic agriculture are thought to have prevailed. G. F. Mitchell (1956, p. 242) pictures the Irish countryside during the Bronze Age as a mosaic in which 'areas of virgin forest, tillage patches, rough pastures and areas of secondary forest in various stages of regenera-tion were becoming closely interlocked'. In the Irish raised bogs there is no clearly defined recurrence-surface—with fresh sphagnum peat overlying dried-out bogland—to mark the widely accepted sub-Atlantic climatic recession at the end of the sub-Boreal. Several such surfaces are present, and it may be that in Ireland the recession came earlier than in England and that anyhow more humid phases are naturally less discernible in the Atlantic zone than in more con-tinental areas: in the Lowland zone, at any rate, the evidence for the onset of more oceanic conditions towards the middle of the last millennium B.C. is more acceptable. In the southern half of England and Wales for example pollen records show a striking expansion of beech and hornbeam at the end of the Bronze Age, though Godwin (1956, p. 341) reminds us that we should look for human as well as climatic causes, and he suggests that in addition to increasing humidity it may have been a relaxation of population pressure on the crests of the chalk and limestone hills that led to their colonisa-tion by beech and hornbeam at about this time. In fact quickening changes in social and economic conditions had been taking place since the early part of the last millennium B.C.

The Late Bronze Age

These changes, accompanying radical improvements in the techniques of metal working and in types of armament, were intro-duced into the Lowland zone by invading groups who are generally considered to have been Celtic speakers. Newcomers at this time and throughout the restless centuries of Celtic expansion included refugees whose localised cultures complicate the archaeological record, especially in the Lowlands. The Highlands and the Atlantic coasts were more conservative, but these areas too in time benefited from the improved metallurgical methods and the new artifacts. Characteristic novelties among the bronze implements were slashing cavalry swords, leaf-shaped spearheads, and socketed axes. Some of these bronzes, it is true, had reached Britain earlier through trade with the continent, but the appearance of cremation cemeteries or urnfields, derived from southwest Germany, clearly demonstrates invasion by groups of settlers who, as horse-riders, were more at home in the Lowlands than in the north and west.

The bronze axe, now perfected in its final socketed form, was produced cheaply in large numbers, speeding up forest-clearance and making possible increased food supplies. Technical advances at this time include casting by the *cire perdue* method and the manufacture of sheet metal. Specialised wood-working tools such as the bronze gouge, the chisel and the saw made their appearance and with them came improved carpentry, facilitating, for example, the construction of timber-framed houses and the production of better furnishings and farm-implements. In the Lowlands the rectangular dwelling-house now appears alongside the circular wattled hut that it was eventually to replace. By the end of the Bronze Age it is possible to recognise a number of regional cultures which are distinguished by standardised types of bronze implements, and which foreshadow the cultural regions later to crystallise around urban capitals. Of towns as yet there was none, but the evidence for fixed settlements is clear. From the late Bronze Age onwards rural settlements and field systems become familiar features. The so-called Celtic field-system constitutes by far the most extensive group of all prehistoric remains in Lowland Britain, especially on the chalk uplands where air photography (Crawford, 1924) has greatly enlarged the distribution areas known from ground surveys.

The Celtic fields, characteristically small and rectangular in shape, are believed to have been fashioned by the ox-drawn plough. A middle Bronze Age date has been claimed for some examples but they became common only in the last millennium B.C., and the majority were made or at least were still being used by the Romano-British population. It would seem that in the late Bronze Age some method of crop rotation was evolved, with fallowing and folding or otherwise renewing the fertility of the soil, which allowed fields and farms to retain their chosen sites generation after generation. Applebaum (1954, p. 106) suggests that some cereals were autumn-sown, and he draws attention to evidence for manuring and the folding of sheep. He thinks it may have been a two-field system. A parallel can be drawn however with the small infield plots of the historic open-field systems of Scotland and Ireland, though the term Celtic fields was applied not for this reason but because of their resemblance in size and shape to the present-day enclosed fields of many parts of the Celtic fringe. The parallel can, however, be extended if, as now appears, some of the associated settlements were hamlets rather than single farms, for hamlets (clachans or farm-towns) occupied by kinsmen characterised the rundale and runrig systems of Ireland and Scotland. Nevertheless most of the excavated habitation sites of the late Bronze Age in southern England were single farms, and they are frequently associated with extensive banked enclosures held to imply ranching activities. Single farms or small hamlets are also characteristic settlements of the period in Scotland and Ireland, where, however, the Bronze Age persisted into the last century or two B.C. In Ireland field boundaries of various types have been observed under the bogs, but those that are securely dated go back to the Neolithic and their irregular shape points to hoe cultivation. The Atlantic and Highland zones must have been predominantly pastoral in prehistoric times as they are today and it is presumed that scrubland and hill pastures were already utilised under some form of transhumance. The peat that covers many megalithic and other cairns and stone circles in the Atlantic and Highland zones began to form for the most part in this sub-Atlantic phase, and the great blanket bogs of the moorlands from now on would have provided extensive if poor summer grazing for livestock.

The Iron Age

The terms Hallstatt and La Tène which were formerly applied to the Early Iron Age Celtic cultures of Britain implied, with their subdivisions and their central European connections, a regular succession of large-scale invasions from about 500 B.C. onwards, and these names have therefore been replaced in the archaeological literature by cultural labels (A, B, and C). Invaders there certainly were, but they were for the most part warrior castes who imposed themselves on native peoples who were already Celtic-speaking. There were also refugees, and at times bands of agricultural colonists. The cultural changes that followed involved far more than the substitution of iron for bronze and of curvilinear for rectilinear art-motifs. New cereal crops were introduced such as spelt, rye, and oats; rye was in time to become an important bread grain in the lowlands, and oats to replace wheat as the corn of the Highland glens and the Atlantic coastlands, food for man and beast. The horse-drawn chariot, which speeded the expansion of the Celtic-speaking warriors, was a powerful novelty, and in the archaeological record the fine craftsmanship of Celtic art is best displayed on horse-trappings, swords, and articles of personal adornment. Similarly the typical field monuments of the Iron Age are the defensive earth-works, often on the grand scale, which crown the hills of the south-ern lowlands and fringe the mountain heartlands of the Highland zone—in the southwestern peninsula, in Wales and Scotland.

These displays of wealth and concentrations of power were made possible by increased production from the land. Sheep now for the first time became more plentiful than the forest animals, pigs and cattle, and their grazing would have helped to check the re-growth of trees in cleared areas. Iron ores are more widely distributed and more easily reduced than copper and tin, and among the more efficient tools that were made available it was the woodman's axe and the plough irons that wrought the greatest changes on the face of the land. An increasing range of uses for heavy timber, including the construction of massive timber-laced defences, speeded up the attack on the woodlands and especially on the oakwoods. It is mainly on the morphology, distribution, and associated relics of the defensive earthworks that the current classification of Iron Age cultures in Britain is based. The A (Hallstatt) culture, however, which is found almost everywhere southeast of the Cotswolds, was apparently peaceful in character, its settlements being undefended farmsteads located in territory previously thinly peopled. The economic and social effects of this first colonisation, which was the ground-swell of the storms brewing in the Celtic homeland, have been compared with those brought into Lowland England by the Anglo-Saxons a thousand years later (Ordnance Survey Iron Age Map, 1962, p. 9). When, from about 300 B.C., bands of warriors brought with them the B (La Tène) culture, the early settlers defen-ded their homesteads and built most of the hill-forts that stud the southern downlands. By the second century the B culture had prevailed in southern Britain, and now many of the downland forts were strengthened and enlarged into multivallate fortresses such as Maiden Castle in Dorset. Altogether, excluding small examples, England and Wales can show no less than 600 hill-forts, some of them exceeding 100 acres in extent. They are most abundant in southern England, Wales, and southern Scotland, and rare in northern and eastern England, a rarity which cannot be explained by freedom from invasion because aristocratic chariot-users were well-established, for example, in the Yorkshire Wolds. As to their function, they would have served as temporary refuges during tribal warfare and they are to be thought of not as tribal centres but as the strongholds of rival groups or septs. Nucleated settlements were on a small scale, and the predominant Iron Age habitation was the single farm. The so-called pit villages of the downlands have been re-interpreted as lone steadings surrounded by their corn-storage pits.

In the southwestern peninsula, besides multivallate forts, there are numerous cliff castles as well as small ring-works which were probably cattle enclosures; well-preserved relics of the south-western culture have been found in the lake-villages of Glastonbury and Meare in Somerset, dating from the first century B.C. Cornwall especially, with its tin-working, shows clear connections at this period, as so often before and since, with Brittany and Galicia; and thence along the Atlantic route Iron Age cultural elements were carried northwards to the Isle of Man and southwestern Scotland, where earlier movements of hill-fort builders from the Welsh Marches and Cheshire had already penetrated. Thence the fort-builders spread to Argyll and along the Great Glen to the Moray Firth area. In northwest Scotland, in the Hebrides and the northern isles, the influence of the Cornish ring-forts may perhaps be seen acting on the round stone huts of Bronze Age tradition to produce the circular dry-walled towers known as brochs. The remains of over 500 of these strongly defended farmsteads are known; they have their beginnings in the first century B.C. but were probably used throughout the period of the Roman occupation (Fig. 26).

Ireland during these last five centuries of the pre-Christian era was still for the most part in the Bronze Age, but by the third century powerful aristocratic groups of the B culture had established themselves in the northeast, coming either from Yorkshire or, as some students think, direct from the continent. Evidence for Atlantic contacts is to be found in the many cliff-forts that line the Irish coasts and perhaps in the ring-forts of the interior—circular enclosures occupied by single farms—but excavation has shown many of these to be of post-Roman date. Very few hill-forts are known but some are of outstanding importance as the fortress-palaces of Gaelic chieftains. Certain sites chosen (e.g. Tara) were long-hallowed burial sites, and the connection of another hill-fort with Christian times is illustrated by its name—Downpatrick. The gradual extension of Gaelic rule and Iron Age culture over Ireland took place through the centuries that were, in Britain, marked by the Roman occupation.

Fig. 26.   THE BRITISH ISLES DURING THE ROMAN OCCUPATION.

CONTOUR AT 200 m.(656 ft)

0   60 miles

0   100 kms

———• ROADS AND TOWNS CIVIL DISTRICTS   • CHIEF IRISH SITES
- - - -○ ROADS AND FORTS MILITARY DISTRICTS   △ TIMBER LACED FORTS
                                                  ▨ BROCH AREAS

Finally, in the last century B.C., we come to the edge of history in southeast England with the emergence of dynasties and leaders and seats of government that are known by name. Tribal names are preserved, for example, in Devon (from Dumnonii) and in Kent and Canterbury (from Cantii). This culture (Iron Age C) was introduced by the Belgae, and by the end of the century had spread over most of the area southeast of a line from Dorset to the Humber. Anticipating in some ways the advance of the Romans whose conquest of north Gaul had provoked its later phases, the Belgic invasion introduced a new concept of political organisation, which is reflected in the cultural landscape of the period. The Belgae had no need for hill-forts but instead tribal capitals were planted in the plains, both *oppida* such as Verulamium (St Albans) and Camulodunum (Colchester) and smaller towns like Canterbury and Leicester. This valleyward movement was accompanied by exploitation of the heavier lowland loams, facilitated by the use of a heavy plough with massive coulter. The contemporary strip-fields that this implement should have produced have not been traced, but they would be difficult to identify in lowlands which, unlike the chalk downs, have since been repeatedly under the plough. Generally speaking, however, the older Celtic field system persisted. At the same time there appeared for the first time in Britain the rotary quern to speed up the process of corn-grinding, wheel-thrown pottery, and an inscribed coinage. Southeast England looked to Gaul for trade, and Strabo tells of luxuries purchased with the export of corn and cattle, hides, metals, slaves, and dogs.

The Roman Period

Apart from brief references in the sixth-century Massaliote Periplus and in the fourth-century account of Pytheas, we learn little about the British Isles from literary sources until we come to Caesar's Commentaries and the writings of Strabo. If from now on we can speak of historical geography in the strict sense, in fact much supplementary information has been derived from field-study and excavations, while for Ireland and north Scotland we must rely almost entirely on these sources and on inferences from the legendary histories of the Celtic world. The conquest begun by Claudius in A.D. 43 was quickly extended over the southeast as far as the Cotswolds. Beyond this line—which has served at many periods both as a dividing line and as a dry communication route (the Fosse Way)—the advance of the Roman armies took the form of three thrusts aiming at the estuary of the Severn and at the mouths of Dee and Tees, where extensions of the English Midlands meet the sea. The three great legionary fortresses of Caerleon (Isca Silurum), Chester, and York were established to defend these salients. To control the northern frontier Hadrian's wall was built along the Solway-Tyne gap early in the second century. Later, in the Antonine Age, a turf wall was erected between Clyde and Forth, and southern Scotland became a frontier zone.

Caerleon, Chester, and York stand near the limits of the Lowland zone and they marked the approximate limits of the Civil Districts of Roman Britain (Fig. 26). Beyond were the Military Districts, planted with forts which were linked by roads. The Military zone corresponded fairly closely with the Highland zone of older cultures, except for the Scottish Highlands which, with the western islands and Ireland, remained outside the Empire. During the Roman occupation, then, the three broad cultural zones of the British Isles—Lowland, Highland, and Atlantic—can again be clearly recognised (Fig. 26). For three and a half centuries the Lowlands, penetrated by Mediterranean standards of culture, were more firmly a part of Europe than they have ever been since, but for this very reason the free interplay of trade, and the processes of cross-fertilisation within the British Isles, between east and west, and north and south, were at a minimum.

The total population of Roman Britain has been estimated at something less than a million. About 60 Roman towns are known, their sites often recognisable by the incorporation of the word 'chester' in the names of their successors. Despite the network of towns, many of them deliberately sited as political instruments with the intention of attracting tribal leaders, the Celtic aristocracy preferred a country life. Many towns had fluctuating fortunes, and everywhere urbanism decayed after the Roman withdrawal. Even in the towns, moreover, for all the Mediterranean splendour of the civic buildings, most of the houses were built in native style, half-timbered. The cultural pull and economic strength of the country-side are demonstrated in the wide scatter of large farms, the villas, occupied for the most part by natives of some substance. They were especially numerous in the Lincoln Wolds and the Cotswolds—where sheep and wool brought great wealth in the third century as they did in the Middle Ages—in the chalk downlands and in the Isle of Wight. Everywhere in the Civil zone native farms and hamlets survived and there was considerable expansion of the Celtic fields and of forest clearance in the lowlands. The Fens were drained by hundreds of miles of wide canals. (A marine transgression which reached its maximum in the first century and brought the silt areas of the Fenlands into being can also be traced in other areas, e.g. the Thames estuary.) The Romans introduced the scythe and minor improvements in the plough, and among cereals oats now assumed an important place, enabling more livestock to be over-wintered. But if the occupation brought little change in the techniques of agriculture or land use—there are only doubtful traces of centuriated fields, and the oldest strip-lynchets of the English hillsides, for example, seem to be of somewhat later date—many useful fruit trees were introduced, including the pear, plum, and walnut, and one of the most enduring and colourful contributions of the period to the rural scene was a host of field and wayside weeds and flowering plants.

In several parts of Britain coal was mined both for domestic and industrial purposes, and salt was produced from Triassic brine as well as from coastal waters. Iron was worked in the Weald, the Forest of Dean, on Tyneside and in the Jurassic belt. But above all Britain was valued for its silver and lead, which were obtained in the Mendips, Shropshire, Flintshire, Derbyshire, and Yorkshire, and which, with Welsh gold and Cornish tin, gave the Highland zone its main economic value. Throughout the Military Districts, however, Roman culture had little effect on life and landscape. Most of the hill-forts were spoiled or abandoned, and no towns arose in their place, though native settlements grew up outside the Roman forts. It must not be supposed that the absence of towns implies a completely pastoral life. Evidence from Wales, in particular, suggests that in later Roman times at least, as in the Early Middle Ages, rural settlement was typically in the form of hamlets occupied by kinsmen (bond tenants) whose cultivation of open fields was supplemented by crops from temporary outfields carved out of the common pasture. A similar system is believed to have prevailed in other parts of the Highland zone, and Jones (1961, p. 196) has claimed that there was a Celtic basis, persisting through the Roman occupation, for the pattern and organisation of early medieval settlement in parts of Lowland England.

Ireland and the Atlantic coastlands of north Britain were very little affected by Roman culture. Isolated from the continent and from their Celtic neighbours, the Gaelic leaders consolidated their grip on Ireland and kept alive the La Tène cultural traditions that were later to merge into the artistic achievement of the Early Christian world. The infiltration of Roman culture was slight until the Early Christian period, though it is perhaps discernible in the travelling earthworks of south Ulster (e.g. the Black Pig's Dyke, Fig. 26) and in the efforts to centralise political power at Tara. A scatter of Roman coins and brooches, and more certainly a few hoards of Roman silver, represent loot. In the third century Irish sea-raiders were harrying the shores of Britain and before long they had established settlements in south Wales and, exploring the sea-ways, planted colonies in the Inner Hebrides and the western Highlands that were to give Scotland its name and its Gaelic tongue. It was from the west, no less than from the north and east, that the defences of the Roman province were overwhelmed in A.D. 367. In the Atlantic zone a blossoming of culture followed renewed contacts with the continent. From the fifth century onwards sub-Roman and Byzantine pottery—found in Cornwall, Wales, southern Scotland, and Ireland—provides archaeological evidence of the revival of Atlantic trade. The majority of the Irish raths—some 30,000 in number—date from the Early Christian period, and pollen counts, showing the rapid decline of the elm, confirm the evidence of archaeology and legendary history that this monastic age was a time of considerable forest clearance, agricultural expansion and population growth (Mitchell, 1956, p. 245). It is suggested that the spread of oats-cultivation in the Atlantic zone was an important factor in the agricultural revival of the Early Christian period (Evans, 1958, p. 7). Finally, it may be asked, in view of the growing body of evidence for extensive forest clearance in many parts of the British Isles during prehistoric and protohistoric times, what woodlands remained for later farmers to clear? The answer must be that much of the historians' 'primeval forest' was in reality secondary growth. It was in the English Midlands, 'sodden and unkind', almost a blank in the archaeological maps, that the most extensive areas of heavy forest remained to be cleared and settled. That story, however, is reserved for English and later comers, who, in their attack upon the woods, their renewal of efforts at draining the marsh, and their attempts at reclaiming the heath, brought yet another geography into being.

References

APPLEBAUM, S., 1954. The agriculture of the British Early Iron Age as exemplified at Figheldean Down, Wiltshire. *Proc. Prehist. Soc.*, **20**, 103-14.
ASHBEE, P., 1960. *The Bronze Age Round Barrow in Britain.* London.
BOWEN, H. C., 1961. *Ancient Fields.* London.
CHILDE, V. G., 1940. *Prehistoric Communities of the British Isles.* London.
— 1950. *Prehistoric Migrations in Europe.* Oslo.
CLARK, J. G. D., 1932. *The Mesolithic Age in Britain.* Cambridge.
— 1952. *Prehistoric Europe: the Economic Basis.* London.

CRAWFORD, O. G. S., 1912. The distribution of Early Bronze Age settlements in Britain. *Geogr. J.*, **40**, 184-203; 304-17.
— 1924. *Air Surveys and Archaeology*. London.
DANIEL, G. E., 1950. *The Prehistoric Chamber Tombs of England and Wales*. Cambridge.
EVANS, E. E., 1958. The Atlantic ends of Europe. *Advanc. Sci.*, **25**, 54-64.
FAIRHURST, H., 1954. The geography of Scotland in prehistoric times. *Trans. Glasg. Archaeol. Soc.*, **13**, 1-16.
FLEURE, H. J., 1951. *A Natural History of Man in Britain*. London.
FOX, Sir C., 1943. *The Personality of Britain*. Cardiff. (1st edition 1932.)
GODWIN, H., 1956. *The History of the British Flora*. Cambridge.
JESSEN, K., and HELBAEK, H., 1944. *Cereals in Great Britain and Ireland in Prehistoric and Early Historic Times*. Copenhagen.
JONES, G. R. J., 1961. Basic patterns of settlement distribution in northern England. *Advanc. Sci.*, **28**, 192-200.
KINVIG, R. H., 1958. The Isle of Man and Atlantic Britain. *Trans. Inst. Brit. Geogrs.*, **25**, 1-27.
KIRK, W., 1957. The primary agricultural colonisation of Scotland. *Scot. Geogr. Mag.*, **73**, 65-90.
MITCHELL, G. F., 1956. Post-Boreal pollen diagrams from Irish raised bogs. *Proc. Roy. Irish Acad.*, **57**, 185-251.
MOVIUS, H. L., 1942. *The Irish Stone Age*. Cambridge.
O.S. Map of Ancient Britain, 1951. 1:625,000. Chessington.
O.S. Map of Roman Britain, 1956. 1:1,000,000. Chessington (3rd Edition).
O.S. Map of Southern Britain in the Iron Age, 1962. 1:625,000. Chessington.
PIGGOTT, S., 1954. *Neolithic Cultures of the British Isles*. Cambridge.
RICHMOND, I. A., 1955. *Roman Britain*. London.
RITCHIE, J., 1920. *The Influence of Man on Animal Life in Scotland*. Cambridge.

HISTORICAL GEOGRAPHY
FROM THE COMING OF THE ANGLO-SAXONS
TO THE INDUSTRIAL REVOLUTION

Introduction

IT has been shown that in Roman times the British Isles comprised three cultural areas associated very largely with physical circumstances. The southeast lowland was a region of agriculture, of towns and of peaceful life over many centuries. To the north and the west, the land is higher, the soils poorer and the climate wetter; here was a zone of many forts and of military rather than civil occupation. Beyond, in a third zone, were those lands never subject to Rome—the Highlands of Scotland (Caledonia) and the island of Ireland (Hibernia); here, tribal societies lived freely in what were also difficult countrysides.

A common characteristic of all three areas can be summed up in the word 'wood'. In the upland areas, oak, pine, or birch covered the countryside up to about 1,500 ft. (450 m.) and in places even to 2,000 ft. (600 m.) or more. Above these elevations stretched moorland or an arctic-alpine vegetation or rock and screes. In the lowlands, oak, ash, or beech were also to be found everywhere except for stretches of marsh, fen, and bog, and for those districts of light soil that had been cleared by successive generations of prehistoric peoples.

The Romans who had come in A.D. 43 bequeathed a substantial legacy to the geography of succeeding ages. The lines of many Roman roads are still in use as arterial ways. The strategical locations of many cities were recognised in Roman as in later times; London itself is a Roman foundation. In the north, the remains of the Roman Walls cross from coast to coast in a distinctive fashion; and in the south many of the traces of early cultivation date from Romano-British times. The legacy of Rome to the geography of Britain is no mean one. But even so, as far as there ever is a new beginning in history, the coming of the Angles, Saxons, and Jutes was such a beginning. It made a decisive contribution to the peopling of the southeast; it determined the language of the area; and it introduced institutions that have formed the basis of all later development.

The Anglo-Saxon settlement

The prelude to the settlement of the newcomers from across the North Sea consisted of plundering raids from as early as A.D. 300 and even before. When the Roman legions were withdrawn, not long after A.D. 400, Britain soon disintegrated into a number of small states, at war one with another, and incapable of withstanding the raiders from overseas. Raiding seems to have passed into settlement about A.D. 450, and Angles, Saxons, and Jutes continued to arrive for the next hundred years or so.

The new villages established by the invaders were, very largely, the villages of later times. Where, for example, Waels and his men settled in Norfolk, there stands Walsingham today. Where Babba made a 'stoc' or settlement in Wiltshire, there Baverstock still stands. From this period date the large number of terminations that give variety and interest to English place-names—ham, ton, stede, cote, worth, and the like. It is true that some Anglo-Saxon sites have been deserted, and that in Norman and later times some new villages came into being. But, in general, the village geography of the sixth to the ninth century has formed the basic element in the pattern of the English countryside up to the present day.

When we peer into the darkness round about A.D. 700 or so, we see that the British Isles as a whole was divided into many small kingdoms both in the southeast, occupied by the newcomers, and in the lands beyond. The process by which the historic kingdoms of the Anglo-Saxons emerged is lost for ever from our sight. By the seventh century, the names of as many as eleven kingdoms were recorded, and there may have been more. Some of these were joined to others, and the result was the historic seven kingdoms known as the Heptarchy (Fig. 27). Their rivalries and warfare did not prevent continued advance to the west. Traditionally, two decisive dates were 577 when the Britons (or Welsh) were defeated at Deorham near Bath, and 616 when they were defeated at Chester. Long before 650, the English had reached the Irish Sea at two points, and the Britons were separated into three groups. In the north, the county-name of Cumberland serves to remind us that here was once Cumbria or the land of the Cymry, as the Welsh still call themselves. In the south, lay the British kingdom of Dumnonia, independent, it would seem, until the eighth century, and its name survives today in that of Devon. Cornwall was raided, so we are told, 'from east to west' in 815. Soon afterwards, if not at the time, it came under Saxon

Fig. 27 POLITICAL DIVISIONS CIRCA A.D. 800.

over-lordship, but by then the force of Saxon colonisation had spent itself and Cornwall did not lose its Celtic character with its independence. Cornish survived as a spoken language until the eighteenth century, and the place-names of Cornwall today are predominantly Celtic.

The Cymry of Wales, cut off from their kinsmen to the north and the south, maintained their independence within their mountains. Little is known of the process by which the boundary between English and Welsh evolved, and only a few echoes of border warfare have come down to us from this period. With the expansion of the Saxon kingdom of Mercia, the frontier had been driven back towards the Welsh foothills, but the era of conquest was coming to an end, and during the reign of Offa the famous dyke that now bears his name was constructed (c. A.D. 790); the line it follows seems to have been the product of negotiation. After twelve centuries, it still remains an impressive monument, cutting straight across hill and valley alike, often running above the 1,000 ft. (300 m.) contour line. Like the English, the Welsh were divided into a number of small kingdoms. Foremost among them was Gwynedd, protected by the mountainous country of Snowdonia. At times, during the ninth and tenth centuries, two or more of the kingdoms were under a single rule, but the details are obscure. In the eleventh century, all the kingdoms were united under the king of Gwynedd, but at his death in 1063, on the eve of the Norman Conquest, Wales once more fell apart into its divisions.

In the north, what later became Scotland was also a land of petty kingdoms. The largest unit was that of Alban or the land of the Picts. To the southwest was Dalriada, conquered before 500 by the Scots, a Gaelic-speaking people from Ireland. Its ruler also became king of Alban about 860, and the name Scotland henceforth began to be used of the united realm to the north of the Forth-Clyde inlets. Strathclyde was a Welsh-speaking area with its own royal line, but it seems to have been united with Scotland about 945. Two further stages in the evolution of the Anglo-Scottish border were marked by the gain of English-speaking Lothian from England in 1018 and the loss of Cumbria in 1092. The English language was to spread throughout the entire country until Gaelic was spoken only in a few remote glens and in some of the Hebrides.

When the island of Hibernia emerged into the earliest historical light, it, like other parts of the British Isles, was divided among various groups whose origins are lost to us among legendary genealogies. According to tradition there were five independent kingdoms, and, of these, the ruler of Midhe seems to have been regarded as the chief king.

The Scandinavian settlement

The destiny of all the various kingdoms of the British Isles took a new turn towards the end of the eighth century, with the arrival of invaders from Scandinavia. Under the year 787, the Anglo-Saxon Chronicle tells us that the ships of the Danes first 'sought the land of the English nation'. In the middle of the next century the raiders began to 'winter', and this 'wintering' passed into systematic settlement in many parts of eastern and northern England. Beyond their settlements, Danish political power stretched up to a line roughly running between the estuaries of the Thames and the Dee. To the northeast of this lay the so-called Danelaw. The English at once began the reconquest of this territory, but it was not until the early part of the eleventh century that an independent Danish political power ceased to exist in England.

While the Danes had been advancing in England, Norsemen from southwestern Norway had established themselves in the Shetlands and the Orkneys. From there, one stream of migration went northward to the Faroes, to Iceland and beyond, while another stream came southward to the mainland of Scotland, to the Hebrides, and into the Irish Sea. A line of Norse kings reigned in the Isle of Man, and Norse kingdoms were centred on the coastal towns of the east and south of Ireland. Norsemen also settled around Solway Firth (in Galloway, Dumfries, and Cumbria), and in Lancashire and Cheshire, and to some extent in north and south Wales. It was not until 1266 that Norway renounced claims to the Hebrides and the Isle of Man; and the Orkneys and Shetlands remained part of the Norwegian kingdom until 1468.

Although Scandinavian political power disappeared from the British Isles, the Scandinavians themselves remained, and the main evidence for their settlement is that of place-names. The most important element in the Danish names of the north and east is 'by' meaning a village; there are, for example, nearly 250 Lincolnshire village-names that end in 'by'. Another common name is 'thorpe' meaning a hamlet or off-shoot settlement. Other frequent Scandinavian terminations include toft (a homestead), thwaite (a clearing), garth (an enclosure) and lundr (wood). The greater number of these words were common to both Danes and Norse, but there were some words peculiar to each, and in the west we encounter such Norse terminations as *erg* (a hill-pasture) and *saetr* (a shieling).

Changing Frontiers after 1066

By the eleventh century the Anglo-Saxons and the Scandinavians had covered most of Roman Britain with their villages, and so had laid the foundations of the later geography of England for all succeeding time. No later disturbing movement of people was to modify the Anglo-Scandinavian pattern, for the Norman Conquest of 1066 was the transposition of an aristocracy and not a folk-movement of people in search of new homes. Twenty years after their coming, the Normans in 1086 instituted the survey that resulted in the Domesday Book. It came at a fortunate moment for it enables us to inspect the economic foundations of English geography after the swirl of the great movements of people was over.

But in 1086, the frontiers of the kingdom had not yet reached their final form. Cumbria, as we have seen, was soon to be gained from Scotland (in 1092), but it remained in dispute and was at times in Scottish hands; so was the territory to the south of Lothian. It is true that all claims to the northern shires of England were re-nounced in 1157, but even so, northern England was long a frontier province that included feudal liberties where the King's writ did not run. Border raiding left its memory—not only in ballads but in castles and defensive towers (called pele towers) some of which can still be seen. The union of the two crowns of England and Scotland did not come until 1707, when the 'United Kingdom of Great Britain' was formed.

The Normans were not content with the *modus vivendi* established between England and Wales. The Welsh, frequently divided among themselves in their mountainous land, were forced to yield before the Norman advance up the valleys of the border and into the plain of Glamorgan in the south. Early in the twelfth century, Flemish immigrants were settled in south Pembrokeshire. The land of this mixture of Flemish, Normans, and English became known as 'Little England beyond Wales', and the linguistic frontier between the monoglot English and the bilingual Welsh persists even today. The Welsh of central and north Wales remained independent under their own kings, but the frontier moved to and fro with the chances of war until 1283 when the northern principality of Gwynedd was con-quered, and the whole country in one form or another was attached to the English crown. There was much unrest and the rebellion of 1400-08 was widespread. Not until the Act of Union of 1536 was Wales completely united with England (Chapter 21).

About a century after their conquest of England, the Normans landed an army in Ireland. The invasion of 1169 began a long phase of Anglo-Norman infiltration. Allegiance was often only nominal and many of the invaders were absorbed by the Irish. The most firmly held part of the island was the so-called 'English Pale' based upon Dublin. During times of English strength it extended far to the west, but at other times it included little more than the immediate vicinity of the city. By the end of the Middle Ages the authority of England had almost disappeared, and Ireland remained to be re-conquered in the sixteenth century. Then, the efforts of the Tudor sovereigns ended in the destruction of the clan system and the subjection of the island. During the seventeenth century, 'plantations' of Englishmen took place upon lands confiscated from Irish leaders. The most important area to be thus affected was Ulster where a substantial settlement of English and Scottish tenants took place. The establishment of this Protestant population was important for the later political geography of the island. When Eire became independent in the 1920s, Northern Ireland remained attached to the United Kingdom.

The political relations of the small kingdoms—Anglo-Scandinavian and Celtic alike—fill much of the early annals of the British Isles. But behind the clash and thunder of this early rivalry and warfare there went on an almost unrecorded process by which the face of the countryside was transformed. An immense struggle, continuing into modern times, resulted in the clearing of the woodlands, in the draining of marshes, and in the reclamation of heathlands.

Clearing the wood

The great achievement of the Anglo-Saxons and the Scandinavians during the centuries immediately after their coming was the clearing of the wood that still covered so much of the countryside. The lumberman with his axe and his pick gave way to the ploughman with his oxen. The Anglo-Saxons called the ploughman the 'grey-haired enemy of the wood', and a memory of his struggle is often preserved in the place-names of today. Names with such endings as -ley, -hurst and -holt tell of the former existence of wood or of clearings in it. So do such endings as -lundr, -skogr and -viothr in the Scandinavian districts. Thus the Anglo-Saxon place-name Brindley is derived from 'brende leah' and means the clearing caused by fire; and the Scandinavian place-name Litherskew comes from 'lithr skogr', the slope with wood.

In spite of some five centuries of clearing, there was still much wood left by the time of the Domesday Inquest of 1086, and large quantities of wood are recorded in many Domesday entries. Later documents show how the arable continued to expand at the expense of the wood, not only in England but also in the Celtic lands of the north and west. The medieval Welsh legend of Kilhwch and Olwen tells how Kilhwch was set the task of clearing a hill of its trees, and then of burning the grubbings on the ground before ploughing and sowing. To the north, in the Lake District and elsewhere, sheep-farming by monastic houses prevented the regeneration of wood on the cleared land. Farther north still, Gaelic place-names indicating the former presence of wood are widespread, and the ancient Caledonian forest of pine and birch was rapidly disappearing. Wood-names and records of clearing are likewise encountered in Ireland.

The demands made upon woodland were various, and all took their toll throughout the islands. One important need was for ordinary domestic purposes and for the building of bridges, castles, and churches. Another demand upon woodland was that of the expanding farm land. A third cause was the demand of industry, especially that of the iron industry; we hear much of the cutting down of wood in the medieval and later iron centres of the Forest of Dean and the Weald. The solution to the problem raised by the increasing scarcity of wood was to find a substitute. About 1709, after the experiments of the sixteenth century, Abraham Darby was smelting with coke at Coalbrookdale, and by the end of the eighteenth century, the use of coke for smelting had become common. There was a fourth demand upon wood. The expansion of Britain's mercantile marine and the development of the Royal Navy from Tudor times onward depended upon an adequate supply of oaks for the hulls of ships. The Dutch wars of the seventeenth century, the maritime wars of the eighteenth, and the Napoleonic Wars formed a heavy and continuous drain upon suitable oak. The problem remained acute until on 9 March 1862, during the American Civil War, the Battle of Hampton Roads demonstrated the superiority of the iron-clad. Within a few months the whole problem of naval construction had to be revised. But although the timber problem soon became only a memory, it left a permanent mark upon the English countryside.

Long before the nineteenth century, the shortage of wood had become a great problem. The shortage seems to have been felt first in Scotland where, as early as 1457, an Act was passed requiring tenants of the king to plant trees. Another Act, in 1503, said that the woods of Scotland were 'utterly destroyed'. This was an exaggeration for there were still stretches of wood in the valleys of the Highlands, and to these, in the eighteenth century, iron ore was brought for smelting; hence the presence of iron furnaces in such unlikely places as Invergarry in Inverness and Inveraray in Argyll.

Dr Johnson in 1773 was struck by the almost complete absence of trees in Scotland. The need for caution in the cutting down of trees in England and in Ireland became vocal in the sixteenth and seventeenth centuries. The Admiralty in its alarm consulted the newly-founded Royal Society which, in turn, asked John Evelyn to report on the problem. The result was the publication in 1664 of Evelyn's *Sylva* which preached the necessity of planting trees to replace the wastage of centuries.

From this time onwards, afforestation changed the appearance of many localities. During the eighteenth century the Royal Dublin Society, the Edinburgh Society for encouraging Arts, and the Royal Society of Arts in London offered awards for tree-planting. The Commissioners appointed to manage the Forfeited Estates, after the rebellion of 1745 in Scotland, 'caused large tracts of the Estates to be enclosed and planted with oaks, firs and other trees, now in a very prosperous condition'—so wrote Thomas Pennant about 1770. One general feature of the new planting was the use of new species. The Scots pine now appeared more abundantly in England, and exotic trees from abroad appeared everywhere—the Douglas fir, the Sitka spruce, and the Japanese larch. An Irish Forestry Department was established in 1903, and the British Forestry Commission in 1919. Their activities have brought a new value to poor hillsides and to sandy heaths. But while important locally, afforestation has not altered the general character of the British landscape as a whole. From an aeroplane we can see little to remind us of the great stretches of wood that covered the British Isles in the Dark Ages.

Draining the marsh

The marsh that confronted the Anglo-Saxon invaders disappeared far more slowly than the woodland. Many alluvial valleys were originally marsh or, at any rate, subject to flooding, and they have been drained by the embankment and regulation of their streams. The history of these small and local transformations has for the most part been lost, but they must be borne in mind when picturing the countryside of the fifth and sixth centuries. Along some valleys, the transformation is still far from complete.

An interesting phase in the story of the taming of many streams was the construction of artificial water-meadows subject to controlled flooding. They are said to have been first made in Britain during the sixteenth century. They reached their most widespread development in the eighteenth century, and were especially important along the streams of the southern counties of Dorset, Hampshire, Wiltshire, and Gloucester. With changing farming conditions, the water-meadow ceased to be a familiar feature of rural economy, although it has not entirely disappeared today.

When we speak of the marshes of the British Isles, we usually think not of these valley-strips but of the great stretches that give a special character to some countrysides. The largest is the expanse of the Fenland itself but there are other tracts of importance—the Levels of Somerset, the warplands of the Humber lowland, the carrs of the Ancholme Valley, the marshes of Holderness, the mosslands of Lancashire, the bogs of Ireland. There are also many other smaller stretches such as those on the boulder clay of north Shropshire, those of the Midland Valley of Scotland, and those of the eastern plain of Scotland. To these must be added the coastal marshes of the Thames estuary and elsewhere.

Of all stretches of marsh, that of the Fenland provided the most spectacular transformation. Here, during the Middle Ages, was a district of swamps and rushes, of wild-fowling and fishing, of turf-cutting and summer grazing. It was drained in the seventeenth century by the Dutch engineer, Cornelius Vermuyden, but technical difficulties of various kinds have more than once brought this success near to disaster. A basic difficulty has been the shrinkage and wastage of the drying peat, with the consequent lowering of its surface below the level of the streams flowing across it. Windmill pumps saved the situation in the eighteenth century, but by 1800 the cultivated land was again relapsing to 'waste and water'. The advent of the steam engine for pumping about 1820 again brought relief, and there have been successive improvements during the nineteenth and twentieth centuries. With its fertile black soil, the Fenland today is one of the most important arable districts in the British Isles.

The draining that took place in Lancashire was different in character. Here was no continuous stretch of marsh but scattered areas called 'mosses' or 'mosslands'. These were drained in a piece-meal fashion in the eighteenth and nineteenth centuries, leaving their names behind them on the modern map; and today, the traveller on the Liverpool-Manchester line can see on either hand a fertile culti-vated countryside. The story with variants has been repeated else-where—in Scotland as well as in England. In the eighteenth century, a large part of the Vale of Menteith (to the west of Stirling) was cleared of its peat bog for farming. The Carse of Gowrie was also transformed from an ill-drained area of mud and standing water into a flourishing countryside. Many other Scottish improving landlords were at work elsewhere in the eighteenth century. One of them, Thomas Hope, who had studied farming abroad, drained the marsh called Straiton's Loch and sowed it down to grass; today, the citizens of Edinburgh still enjoy the grass park known as the Meadows. In Wales, there were also local transformations, and at the end of the century the arm of the sea between Caernarvon and Merioneth was reclaimed, a change lamented by T. L. Peacock in chapter seven of *Headlong Hall* (1816).

The many peat bogs of Ireland had been used largely as a source of fuel from time immemorial, but in 1742 an Act was passed 'to encourage the reclaiming of unprofitable bogs'. With the help of the potato, there were many local changes. An official report of 1810 said that single patches of up to 10 or 12 acres (4-5 ha.) could be seen in a state of semi-reclamation around the edges of most bogs. From about the same time, we also hear of 'daily encroachments' upon the bogs. Little seems to have been done in the twenties and early thirties. In 1845, however, the Report of the Devon Commission gave many instances of improvement. A West Meath land-owner, for example, had spent £30,000 over twelve years in bringing into cultivation a large tract of low-lying bog. But, taken as a whole, the Irish bogs remained to engage the enterprise of twentieth-century reclamation and improvement schemes.

Reclaiming the heath

Generally speaking, the reclamation of the heathlands started later than the clearing of the woodland and the draining of marshes. The dry light soils of many parts of lowland England were inherently infertile, and their cultivation had to await the coming of new crops and new methods of husbandry. The full value of sheep to arable farming could not be realised until the introduction of rotations involving such crops as turnips, clover, and the artificial grasses. When sheep were folded on these crops, it was said that 'the foot of the sheep turned sand into gold'. The new ideas advocated by the agricultural writers of the sixteenth and seventeenth centuries thus increased the technical mastery that made reclamation possible.

The reward was reaped in the eighteenth century, and on the light soils of western Norfolk there were remarkable changes. Here, at the beginning of the century, great expanses of warren met the eye, and, so we are told, 'two rabbits struggled for every blade of grass'. It was to Raynham that the second Viscount Townshend retired in 1730 from the vexations of politics, and the rest of his life was given up to the development of his estate. In particular, he advocated what was to be known as the 'Norfolk Four Course System' in which wheat, turnips, barley, and clover followed one another in rotation. The success of his effort was spectacular, and within a few years the warrens around Raynham were converted into productive arable land. Others shared in the rewards to be gained from the Norfolk husbandry. The young Duc de Rochefoucauld, who travelled through western Norfolk in 1784, noted some of the changes of the preceding thirty or forty years, and could only exclaim: 'The fertility of the land is wholly artificial'.

Elsewhere in the kingdom many other tracts of light soil were being reclaimed after the manner of western Norfolk. The Lincoln-shire Wolds were transformed from being a countryside of warren, gorse, and rabbits into one of prosperous cultivation; so were the heaths of the oolitic limestone belt that stretches north and south of the city of Lincoln; so were the Yorkshire Wolds. It would not be difficult to find yet other districts that owe their present character to the hand of the eighteenth-century improver.

But there were limits to the magic of the Norfolk husbandry. Some expanses of coarse sterile sands remained in their barren state until they were given a new value by the development of afforest-ation especially after the establishment of the Forestry Commission in 1919. The Breckland, in East Anglia, has been very largely trans-formed by the planting of conifers. The same is true of the Suffolk Sandlings, the Dorset heathlands, the Bagshot area, and Cannock Chase. Other stretches of heath and common remain as inliers of an older and wilder landscape surrounded by improvement. A number of these have been used as military training grounds and some have been adapted for golf-courses, but a few still appear as open tracts of *Calluna* and *Erica*. Described in the eighteenth century as 'horrid and frightful' these open spaces have acquired a new value in the modern age as areas of recreation. London is for-tunate in having so many of these open tracts nearby—on the Bag-shot Series, on the Lower Greensand, on the Hasting Beds and, to a less extent, on the Blackheath Beds. The struggle for the preserva-tion of these open spaces, and others elsewhere in the realm, forms an interesting chapter in the history of the countryside during the nineteenth century.

The improvements on the light soils form only one aspect of the 'New Husbandry' of the eighteenth century. Agricultural innovation was in the air, and the initiative came largely from some of the great landowners. The amelioration of the soil by marling, liming, and manuring; the invention of new implements of tillage, especially that of Jethro Tull's drill for sowing; experiments in live-stock breeding, particularly those of Robert Bakewell; the introduction of new crops and methods; all were manifestations of a mood of enterprise. It was the Age of the Improver.

The spirit of improvement was increasingly felt in Wales after the middle of the century. Travellers about the year 1770 were noticing that the inhabitants of Welsh districts along the Border had 'in some degree adopted the English manner of tillage', whereas the remoter they were from the English counties the less there was of 'the spirit of industry and improvement'. Certainly, turnips could be only rarely encountered to the west of the moorland core of Wales, and they were not very abundant even along the Border. Potatoes were everywhere more important than turnips in the scheme of cropping. This was the result partly of climate and soil, but, even so, a patriotic Welshman could say in 1812 that the agriculture of Wales was 'a century, at least', behind that of England.

Agricultural improvement also came late to Scotland. The Act of Union of 1707 did not bring immediate benefits, but, by the middle of the century, after the rebellion of 1745 had been suppressed, there were many signs that changes were afoot. As in England, the initiative came through agricultural societies, farmers' clubs, and individual landowners. Clover and sown grasses were grown in the Lothians in the 1720s, and turnips appeared by 1750. From here, they spread rapidly through the eastern seaboard of Scotland. On the lighter soils, the turnip was of especial value, but, in this northern land of cool summers, the Norfolk system was rarely adopted in its original form; oats commonly replaced wheat. A frequent rotation was: oats, turnips, oats, grass, grass, grass; and there were many other variations. Potatoes seem to have been introduced as a garden crop from Ireland in the early years of the century. They soon spread as a field crop, and by 1790 they had taken their place in rotations, sometimes completely replacing the turnip. The *Old Statistical Account* (1791-99) refers time and again to this 'most useful root'. It was especially common in the Highlands and in the Hebrides where it proved suitable for 'breaking in' waste ground. Someone could write in 1808 that 'during fifty years past there have been no additions made to the cultivated land in the Highlands but by this practice' of planting potatoes.

Irish farming was far behind that of the United Kingdom, and Arthur Young, in his *Tour of Ireland* (1776-78), found it marked by an 'extreme inferiority of management'. Even so, there were many

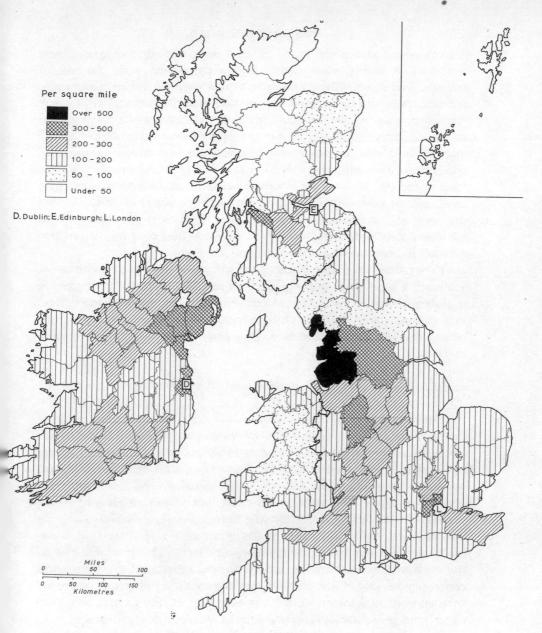

Miles
0   50   100

0   50   100   150
Kilometres

Fig. 28. POPULATION 1821.

improving landlords in the eighteenth century, and Young was able
to give several instances of improvement. Thus, the district around
Collon (to the northwest of Drogheda) was 'a sheet of corn' whereas
twenty-two years earlier it had been 'a vast sheep-walk, covered
chiefly with heath, with some dwarf furze and fern'. It had been

heavily limed and sown with rye and oats. Young also gave a few instances of 'furzy waste land' being improved with the aid of turnips, but Irish tillage as a whole was marked by an absence of turnips. Not the turnip but the potato was the critical root crop. Introduced late in the sixteenth century, it had spread rapidly, and in the eighteenth century it was an important instrument of reclamation, not only on moor and bog but also on heathy slopes. In the decades following the 1780s there was a great extension of arable land in Ireland, and a shift in emphasis from pasture to tillage. 'The thick coat of whins which clothed so many of our small hills', it was said in 1816, 'are vanishing rapidly from the face of our country, and exclusively by potato culture'. But we must add that there was also a great increase in the area devoted to grain.

From about this time began a rapid increase in the population of Ireland. Cause and consequence were intermixed. Pressure of population was an incentive to reclamation, but the reclaimed land in turn stimulated the growth of population during the half-century before the Famine. Figure 28 shows how dense was the population in 1821.

Field systems and Enclosure

For the greater part of its history, the agricultural land of much of England would have looked strange to us today. Over a broad Midland zone, extending from Dorset northwards into the North Riding, most villages were surrounded by those great stretches of arable land known as open fields. In the rest of England, to the south and east and to the north and west, open-field cultivation either had never existed or had disappeared silently before the sixteenth century. In the Midland belt, the open fields remained unenclosed in some places for as long as another three centuries. The complexities of the enclosure movement by which they disappeared are many and controversial, but at any rate we can say that after about 1750 enclosure rapidly took place under various Acts of Parliament until by 1850 open fields had disappeared from all but a few villages.

To our eyes the unenclosed landscape would have looked bare, with, as William Cobbett wrote in 1822, 'all the nakedness, without any of the smoothness, of Downs'. The fences around the enclosed fields were made by planting 'quick' or live cuttings, usually of hawthorn; so was spread the ubiquitous English hedgerow, and from eye-level the countryside came to look much more wooded than it really was.

The hedgerow was not the only geographical consequence of enclosure. The disappearance of open fields was frequently accompanied in the period 1450-1550 by the conversion of arable to pasture, and much of England came to look greener than before. A sheep-run needed far fewer men than the cultivated arable, and from this period date the majority of the 1,700 or so deserted villages in England. In spite of these changes it was not until the eighteenth century that the Midland countryside began to assume its twentieth-century character. As Arthur Young wrote in 1774: 'The fact is this; in the central counties of the kingdom, . . . there have been within 30 years large tracts of the open field arable . . . enclosed and laid down to grass, being much more suited to the wetness of the soil than corn'. By the time the enclosing movement was over, the broad distinction between the arable and the grazing districts of England had been drawn. James Caird's map of 1852 shows the contrast between 'the chief Corn Districts' of the south and east and 'the principal Grazing, Green Crop and Dairying Districts' of the Midlands and the west. There is another generalisation that covers most of the facts: the main arable areas had come to be on light soil or drained fen; the heavier clays were under grass. The condition of these heavier clays had been greatly improved during the eighteenth and nineteenth centuries by underground tile-draining; but the full effect of this could not be felt until the invention, in the 1840s, of machines that produced large quantities of cheap tiles.

The primitive agriculture of Scotland was characterised by the infield-outfield system under which the arable land of a township was divided into two unequal parts. That nearest the cultivators' houses was called the infield. It received all the manure of the settlement and was cropped continuously year after year. Beyond, lay a large outfield comprising some five to ten enclosures from the waste. Each enclosure was cropped for a few seasons and then allowed to revert to its former condition until its turn to be ploughed came round again. The arable land was disposed in ridges; the holdings of tenants were intermixed, and in some places there was an annual re-allotment of strips. The main crops were oats or barley or a mixture of both.

Such arrangements began to disappear with the Improving Movement of the eighteenth century. Because of the differences in land tenure between the two countries, enclosure in Scotland did not carry the same connotation as in England. There were no common rights to be extinguished, so that landowners and tenants could abolish the old system in their own way. One feature of the new order in agriculture was the granting of longer leases so that a tenant could reap the reward of his labour. In the early decades of the 1800s change was apparent everywhere except on some of the arable patches in the more inaccessible Highlands.

The infield-outfield system—or something very much like it—had also once been found to the south of the Border, on the mountainous west of England and in Wales. It also occurred elsewhere, and we may perhaps regard it as a device for utilising poor soils—on the Wolds of Yorkshire and Lincolnshire, on the heaths of Nottingham and Stafford, of Norfolk and Suffolk and of other counties. Agricultural improvement and enclosure changed the character of these areas in the eighteenth century.

Throughout Ireland there was a system comparable with that of Scotland—shifting outfield supplementing an infield. The infield was usually ploughed in ridges, and the outfield, more often than not, was spade-dug. Individual holdings were dispersed in a large number of fragments. There are many obscurities associated with the infield-outfield of Ireland. As in Scotland, there were no legal common rights to extinguish, and the system had all but disappeared by the middle of the nineteenth century. Subsistence farming was giving way to commercial agriculture. New crops, new ideas, and hedged fields were producing a new countryside.

Rural settlement

In a very general way, nucleated villages are and have been characteristic of the English lowland, especially in the two- and three-field area. Dispersed settlement with isolated houses and hamlets, on the other hand, is associated not only with northern and western England but with Wales, Scotland, and Ireland. These statements are only the broadest of generalisations. There has always been much dispersed settlement in the lowland zone, especially in areas that had been wooded in Anglo-Saxon times. The first Ordnance Survey maps of Warwickshire, for example, appeared in the 1830s, and they show a contrast between the nucleated villages of the south and the farms and hamlets of the north, a distinction corresponding to that made by seventeenth-century topographers, between the southern 'Feldon' or open country and the northern 'Woodland' where lay the Forest of Arden. In many Midland parishes, dispersed houses were built in the years following parliamentary enclosure. Where once had been open fields now appeared dwellings with names that occasionally provide clues to their dates, e.g. Quebec Farm, Bunkers Hill Farm.

There were, on the other hand, nucleated settlements within the main areas of dispersion. Hamlets or clachans around an ancient church, or at a bridgehead, or near a large stretch of arable, could reach the size of villages. Such were to be found for example along the Anglo-Normanised coastal plain of south Wales, or in parts of Ireland, or in the crofting areas of the western Highlands and Hebrides. The history of these settlement-types is as yet much too obscure to allow us to attempt any simple explanation of their origins.

Landscape gardens

The landscapes produced by reclamation and agriculture were merely the incidental by-products of economic activity. But there were some localities where scenery was deliberately created to please the eye. The eighteenth century, with its increasing wealth and its developing artistic theories, saw a great and wide-spread development of landscape gardens and parks. Many of the 'improving landlords' and 'spirited proprietors' of the age began to vie with one another in the embellishment of their estates. The making of a landscape garden became an exercise in which stretches of grass, expanses of water and clumps of trees were important elements; such arrangements often included not only rustic pavilions and artificial ruins but classical temples and even pagodas. The outstanding gardeners of the century were William Kent (1685-1748), Lancelot Brown (1715-83), and Humphry Repton (1752-1818). Their influence was to be seen not only around the great palaces of the realm—Blenheim, Chatsworth, Stowe, and the like—but also around what the county gazetteers were in the habit of calling 'a neat mansion pleasantly situated in a park'. Landscape gardens and parks became widespread throughout England, especially within a radius of thirty miles of London. As Uvedale Price wrote in 1794, these embellishments gave 'a new and peculiar character to the general face of the country'.

There were far fewer gardens in Highland Britain—especially in Wales and Scotland—where physical, economic, and social conditions combined to produce a less favourable setting. But, more particularly in Scotland, the building of country houses and the planting of gardens became frequent after the middle of the century. Ardent improvers, like Lord Kames (1696-1782) at Blair Drummond in Perthshire, strove to embellish the scenery as well as improve the agriculture of their estates. One of the causes of the financial difficulties of Sir Walter Scott (1771-1832) was the lavish scale of his gardening and tree-planting at Abbotsford. This activity of Scottish lairds was paralleled to a less degree by that of Irish landowners, and Arthur Young, in 1776, was able to observe some of the results. The estate of Dundrum in County Tipperary, for example, had been 'ornamented in the modern style of improvement', with a 'very noble lawn . . . scattered negligently over with trees'. Other parks figured prominently in the Irish scene, though, except near Dublin, they were not as frequent nor as large as those of England.

Mountains and moorlands

Above the agricultural and improved countryside rise the uplands of Britain with poor soils and generally high rainfall. The upper limit of improvement is rarely sharp, and there are many marginal areas where land has been enclosed and improved only to revert to rough grazing. Field-names ending in such words as ridding, stubbing or intake sometimes tell the story of the upward advance of improvement. The wood that once covered these slopes up to some 1,500 ft. (450 m.) or more was cleared for domestic purposes or for iron-smelting, and its regeneration has been prevented by sheep-grazing and by burning.

The Middle Ages saw a great development of sheep-farming associated with the Cistercian and other monastic houses that were established in wild and solitary places after A.D. 1100 or so. By the sixteenth century, great stretches of the Pennines, of the Lake District and of Wales had become sheep-walks. The native red deer was to be found only in the more remote parts, especially towards the north and in the Southern Uplands of Scotland. Much of the character of these mountains as a whole is due to their long-continued use as sheep-pastures and to the dry-stone walls that were built during the eighteenth and nineteenth centuries.

The most characteristic type of upland grassland is that dominated by sheep's fescue (*Festuca ovina*) and the bents (*Agrostis*). Above this generally comes a variety of other plant associations dependent upon elevation, climate, soil, slope, and drainage, to say nothing of selective grazing and human interference: cotton grass and sphagnum on very wet peat usually above 1,200 ft. (360 m.); wet grass (*molinia*) or dry grass (*nardus*) moors; heather moor, sometimes on peat sometimes not, but always on drier or better drained slopes. There are many gradations among these, and between these and *Festuca-Agrostis* grasslands. All this upland, mostly above the 1,000 ft. (300 m.) contour, falls into the category of rough-grazing.

Some of these features are repeated on a smaller scale in the south of England (in and around Dartmoor and Exmoor) and over scattered areas in Ireland.

The Highlands of Scotland, on the other hand, are far more extensive, and they remained for long in a wild state with not only deer but wolves and possibly bears and elks; the last certain record of wolves comes from Perthshire in 1680 although some are said to have lingered on in the Highlands until the 1740s. There were also semi-wild herds of cattle, and the cattle trade with England took on a new prosperity after the Union in 1707. The social changes after the rebellion of 1745 brought further economic and geographical consequences. The old relationship between chief and clansman was destroyed; and many landowners now aimed at converting their estates into sheep-walks. The invasion of the Highlands by farmers from the south, and by southern breeds of Blackface and Cheviot sheep began about 1760 and reached Caithness by about 1800. Sheep came to replace cattle as the important animal export from the Highlands. The new sheep-walks could be managed by only a few shepherds and their dogs, and the crofters of many a glen were evicted from their homes, leaving behind abandoned dwellings soon to be in ruins. Some crofters emigrated. Some moved to townships near the coast, where the kelp industry, based on seaweed, yielded soda for soap and glass; but its heyday was soon over in the early decades of the nineteenth century. Those who remained in the Highlands kept themselves alive largely with the help of potatoes, but the widespread failure of the potato crop of 1846 helped to swell the volume of emigration.

By this time a new factor had become important in the economy of the Highlands. The price of wool was falling and deer-stalking was becoming fashionable with wealthy Englishmen. The sheep with their shepherds, and the few remaining crofters, were now replaced over large areas by deer-stalkers and gillies. The zenith of the deer-forest came just before the First World War, when the area devoted to the sport in Scotland amounted to over $3\frac{1}{2}$ million acres. Another sport that has affected the Highlands is grouse shooting. The habitat of the grouse is heather moor and there are extensive semi-natural grouse moors on the eastern side of the upland zone, particularly in Perthshire and to the south in Yorkshire.

The twentieth century was to bring yet other changes to these open areas of rough pasture and moorland in the British Isles. Afforestation since the eighteenth century, and particularly since 1919, has altered the appearance of many localities in England,

Wales, Scotland, and Ireland. Other mountain districts have benefited from improved grassland management, although neglect has
sometimes resulted in the spread of bracken and gorse. Much of the
upland zone as a whole has served as a catchment area to sustain the
reservoirs that provide a water-supply for the cities of the industrial
revolution. Finally, much of the area also provides open spaces for
public recreation. Here are the National Parks of England and
Wales, and the areas of Special Control in Scotland.

Towns and the seats of industry

There was apparently but little or no continuity between the
towns of Roman Britain and those of later times; the very sites of
some Roman towns were deserted during the tempest of the invasions. But with the firm establishment of the Anglo-Saxon and
Scandinavian settlers, there once more came into being centres with
an economy different from that of the surrounding agricultural
countryside. These new centres were sometimes on Roman sites and
sometimes not. Some of them grew up as market towns serving as
foci for the villages around; those favoured by location became
regional capitals for wider areas. Other towns along the coast
developed into ports with overseas connections. A number of towns
originated as seats of administration for king, army, or church. Such
were some of the midland boroughs, each surrounded by a shire to
which it gave its name—Bedford, Leicester, Nottingham, and the like.

Not only were existing settlements granted borough status by
charter, but, between about 1200 and 1350, a number of new towns
were deliberately created by kings, nobles, and churchmen, all
interested in increasing their incomes from the profits of trade and
craft. Other motives were also at work. When Edward I (the founder
of many *bastides* in France) conquered Wales in 1282-3, he established towns with castles not only to hold but to assimilate the Welsh.
Such was the origin of centres like Caernarvon, Conway, Flint, and
Harlech where tradesmen and garrison intermingled. The medieval
boroughs of Ireland were likewise English outposts in an unfriendly
country. There were no new creations in the years following 1350
because the medieval economy was contracting. Even the recovery
in Tudor and Stuart times saw the country well enough stocked with
town centres, and there were no additions until the factory towns
and the watering places of the eighteenth century and after. The
exception to this generalisation was Ireland where new towns were
founded as part of the Tudor and Stuart plantations.

Some of the deliberate creations never flourished. Those of Cause in Shropshire and Hedon in the East Riding were in decay by the fifteenth century. Those planned at Newton in Purbeck and at Bere in Merioneth were never even built. Whatever the origin of a town, it was trade and industry that in the long run played the most important part in its survival and growth. All figures about the sizes of medieval towns must be very speculative, and the most that the following estimates can do is to give some idea of orders of magnitude. By 1500, London seems to have had a population of some 60,000. Far below came York, Norwich, and Bristol each with maybe 10,000 to 15,000 inhabitants. Dublin may also have had 10,000 or more, and Edinburgh not quite that number. Below these came a dozen or so towns with between 5,000 and 10,000 people apiece. The size of most market towns that served their surrounding countrysides seems to have been well below the 2,000 mark. There can for example have been few, if any, places in Wales with a population of over 2,000, apart from Cardiff. Estimates of total population are equally hazardous. Wales may have had a quarter of a million people in 1500; Ireland and Scotland may have had three quarters of a million each; England on the other hand, may have had upwards of $3\frac{1}{4}$ million. This makes a possible total of about five million inhabitants for the British Isles round about 1500.

By 1801 this total had become about 16 million; this figure includes only an estimate for Ireland because there was no Irish census until 1821. London had some 900,000 people in 1801. Dublin came next with an estimated total of about 170,000. No other city had over 100,000 inhabitants. There were five cities with over about 70,000 people each: Edinburgh, Glasgow, Manchester, Liverpool and Birmingham; it is difficult to give precise figures because different limits can be taken for each city.

By 1821, the total population of the British Isles had reached nearly 21 million. The details are set out below:

Table 10. Population in 1820

	Area in sq. miles (sq. km.)	Population	Inhabitants per sq. mile (per sq. km.)
England	51,143 (129,870)	11,321,964	221 (87)
Wales	7,398 (19,160)	718,353	97 (37)
Scotland	31,324 (81,130)	2,091,521	67 (26)
Ireland	31,849 (82,490)	6,801,827	210 (82)
British Isles	121,714 (312,650)	20,933,665	172 (67)

219

Two general points may be noted about the distribution of this population (Fig. 28). One is the relatively high densities encountered in Ireland which was as thickly populated as rural England in general. The consequences of the Famine of 1845, and the rural depopulation that continued for the remainder of the century, were drastically to change this position. The second feature that is reflected in Figure 28 is the rise of new industrial areas—Lancashire, the West Riding, the Midlands and, to a less extent, the Lowlands of Scotland. By 1700 almost all the coalfields had begun to be worked, but they were not yet centres of population; the distribution of population was still upon the medieval pattern, and the most populous tract of England lay on either side of a line joining London and Bristol. By 1800 all had changed. As Arthur Young wrote in 1791: 'all the activity and industry of this kingdom is fast concentrating where there are coal pits'. The iron-smelting centres of the Forest of Dean and of the Weald had been superseded by those of the Midlands, of south Wales, of Furness and of the Scottish Lowlands. The textile centres of the West Country and East Anglia were being surpassed by those of Lancashire and the West Riding. A variety of small rural industries were also concentrating in populous centres. The beginnings of the Industrial Revolution reach back into the eighteenth century. Railways had their origin in the tramways that were in use before 1700 on the coalfields. The advent of the locomotive engine ensured the success of their wider application. The opening of the Stockton and Darlington line in 1825 and of the Liverpool and Manchester line in 1830, may be said to mark the end of the beginning of the Industrial Revolution in Britain, and thus to constitute a divide in the history of the changing landscapes of the British Isles.

References

CONNELL, K. H., 1950. *The population of Ireland, 1750-1845.* Oxford.
DARBY, H. C. (Ed.), 1936. *An historical geography of England before A.D. 1800.* Cambridge.
DODD, A. H., 1933. *The industrial revolution in North Wales.* Cardiff.
FREEMAN, T. W., 1950. *Ireland: Its physical, historical, social and economic geography.* London.
HAMILTON, H., 1932. *The industrial revolution in Scotland.* Oxford.
HANDLEY, J. E., 1953. *Scottish farming in the eighteenth century.* London.
HOSKINS, W. G., 1955. *The making of the English landscape.* London.
SMITH, W., 1949. *An economic geography of Great Britain.* London.
SYMON, J. A., 1959. *Scottish farming past and present.* Edinburgh and London.

12

HISTORICAL GEOGRAPHY: THE INDUSTRIAL REVOLUTION

Introduction

THE industrial, agrarian, and transport revolutions in the British Isles were the product of a long series of economic and technological changes. Their profound geographical consequences altered the British landscape and came to be reflected in the changing distributions of population. From the mid-eighteenth century technological innovations, and the harnessing of capital and productive skills to manufacture, led to the development in the British Isles of the first modern industrial state. Agriculture, too, underwent a technical and tenurial revolution which increased production and permitted a great increase in population in the later eighteenth and nineteenth centuries. Revolutionary improvements in transport made possible the interchange of men and materials essential to the progress of industry, agriculture, and trade. Such 'revolutions' were, however, a series of movements progressing at different rates over different periods of time. Thus, while the years between 1750 and 1914 have a certain coherence as the period of birth, maturity and, in certain respects, the decay of Britain's industrial revolution, they are far from presenting a single undifferentiated phase of growth.

In 1700 the British Isles were largely rural and agricultural, exporting surplus grain and other raw materials, with only one major industrial export, woollen cloth; only London, with a population of about 675,000, was a large town by modern standards. From 1700 to 1750 population increased slowly from about 10 to 10·8 millions, two-thirds of the labour force being employed in agriculture. By 1821, when the first phase of the industrial revolution had run its course (Ashton, 1948) one third of the working population in Britain and over one half in Ireland were still engaged in agriculture. By 1911, when the population was 45 millions, only 8% were engaged in agriculture in Britain and 40% in Ireland. Except in Ireland the mainly-rural population of the eve of the railway age had been largely replaced by a nation of industrial workers and town dwellers. The economy leaned on food and raw material imports paid for by manufactures and coal.

Here, then, within a century and a half are all the features of an economic revolution: the challenge of a period of rapid population increase; an era of application of scientific discoveries to technology; a phase of high capital provision and sustained economic growth.

Prelude: The early eighteenth century

The 'take-off' in the British economy about 1780 (Rostow, 1960) saw the rate of industrial growth increase from under 1% per annum, or less, to between 3 and 4% per annum, where it remained, on average, for about a century (Hoffmann, 1955). But in agriculture there was a lengthy process of improvement from the late-sixteenth to the mid-nineteenth century rather than a 'revolution', associated with a few 'improvers' like Jethro Tull, 'Turnip' Townshend, and the Cokes of Holkham, important as these were in implementing new ideas (Fussell and McGregor, 1961). As Darby has shown, the breakdown of communal farming had begun by the end of the fifteenth century, though in many places open fields and commons remained to the nineteenth century. In Scotland and, especially, in Ireland the social and economic forces holding together traditional communities were not swept away until the late-eighteenth and mid-nineteenth centuries respectively. Elsewhere enclosures advanced steadily, and with marked acceleration from the 1730s, and new crops and grass leys progressively replaced open-field fallows and, together with improved stock, opened the way to mixed farming. Farming regions based on specialist production best suited to local soil and climatic conditions began to emerge.

The key to regional specialisation in both industry and agriculture lay in improvements in communications, especially in river navigation (Willan, 1936) and road turnpikes (Jackman, 1961), from the late-seventeenth century.

Despite such advances the rate of population growth was slow, rather less than 0·2% per annum between 1700 and 1750. Overall densities were, with limited exceptions, still low. According to Daniel Defoe (1724-6) 'the country south by Trent is the richest by far and the most populous', the greatest densities in a belt extending from Somerset and Gloucester to East Anglia including not only some of the best-farmed land in Britain but also the prosperous West Country and East Anglian woollen manufacturing regions. But Defoe also observed that the cities of the south were 'matched, if not out-done, by the growing towns of Liverpool, Hull, Leeds, Newcastle and Manchester, and the cities of Edinburgh and Glasgow';

it was in such towns, many of recent growth, that the expression of accelerating commercial and industrial activity was to be sought.

The British Isles were by no means unimportant industrially in the early-eighteenth century (Court, 1954). Its long-famed woollen industries provided more than one half the value of exports (Robinson, 1954). Flax spinning and linen weaving were important in eastern Scotland, Lanarkshire, and Renfrewshire (Pryde, 1961). In Ireland linen and, to a lesser extent, woollens figured in an export trade otherwise dominated by agricultural produce. Silk-weaving was well-established in London, Macclesfield, Coventry, and Norwich; cotton was a growing manufacture in east Lancashire and on Clydeside. The metallurgical industries were varied and widespread and newer industries such as pottery, paper- and glass-making had developed considerably from the seventeenth century.

Moreover, significant (though limited) technological advances were made even before 1750. In the iron industry these initiated significant locational changes (Flinn, 1958). In 1700 iron smelting, located by ore, charcoal for fuel, and water power for blast, was found principally in the Weald, the Forest of Dean, around Sheffield, and in Furness and the west Midlands. But declining ore resources, as in the Weald, and a general scarcity of wood for charcoal led to the migration of furnaces both within individual regions, as in the west Midlands (Johnson, 1951), and from one region to another, as with the smelting of Furness ore at Invergarry in Inverness-shire (Ashton, 1924). More important in shaping a new pattern of location was the successful smelting of iron with coal by Abraham Darby at his Coalbrookdale works, Shropshire, from 1709 (Mott, 1961). The sulphur-free 'sweet clod' coal, local ore, and water power from Severn tributaries gave unique site advantages to this revolutionary enterprise which, together with advances in casting and boring, laid the foundations for rapid progress in the late-eighteenth century.

The use of power in industry was, as yet, limited, though water power had long been an important locating factor notably in textiles. But machinery was limited and many industrial processes were handicrafts. Moreover industrial activity was generally on a small scale, carried on in the home or in small workshops in a domestic system integrated by entrepreneurs who were merchants as much as industrialists. Such industry was widely dispersed and rurally located; the 'growing towns' of which Defoe spoke were commercial centres and ports serving hinterlands of domestic

223

industry. Even so, the seeds of change were being sown, as when, in 1719, Thomas Lombe built the first true factory in the British Isles at Derby, employing 300 workmen and using water power from the river Derwent to drive machinery for silk-throwing (Clapham, 1939).

The Industrial Revolution, 1750-1820

There is ample evidence of acceleration in the rate of industrial growth from about 1780, a period rich in technical innovation. It was accompanied by the rapid growth of population throughout the British Isles, numbers nearly doubling between 1750 and 1821 at an average annual rate of increase of 1·32%, due largely to a decline in the death rate and to a somewhat increased birth rate from the 1780s (Krause, 1958). Large scale movements of people led to considerable changes in distribution. Water power and then steam power harnessed to new machines began to break down traditional industrial methods and organisation, and sponsored new types and locations of industry: the necessary mobility of men and materials was permitted by the growth of a national network of waterways and roads. Increased investment (Ashton, 1948), new forms of capital raising (for example, through country banks), and pioneering technology, all contributed to Britain's ability to make and sell cheaply for both home and overseas markets.

By the 1820s manufactures accounted for 90% of British exports, with cottons (48%) and woollens (12%) dominant (Robinson, 1954). Industrial raw materials, notably cotton, and foodstuffs formed the bulk (91%) of imports, imported foodstuffs comprising one seventh by value of Britain's food consumption. Thus population outstripped food production, despite large-scale reclamation of wastes and commons (especially on heathland and moorland), the rapid enclosure of open fields in Britain (though not yet Ireland), and increased yields from improved farming. Although the proportion of the population in Britain employed in agriculture fell to about one third, productivity increased. Specialist farming regions crystallised, for example in the sheep and barley husbandry of light soils in eastern Britain, and the grazing areas on heavier soils in the English Midlands, as was observed by contemporary agricultural writers like Young and Marshall and the county reporters to the first Board of Agriculture (1793–1815) (Darby, 1954). But much agriculture was still backward and the unevenness of progress by the 1820s may be gauged from William Cobbett's

Rural Rides. Rural industry was still widespread, however, and many small farmers also had a trade to follow.

Geographical changes in the location and scale of industry were of crucial importance. The industrial revolution was based firmly upon iron which, with engineering, lay at the very heart of the new technology. The first vital steps had been taken early in the eighteenth century, but, from about 1760, the extension of coke-iron smelting and the perfecting of casting processes by Darby, Wilkinson, and others led to the growing use of iron for machinery and constructional purposes as in the Severn bridge, Ironbridge built in 1779, and the Arkwright and Strutt mill, Belper built in 1795 (Green, 1960). Advances in working wrought iron by the Cranage brothers from 1766, and in iron puddling by Cort (1784) and Onions, facilitated the replacement of wood by iron; thus pig iron production trebled between 1788 and 1806 and, from partial dependence on imported Swedish bar iron before 1750, Britain became an exporter of pig by the early 1800s. New areas of manufacture developed rapidly after mid-century: in Scotland, Roebuck established the Carron works in 1759; the Shropshire ironmasters, the Guests, set up a works at Dowlais, Merthyr Tydfil, in 1760; smelting was carried on at Workington from 1762. The once dominant Wealden industry completely disappeared by 1820; the Forest of Dean gave way to south Wales, which produced 42·5% of British pig iron by 1830, mainly in the northeastern part of the coalfield; east Shropshire and the Black Country rapidly increased production to 32·5% of the total by 1830 (Scrivenor, 1854; Roepke, 1956; Mitchell, 1954). Until the mid-nineteenth century British iron smelting rested on coal and coal-measure ores, with the locational influence of coal dominant because of the larger amounts required in smelting and to provide steam power for blast.

Though less concentrated geographically than smelting, iron-working increasingly acquired a coalfield location. But the unit of production remained small and, despite inventions such as the water-powered slitting mill, mechanisation was limited, even in the Black Country (Court, 1938; Allen, 1929). Engineering progress in this period was mainly associated with the steam engine. Newcomen's engine (1708) was extravagant in its use of coal and largely confined to pumping in mines and collieries where it helped to develop techniques of deeper mining. The Watt steam engine (1769)—manufactured under patent from 1775—was more efficient and, by 1781, made it economically and technically possible to drive machinery by rotary motion. The Boulton and Watt partnership in Birmingham and, from 1795, at the Soho works, Smethwick, symbolises the technical advantages of the age, and the distribution of Boulton and Watt steam engines in 1800, when their patent expired, gives some indication of the major industrial regions of the period (W. Smith, 1949). The engines were found mainly in the textile districts, especially east Lancashire, the mining areas, such as Cornwall, and iron-manu- facturing areas, especially the west Midlands. But engines built to a pirated Watt design were probably numerous in Lancashire (Musson and Robinson, 1959) and in Cornwall, and in Derbyshire Newcomen engines predominated even at the end of the century (Nixon, 1961). The early steam engines were wasteful in their use of fuel and despite the development of cheap bulk transport by water during the canal era of 1759 to 1830, easy access to coal was vital to industry and long hauls were generally avoided: for example, in 1761 the Duke of Bridgewater's Worsley collieries were linked by canal to Manchester, ten miles away, and halved the cost of coal there. Most canal acts were secured for, and the dens- est network of canals completed in, the coalfield industrial regions of the west Midlands, Lancashire, and west Yorkshire, these being linked by important trunk canals such as the Trent and Mersey, the Grand Union and the Leeds and Liverpool. Canals were of great importance to inland manufacturing regions and the canal-side industrial site, now often a relict site, is an enduring reminder of this in the landscape, nowhere more so than in the former Wedg- wood Etruria Pottery, Stoke, built in 1769 (Hoskins, 1955).

Water transport opened up wider markets for bulky com- modities. Coal travelled coastwise from northeast England to east coast ports, notably London, thence to be distributed inland by river and canal. Coal production, long limited by techniques of working, restricted industrial use and costly transport, trebled be- tween 1770 (6·2 million tons) and 1826 (21 million tons), though mining was still confined to the more accessible coal measures in industrial regions or near tidal water.

The textile industries progressed enormously during this period. Hargreaves' 'jenny', capable of spinning many threads at once, and Arkwright's 'frame', patented in 1769 to spin the stronger warp twists, made rapid production of all types of cotton yarn possible. The jenny could be hand-operated in the home but the frame required power initially supplied by water mills. In the 1780s Crompton's 'mule', a machine capable of spinning all types of fine yarn in quantity, opened the way to world markets in fine muslins. But innovation in spinning progressed more rapidly than in weaving and the dominance, by the 1820s, of factory-production in cotton was not general throughout the textile industry. Water for power, and for washing and bleaching, dominated the siting of the early cotton industry; mills were often in remote valleys where such site advantages overcame disadvantages of communication. Although to a lesser degree than in the mid-nineteenth century, the cotton industry achieved a marked regional distribution. Daniel Crompton's census of 1811 (Daniels, 1930) showed that east Lancashire and adjacent areas had 80% of British spindles; the east Midlands, which for a short time in the pioneer phase of factory development in the 1780s rivalled Lancashire as a spinning area, was important, but much less so than Lancashire for steam-powered manufacture (D. M. Smith, 1962). In Scotland the harnessing of steam power to cotton was rapidly displacing linen in the Clyde valley, while in northern Ireland the introduction of steam to a cotton factory at Lisburn in 1789 led to a rapid, but short-lived, extension of the industry in Belfast and the Lagan valley (Green, 1949; Freeman, 1960). Cotton weaving, though less a factory industry, was similarly concentrated at this date; indeed the proportion of cotton cloth made in Lancashire was probably greater.

Similar regional specialisation was developing in the linen and woollen industries, though because of slowness in adopting new processes this was less marked than in cotton. Linen manufacture remained widespread in eastern Scotland, especially in Forfarshire, Fifeshire, and Perthshire (Turner, 1953); in Ireland the Lagan valley was an important flax-spinning and linen-weaving area; other domestic producers were scattered in the West Riding and in the West Country.

Specialist woollen regions had long existed in the West Country and, for worsted and fine patterned cloths, in East Anglia. Both were being displaced by the West Riding of Yorkshire by the late eighteenth century. Although slower than cotton to adopt factory organisation and power-operated machinery, domestic industry was being rapidly displaced in the west Yorkshire woollen industry by 1820. In the hosiery districts of the east Midlands, however, in the hosiery and tweed area of the Tweed valley, the flannel industry of Wales, and in Ireland, domestic craftsmen still dominated, though small water-powered mills were growing in number. Thus, woollen manufacture was less concentrated in location and the unit of production was smaller than in cotton.

Indeed 'the Lancashire cotton operative was not the representative workman of the Britain of King George IV' (Clapham, 1939,

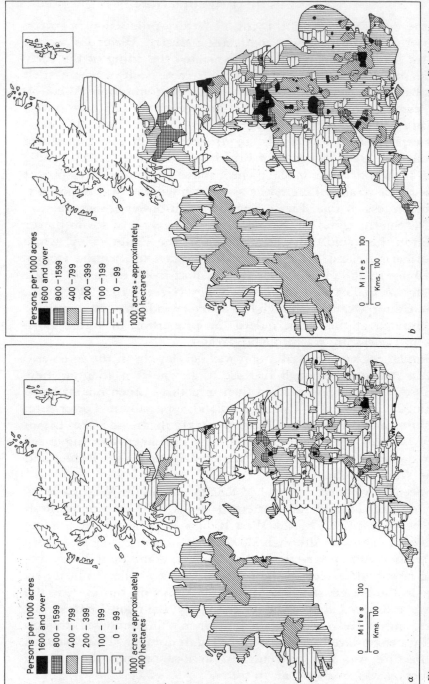

Persons per 1000 acres

- 1600 and over
- 800 – 1599
- 400 – 799
- 200 – 399
- 100 – 199
- 0 – 99

1000 acres = approximately 400 hectares

b

Persons per 1000 acres

- 1600 and over
- 800 – 1599
- 400 – 799
- 200 – 399
- 100 – 199
- 0 – 99

1000 acres = approximately 400 hectares

a

Fig. 29. THE DISTRIBUTION OF POPULATION IN THE EARLY AND MID-NINETEENTH CENTURY. Based on (*a*) the first censuses for Britain (1801) and Ireland (1821) and (*b*) the censal year of peak rural population in Britain (1851) and Ireland (1841); densities are given for registration districts in England and Wales and counties in Scotland and Ireland.

p.41). Handloom weaving was still important; industries such as clothing, boots and shoes were wholly handicrafts and, with smiths, wrights, and many others, numerous craftsmen were to be found in every large village and market town (Lawton, 1954).

At the first census of 1801 (1821 in Ireland—Connell, 1950) many of the higher population densities occurred in industrialised countrysides, notably in the textile districts of east Lancashire and west Yorkshire, in the Black Country and along the lower Clyde (Fig. 29) and in some mining areas. The low densities in agricultural areas of Highland Britain contrasted markedly with the relatively dense population of much of Lowland Britain. In Ireland, too, relatively high population densities point to overcrowding by a peasantry already seeking relief by seasonal migration to Britain as labourers and harvesters, with a growing tendency to permanent emigration (Freeman, 1957).

Town growth, though rapid, was still relatively restricted. In England only one third of the population was urban and in Scotland about one quarter; in Ireland there were no large towns outside Dublin and Belfast. Not until the railway age did urbanisation dominate Britain, though many commercial and industrial towns were growing very rapidly in the late eighteenth and early nineteenth centuries. But rural population also grew quickly; agriculture was expanding and rurally-located industries and crafts gave diversity to the economy of the countryside.

The mature economy, 1820–1880

In the sixty years astride 1850, the industrial revolution reached full maturity in the British Isles. In the 'drive to maturity' (Rostow, 1959) industry was diversified, a wider range of products found its way into world markets, and Britain became the workshop of the world. Industrial productivity continued to grow at rates of 3 to 4% per annum until the 1870s. Although agricultural production also increased, population grew faster and by the late 1870s the British Isles were markedly dependent on imported food, producing only one half of their requirements of grain, meat, dairy produce, and wool.

Important technical developments in this period did much to shape the geography of modern Britain, none more than the fuller utilisation of steam power in industry, agriculture, and transport. Machine-making and engineering made remarkable advances in this age of the great engineers. Although in the 1850s Britain still depended on textiles for 63% of her exports—40% in cottons

(Robinson, 1954)—her supremacy in textiles was being challenged by the 1870s, and other exports, especially metals and metal products, grew in importance. Thus the continued expansion of the economy depended on a wider range of exports to wider markets, including South America, southeast Asia and the Far East, and tropical Africa; British shipping dominated world trade to the benefit of ship-building and marine engineering. The earnings from commerce and investment overseas gave substantial 'invisible' exports to off-set the unfavourable trade balance which became appreciable after 1820 (Chambers, 1961).

Despite increased food production the agricultural labour force declined after the 1840s, with consequent rural depopulation. But greater productivity per acre and per unit of manpower in the 'High Farming' period of the 1850s and 1860s followed better farming techniques and increased mechanisation, which, from the 1830s, enabled the agrarian revolution to come to full fruition on heavy as well as light land. By mid-century most of the cultivated land was enclosed and farms were larger; even in Ireland changes in tenure and farming were taking place, initiated in part by the potato famine of the late 1840s. Caird's classic account of English agriculture in 1850 and 1851 and the agricultural statistics available from 1866 both show the dominance of arable farming on the lighter soils of eastern Britain and of grazing on the moister soils of the west, the Midlands, and in Ireland.

In many ways the harnessing of steam to railways and sea transport was the most significant feature of the age. Although railways had previously been used in colliery districts (notably Tyneside and south Wales), not until the successful design of steam locomotives by Hedley (from 1813) and Stephenson (from 1814) was their potential fully realised. Bulk production of iron rails was one important cause of the ten-fold increase in pig-iron production between 1828 (0·70 million tons, 0·71m. metric tons) and 1884 (7·57 million tons, 7·69m. metric tons). More coal was required for railways and steamships, to drive machinery in a widening range of industries, for domestic fuel and, after mid-century, for export. Coal output rapidly increased from 21 million tons in 1826 to 64·5 millions (65·5m. metric tons) in 1854, according to the first mineral statistics, and to 154 million tons (156·5m. metric tons) in 1880: coal made a significant contribution to the national income, directly and indirectly. Improvements in mining techniques led to the exploitation of the 'concealed' coalfields (except in Kent) after the 1820s (Fig. 31); deeper mining in the

Northumberland and Durham coalfield helped to make it the leading coal producer in Britain in 1855 with 24% of total output. Many fields with small but accessible reserves which had been closely associated with early industrialisation were still leading producers; Staffordshire (11·4%) was nearing the peak of its production and although it had the largest number of collieries it had one of the lowest outputs per colliery; Lancashire (15·1%) was second in production, but the Shropshire and Denbighshire fields were declining; south Wales (13·3%) and Yorkshire (12·0%), though important, were still to approach their full development, and Scotland (11·4%) was rapidly increasing its output.

Fuller mechanisation and steam-power operation led to further concentration of factory industry on coalfields and in towns. But in 1851 there were only an estimated $1\frac{3}{4}$ million mechanised workers in Britain as compared with $5\frac{1}{2}$ million non-mechanised, and while textiles employed 12·6% of the working population of the British Isles (1·61 millions) there were still 27·6% employed in agriculture (3·52 millions) and 12·1% (1·54 millions) in domestic service. However the balance was changing: while the employed population of the British Isles increased by 12·3% between 1851 and 1881, the numbers in textiles fell by 20·1% to 9% of the employed population as compared with increases in employment in metals, machinery, and engineering from 4% to 6·4% and in coal from 2·4% to 3·6%. Textiles, the dominant export to the 1870s, had declined relatively to 43% of total exports in 1890, when metals and engineering products provided 25% and coal 7% of exports (Robinson, 1954).

Significant changes also took place in the distribution of population (Fig. 30). The railway network initiated in 1830 grew rapidly and gave new mobility, and a new nodality to many towns. Labour and materials were assembled in great urban and industrial regions: even in 1851 over 50% of England's population was urban and many 'rural' districts were being industrialised; by 1881 over 70% of the people were town-dwellers. The nuclear industrial regions of 1801, west Yorkshire and east Lancashire, the Black Country and Birmingham, Tyneside, central Scotland, and London, grew increasingly more extensive and more populous; other marked concentrations had emerged in the Durham and south Wales coalfields and in parts of the east Midlands. In southeastern England the development of many towns, notably along the coast, presaged the rapid urbanisation of the late-nineteenth century. In Scotland also the bulk of population increase occurred in industrial

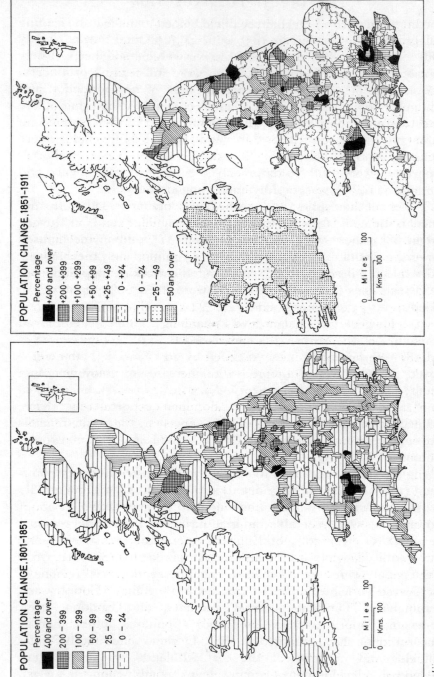

Fig. 30. POPULATION CHANGES IN THE NINETEENTH CENTURY. Percentage changes are shown for the periods 1801-51 and 1851-1911 in Britain, and 1821-41 and 1841-1911 in Ireland. Based on the same administrative units as Figure 29.

areas, especially in Glasgow and the central coalfields. In Ireland the only notable increases of population after the 1840s were in Belfast and its industrial hinterland and, to a lesser degree, around Dublin. People left the countryside in large numbers; the proportion employed in agriculture fell from one third in Britain and nearly one half in Ireland in 1821 to 13% and 42% respectively in 1881.

The transfer of population from country to town took place on an unprecedented scale in the first two decades of the railway age. In the large towns of England the proportion of net townward movement to total population increase was never less than 37% in any one decade between 1821 and 1881, and in London it was generally over 20% (Weber, 1896). New towns rose at incredible speed; iron centres like Middlesbrough and Barrow, railway towns like Crewe and Swindon, resorts like Blackpool and Bournemouth. Although population increased throughout Britain to 1851 and in Ireland to the eve of the potato famine in 1845, most rural areas experienced their maximum increase between 1811 and 1821. Thereafter there was a slackening of rural growth leading to decline from mid-century (Fig. 30).

In 1851, Augustus Petermann designed what is perhaps the first distribution map showing 'the places where certain well-defined works and manufactures are concentrated' (Census, Great Britain, 1852, p. xxvii). With similar data added for Ireland this map has been used as the basis of Figures 31 to 33. The great concentration of industries on the coalfields in 1851 was nowhere more marked than in the iron industry (Fig. 32). Its location was dominated by coal and coal-measure ores, and, of the total of 2·7 million tons of pig iron in 1852, south Wales had 24·7%, central Scotland 28·7%, and Staffordshire 30·2%. In the west Midlands, the cradle area of the coke-iron industry (in Shropshire) declined after 1830, and, like Denbighshire, was of little account. But the Black Country was synonymous with iron, its furnace-ridden landscapes a source of wonder to many foreign travellers, its metal industries varied and highly skilled. However, by 1865 production of iron fell short of requirements in the region and after 1870 it lost ground rapidly as raw materials were exhausted (Allen, 1929). South Wales's importance was initially based on local coke and clay-band ores around Merthyr Tydfil, but rising costs of local ore caused the industry to move to coastal sites using imported ore, and also coal brought down-valley by rail in increasing quantities after 1870. Scottish iron smelting, using black-band ores, increased to a quarter of British production after the development of

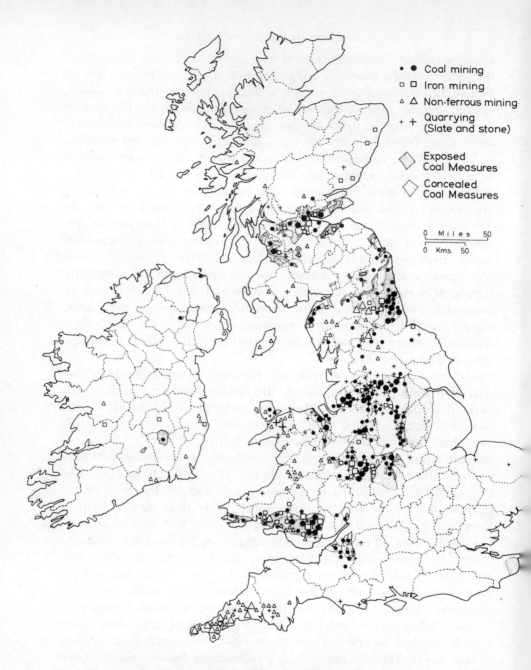

Fig. 31. EMPLOYMENT IN MINING INDUSTRIES, 1851. Based on A. Petermann's map of occupations, Census of Great Britain, 1851, and on the Census of Ireland, 1851. Symbols are placed in districts where numbers occupied in specific industries were important; large symbols signify districts of special significance.

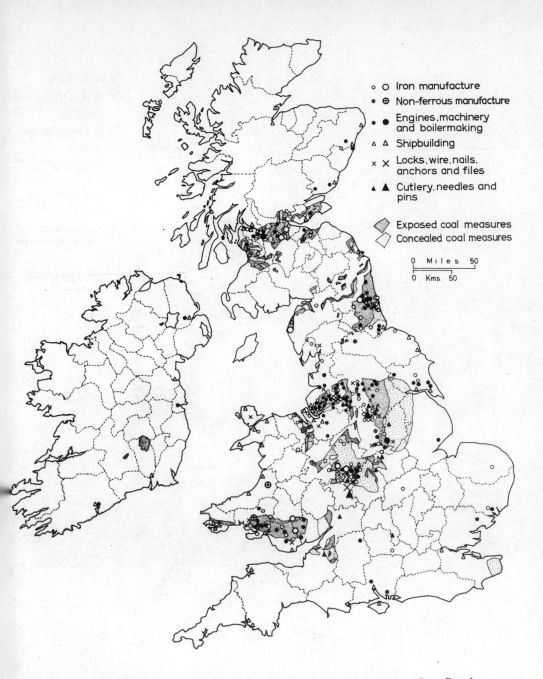

Fig. 32. EMPLOYMENT IN METALLURGICAL AND ENGINEERING INDUSTRIES, 1851. Based on A. Petermann's map, Census of Great Britain, 1851, and on the Census of Ireland, 1851. Symbols are on the same basis as in Figure 31.

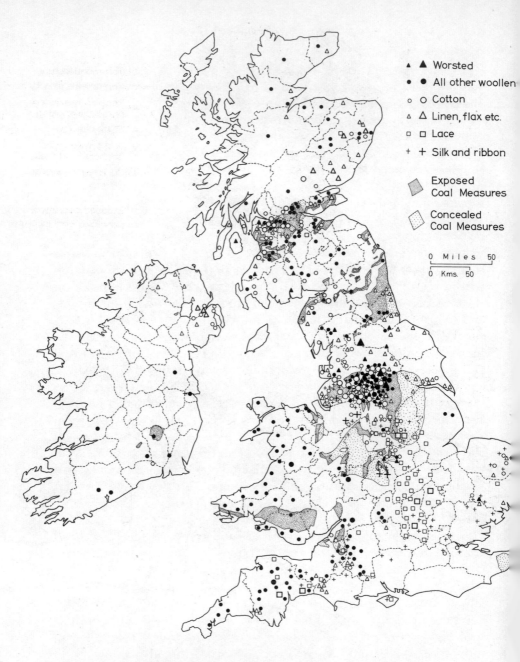

Legend:

▲ ▲ Worsted
● ● All other woollen
○ ○ Cotton
△ △ Linen, flax etc.
□ □ Lace
+ + Silk and ribbon

Exposed Coal Measures

Concealed Coal Measures

0　Miles　50
0　Kms.　50

Fig. 33. EMPLOYMENT IN THE TEXTILE INDUSTRIES, 1851. Based on A. Petermann's map, Census of Great Britain, 1851 and on the Census of Ireland, 1851. Symbols are on the same basis as in Figure 31.

Neilson's hot blast process in 1828. But the rapidly-growing Tees-side industry, using coking coal from southwest Durham and, initially, Coal Measure ores, pointed to a new phase of development in the mid-nineteenth century based on Cleveland ore.

Iron working and machine-making were much less tied to raw materials, often being located near the industries for which they manufactured. Skilled labour encouraged the development of congeries of metal industries in such areas as Sheffield, and Birmingham and the Black Country where specialist sub-regions developed, for example nail-making around Halesowen, or locks and keys at Willenhall and Walsall (Wise, 1950). Many textile firms made their own machinery, the wrights of an earlier period becoming millwrights and machine makers (Clapham, 1926–38). The emphasis was mainly on skilled craftsmanship and, in 1851, the unit of production was generally small. Moreover only 4% of the working population were employed in all forms of metal-working, tool-making, engine- and ship-building in the British Isles, though by 1881 the proportion had increased to 6·3%. Despite some big units, e.g. the locomotive-builders Hawthorns of Gateshead and Kitsons of Leeds, the increase in size and production of engineering firms awaited standardisation of tools and processes, though important progress was made in this period by such pioneers as Maudsley of Lambeth and Nasmyth of Manchester (Smiles, 1861-2; Musson, 1957). In part, therefore, engineering developed to serve other industries on the coalfields, in part it arose from the application of machinery to new uses, as in the locomotive workshops of Crewe, Swindon, and Darlington, the agricultural machine shops of Ipswich and Leiston and in the marine engineering of Clydeside, Merseyside, and north-east England.

Constant technical improvements and increased mechanisation stressed the advantages of concentration in the textile industries (Fig. 33). By 1851 Lancashire's dominance in cotton was over-whelming; weaving was largely mechanised by the 1840s, attracting labour from hand-loom weaving areas to Lancashire mills. Early competitors in the east Midlands and Belfast declined as the industrial revolution in cotton ran its course and the Paisley cotton industry survived only in such specialisms as thread-making.

No one region dominated other branches of the textile industry to the same degree. Only in the worsted trade of the Bradford district, which had completely ousted the Norwich region, was concentration complete. But of other woollen manufactures, only 40-50% was found in west Yorkshire: many small water-powered mills remained in Wales where, as in the West Country, there were many out-workers. In the east Midlands, most hosiery was still made by workers in their own homes, using frames provided by the manufacturer.

A similarly-wide dispersal of lace-making prevailed until the rapid growth of the Nottingham factory industry after c.1860. Linen manufacture remained in part a rural industry in eastern Scotland (Turner, 1953) and in parts of Yorkshire and the West Country, though Belfast dominated British production following the development of wet spinning after 1825 and the consequent conversion of mills from cotton to flax spinning.

In addition to such major industries there were still, in 1851, large numbers of other craft workers. The 1851 census recorded some 500,000 cotton workers; the next largest industrial groups at about 250,000 were boot- and shoe-makers, then milliners and dress-makers. There were more tailors than woollen workers, more blacksmiths than iron workers. Such craftsmen were distributed throughout the country in small and little-mechanised units of production in village and town alike in rough proportion to the population they served (Lawton, 1954). But after the 1850s employment in such industries fell as factory production developed, for example in the boot-and-shoe and clothing industries from c.1870. The consequences for the population of rural areas were profound, but may best be reviewed with population trends between 1851 and 1911.

The Great Depression, 1873-1896, to the First World War

From about 1873 to 1896 economic growth in Britain slackened; average annual increases in industrial productivity fell below 2% (Hoffmann, 1955); key industries such as coal, iron, and steel, and even engineering, periodically suffered severe unemployment (Musson, 1959); while dependence on imported food and raw materials increased, exports faced growing competition. Such difficulties, symptomatic of long-term economic problems, were reflected in changes in industrial location, in population distribution and in agriculture, and anticipated the further redistribution of capital and manpower in the twentieth century.

The textile industries, for over a century the main prop of the economy, produced only 34% of United Kingdom exports in 1913 as compared with 56% in 1870 (Robinson, 1954). Cotton declined further in the east Midlands and in Scotland where it survived only in Paisley and the Irvine valley. Even in Lancashire, compared with the great growth of the 1850s, there was a period of slow growth, despite new markets in the Far East and in Africa (Chambers, 1961). At the end of the century many cotton towns in east Lancashire were losing population by migration, though cotton production did not reach its peak until the eve of the First World War and new factories replaced old in Lancashire after the Great Depression. A high degree of concentration into West Riding factories was also seen in the woollen industries by 1911, though some hand-weaving of tweeds still survived in western Scotland and in Ireland. The knit-wear and hosiery industries became factory industries after the 1860s, mainly in the east Midlands but with specialist woollen knit-wear in the Tweed valley. Belfast further dominated the linen industry, and east Scotland sought recompense in the virtual British monopoly of jute and allied industries in Dundee and Fifeshire (Turner, 1952). Such intense specialisation within limited areas became highly characteristic of British industry, not least in the older staples such as textiles, and, whilst it may have led to maximum efficiency of production, it also created single-industry towns particularly vulnerable in trade depressions.

Metals and engineering products increased their place in exports to over one quarter by 1913, and together with new industries, including chemicals and electrical engineering, helped to replace textiles. Changes in Birmingham and the Black Country after the 1870s epitomise those in British industry at large: the coal-iron staples declined but metal-working and engineering remained important; new trades were developed, some, such as electrical and assembly industries, based on traditional skills, others, like chemical and subsidiary industries and food processing, breaking newer ground (Allen, 1929). Many new industries were less tied to raw materials, and a coalfield location became less dominant in industry, though the coalfields themselves flourished on an unprecedented demand for coal, including exports valued at 10% of the total in 1913 which helped to close the trade gap left by the relative decline of cotton; in that year the output of coal reached a peak of 287 million tons (291·5m. metric tons), 94 millions (95·5m. metric tons) of which were exported.

Profiting from the mobility offered by railways and electric power transmission, assembly and consumer industries increasingly sought large markets and sources of labour; London, always a major centre of such industry was not only the largest conurbation but one of the biggest and most varied industrial regions in the British

Isles (Hall, 1962). With increasing dependence on imported food and raw materials, flour milling, oil-seed crushing and tanning joined sugar refining and tobacco manufacture at the major ports, which grew as industrial, as well as commercial, centres. The chemical industries, also partly dependent on imports, grew rapidly from the mid-nineteenth century. In mid-Cheshire and along the middle Mersey they were closely associated with salt (W. Smith, 1953); together with derivatives from coal and metallurgical industries they provided a new heavy industry in northeast England, on Clydeside, and in the west Midlands.

There were marked changes in the iron industry as the displacement of wrought iron by steel for many purposes and new smelting processes placed new geographical values on previous locations. By 1884 Staffordshire's share in pig-iron output had decreased to 8%; production in south Wales dropped to 12% in 1884 and to 9% by 1913, when Scottish production fell to 13%. Using Cleveland ores northeast England rapidly expanded production to 33% of the total by 1884 and nearly 40% in 1913, while Furness and west Cumberland produced 20% and 12% in those years. Increasing dependence on imported ores moved blast furnaces to the ports and more economical use of coal in smelting also favoured sites other than on the coalfields. Bessemer's revolutionary paper to the British Association in 1856 was significantly entitled 'The manufacture of Iron without Fuel'. Initially this process was confined to non-phosphoric ores, favouring west Cumberland haematite and imported ores. But in 1879 the Gilchrist-Thomas process opened the way to the use of phosphoric ores in steel manufacture, although the output of basic steel did not approach that of acid steel until 1913. Thus the development of smelting located on lean Jurassic ores led to the production in the east Midlands of 12% of British pig iron in 1913.

Steel made a great impact on the engineering industries. In shipbuilding, the iron ship gave way to steel on the Clyde in the 1880s, and shipbuilding and marine engineering here and in Belfast, Furness, northeast England, and on Merseyside created a vast modern industry. Precision and standardisation (e.g. by die stamping) led to general advances in engineering; more accurate machine parts and wide application of such new inventions as hydraulic machinery led to mechanisation of an increasing range of industrial processes. By the end of the century handicraft work had declined, to the detriment of rural industry.

The concentration of population in large towns and industrial

areas attracted a wider range of industries and services, while
rural losses were further emphasised by trends in agriculture.
Despite the prosperous years of 'High Farming', the labour force
fell from the 1850s with increased mechanisation. Improvements in
draining heavy clayland with the mole plough and mass-produced

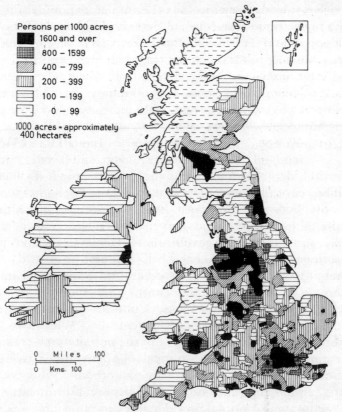

Persons per 1000 acres

- 1600 and over
- 800 – 1599
- 400 – 799
- 200 – 399
- 100 – 199
- 0 – 99

1000 acres = approximately
400 hectares

0   Miles   100
0   Kмв.   100

Fig. 34. THE DISTRIBUTION OF POPULATION, 1911. Based on the
censuses of England and Wales, of Scotland, and of Ireland, 1911.
Densities are given for the same administrative units as in Figures
29 and 30.

tile pipes, and the development of chemical fertilisers increased
yields. Mixed farming in particular benefited from increased
home markets for stock and cash crop products.

Nowhere was depopulation more marked than in Ireland (Fig.
30), where, despite a backward peasant agriculture excessively
dependent on potatoes, overpopulation had been assisted by
seasonal labour migration. The demographic catastrophe of the
potato famine of 1845-48 led to a fall of 19.5% in the population
of Ireland (Cousens, 1960) and an increase of 74% in the Irish-born

241

population of Britain between 1841 and 1851 (Lawton, 1959). Crowded into some of the poorest areas of British cities like London, Liverpool, Manchester, and Glasgow, the flood of Irish migrants had pronounced effects on their social and demographic structures; indeed in parts of Liverpool in 1851 up to 50% of the population were Irish by birth (Lawton, 1955). Similar depopulation was the outcome of the same causes in the Scottish Highlands (Gray, 1957). Rural depopulation throughout the British Isles continued from the 1870s when agriculture, competing with new lands in the Americas and Australasia for home markets in wheat, wool and, later, meat, had to economise further in production costs. Much marginal land went out of cultivation and, although lower food prices benefited the industrial worker, arable farming was badly hit.

In 1911 over 80% of the population of England and Wales was urban, in Scotland three quarters: even in Ireland, following severe rural depopulation, some 40% were town-dwellers. The remarkable concentration of population (Fig. 34) into the conurbations of Clydeside, northeast England, south Lancashire, west Yorkshire, the west Midlands, and south Wales resulted not only from the early industrial revolution but also from mid-Victorian urbanisation which extended the built-up areas outwards to create a blanket of terrace-housing wrapped around commercial and industrial cores. At the end of the century migration was especially marked to London and the Home Counties where, in 1911, over one quarter of the population of England and Wales lived; in the outer suburbs half to three quarters of the population were migrants. Similar rapid increases were typical of many other towns. Such long-continued migration from the countryside, the product of declining employment in both agriculture and industry, led to general reduction of population densities in rural districts (Saville, 1957).

Between the censal year of peak rural population (1851 in Britain, 1841 in Ireland) and 1911 (Fig. 30) areas of growth were few, mainly in the expanding conurbations and other towns. But some older industrial areas grew very slowly and, as in east Lancashire and parts of the Black Country, were losing population by migration in the decades before the First World War. The problems of urban sprawl, and of the drift to the southeast were already present: rural depopulation had been there since mid-century. As with the economy, so the rate of population growth had begun to slacken with a decrease in the birth-rate from about 1880. Thus, the First World War was a watershed in the geography of the British

Isles. It marked the end of a century and a half that was crucial in the shaping of the geography of present-day Britain and in which many present problems are rooted. But it was also a period of great achievement in which a small, mainly-rural population of some 10 millions was transformed into an urban and industrial nation of 45 millions, manufacturing for much of the world, supporting itself at generally rising standards of living and pioneering technical development of many kinds.

References

ALLEN, G. C., 1929, *The Industrial Development of Birmingham and the Black Country.*

ASHTON, T. S., 1924. *Iron and Steel in the Industrial Revolution.*
— 1948. *The Industrial Revolution.*

CENSUS, GREAT BRITAIN, 1852. *Census of Great Britain, 1851, Vol. I.*

CHAMBERS, J. D., 1961. *The Workshop of the World. British Economic History from 1820 to 1880.*

CLAPHAM, J. H., 1926–38. *An Economic History of Modern Britain*, I. (1926) Britain on the Eve of the Railway Age; II. (1932) The Early Railway Age.
— 1949. *A Concise Economic History of Britain from the Earliest Times to A.D. 1750.*

CONNELL, K. H., 1950. *The Population of Ireland, 1750-1845.*

COURT, W. H. B., 1938. *The Rise of the Midland Industries.*
— 1954. *A Concise Economic History of Britain from 1750 to Recent Times.*

COUSENS, S. H., 1960. The regional pattern of emigration during the great Irish famine, 1846-1851. *Trans. Inst. Brit. Geogrs.*, **28**, 119-34.

DANIELS, A. W., 1930. Samuel Crompton's census of the cotton industry in 1811. *Econ. Hist.*, **2**, 107-10.

DARBY, H. C., 1954. Some early ideas on the agricultural regions of England. *Agric. Hist. Rev.*, **2**, 30-47.

DEFOE, D., 1724-6. *A Tour through the Whole Island of Great Britain.* (Everyman Edition, 1928, Ed. G. D. H. Cole.)

FLINN, M. W., 1958. The growth of the English iron industry, 1660-1760. *Econ. Hist. Rev.*, **11**, 144-53.

FREEMAN, T. W., 1957. *Prefamine Ireland; a Study in Historical Geography.*
— 1960. *Ireland; a general and regional Geography*, 2nd Edition.

FUSSELL, G. E., and McGREGOR, O. D., 1961. Introduction to LORD ERNLE, *English Farming, Past and Present.* (6th Edition.)

GRAY, M., 1957. *The Highland Economy, 1750-1850.*

GREEN, E. R. R., 1949. *The Lagan Valley, 1800-1850.*
— 1960. Industrial archaeology. *Antiquity*, **34**, 43-8.

HALL, P. G., 1962. *The Industries of London since 1861.*

HOFFMANN, W. G., 1955. *British Industry, 1700-1950.* (Translated by W. O. Henderson and W. H. Chaloner.)

HOSKINS, W. G., 1955. *The Making of the English Landscape.*

JACKMAN, W. T., 1961. *The Development of Transportation in England.* (2nd Edition, with introduction by W. H. Chaloner.)

JOHNSON, B. L. C., 1951. The charcoal iron industry in the early eighteenth century. *Geogr. J.*, **117**, 167-77.

KRAUSE, J. T., 1958. Changes in English fertility and mortality, 1781-1850. *Econ. Hist. Rev.*, **11**, 52-70.

LAWTON, R., 1954. The economic geography of Craven in the early nineteenth century. *Trans. Inst. Brit. Geogrs.*, **20**, 93-111.

— 1955. The Population of Liverpool in the mid-nineteenth century. *Trans. Hist. Soc. Lancs. Chesh.*, **107**, 89-120.

— 1959. Irish immigration to England and Wales in the mid-nineteenth century. *Irish Geogr.*, **4**, 35-54.

MITCHELL, J. B., 1954. *Historical Geography*.

MOTT, R. A., 1961. Abraham Darby (I and II) and the coal-iron industry. *Trans. Newcomen Soc.*, **31**, 49-93.

MUSSON, A. E., 1957. James Nasmyth and the early growth of mechanical engineering. *Econ. Hist. Rev.*, **10**, 121-27.

— 1959. The Great Depression, 1873-1896; a re-appraisal. *J. Econ. Hist.*, **19**, 199-228.

MUSSON, A. E., and ROBINSON, E., 1959. The early growth of steam Power. *Econ. Hist. Rev.*, **11**, 418-39.

NIXON, F., 1961. The early steam engine in Derbyshire. *Trans. Newcomen Soc.*, **31**, 1-28.

PRYDE, G., 1961. *Scotland from 1603 to the Present Day*.

ROBINSON, E. A. G., 1954. The changing structure of the British economy. *Advanc. Sci.*, **11**, 182-93.

ROEPKE, H. G., 1956. *Movements of the British Iron and Steel Industry, 1720-1951*.

ROSTOW, W. W., 1960. *The Stages of Economic Growth*.

SAVILLE, J., 1957. *Rural Depopulation in England and Wales, 1851-1951*.

SCRIVENOR, H., 1854. *A Comprehensive History of the Iron Trade*.

SMILES, S., 1861-2. *Lives of the Engineers*.

SMITH, D. M., 1962. The cotton industry in the east Midlands. *Geography*, **47**, 256-69.

SMITH, W., 1949. *An Economic Geography of Great Britain*.

SMITH, W. (Ed.), 1953. *Merseyside: a Scientific Survey*.

TURNER, W. H. K., 1952. The evolution of the pattern of the textile industry within Dundee. *Trans. Inst. Brit. Geogrs.*, **18**, 107-119.

— 1953. Some eighteenth century developments in the textile region of east central Scotland. *Scot. Geogr. Mag.*, **69**, 10-22.

WEBER, A. F., 1896. *The Growth of Cities in the Nineteenth Century*.

WILLAN, T. S., 1936. *River Navigation in England, 1600-1750*.

WISE, M. J. (Ed.), 1950. *Birmingham and its Regional Setting;* chapters on the Industrial Revolution.

13

SOME PROBLEMS OF LAND USE

WITH the success of the industrial revolution, the growth of population, and the enjoyment of a high standard of living in the British Isles, problems of land use inevitably arose, as the demand for land pressed upon supply. The land available within the British Isles provides, for all purposes, only 1·4 acres (0·6 ha.) of land per head of population compared with 3 acres (1·2 ha.) in France, 13 acres (5 ha.) in the United States, and 25 acres (10 ha.) in the Soviet Union. Moreover, the achievement of a balance at once socially and economically acceptable, between the distribution of population and land, is complicated by the great variety of land types and by the marked regional differences in their use and in the demand for them.

Variations in the intensity of use and in competition for land are particularly related to the progressive concentration of population in urban-industrial and commercial areas, notably within Great Britain. This process of localisation is continuing, though its effects and their distribution are changing and presenting new problems.

The land and its use capacity[1]

Land within the British Isles varies greatly in its capacity and, thus, in the return it provides from a given type of use. This variation is related in part to physical attributes of the land, especially in uses such as forestry and farming. Returns from land also depend on certain institutional controls, such as the manner in which the land is held and the official restrictions that are placed upon its use. They depend further, and in some respects increasingly, on the connection of the land with major centres of population and economic activity, and major lines of communication.

Types of land. The physical diversity of the land within the British Isles, as indicated by its generalised soil groups, is shown in Figure 35. Soils are here treated in terms of their characteristic association with major types of terrain.

[1] The use capacity of the land refers to its ability, in all respects, to provide a net return above the production costs arising from its use.

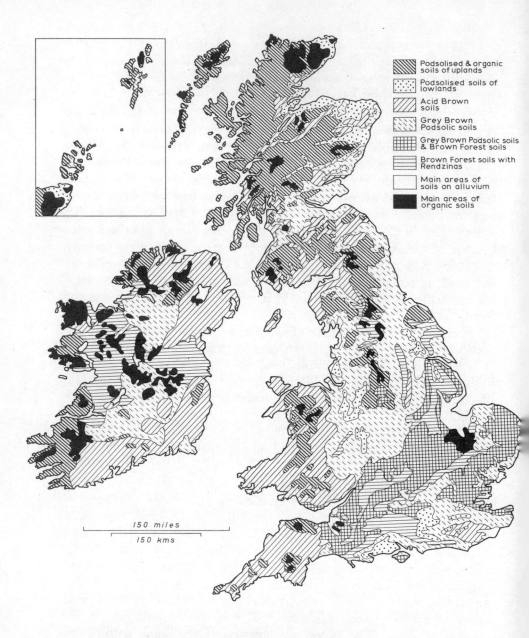

Legend:

- Podsolised & organic soils of uplands
- Podsolised soils of lowlands
- Acid Brown soils
- Grey Brown Podsolic soils
- Grey Brown Podsolic soils & Brown Forest soils
- Brown Forest soils with Rendzinas
- Main areas of soils on alluvium
- Main areas of organic soils

150 miles
150 kms

Fig. 35. GENERALISED SOIL TYPES. Adapted from a soil map of the British Isles, prepared by D. A. Osmond for F.A.O., a schematic soil map of Ireland, prepared by P. Ryan, and the Ordnance Survey map of peat bogs in Ireland.

Lowland soils are largely restricted to England and Ireland. They are associated with gradients that vary from the flat or gently-sloping surfaces of alluvial and fen areas to the more accidented drumlin or scarpland country. Gradients are, however, seldom prohibitive for farming or other uses.

Acid Brown soils occupying lowland sites occur principally in Ireland and in the wetter western parts of Great Britain; here they are mainly devoted to farming, though commonly at a lower intensity in Ireland. Podsolised soils in northeastern Scotland support important farming areas; elsewhere, notably in eastern and southeastern England, such soils are most typically associated with free-draining siliceous parent materials and are often given over to forestry, to recreation, or to military uses.

The more productive Grey-Brown Podsolic soils and Brown Forest soils occupy the greater part of the lowlands in both Ireland and Great Britain. They provide the most extensive areas of good agricultural land, and their capacity to support a more intensive use through the increased employment of fertilisers and machinery has done much to raise farm output and thus to offset losses of land to building and related purposes. The agricultural significance of the Brown Forest soils and Rendzinas, associated with chalk and limestone areas, has also increased through improvements in farming technique, particularly on the chalk downlands of England.

The most extensive areas of alluvial soils are on the margins of the English lowlands; in the Fenland they are juxtaposed with mild organic (fen) soils. Both kinds of soil support some of the most productive pastures and intensive cropland in Britain. In Ireland and Scotland the lowland organic soils are acid and are principally associated with raised bog and blanket bog. Attention is being given to the reclamation of bog land for agriculture or forestry.

Soils of the *intermediate lands* are associated principally with dissected plateau and hill country, at heights of roughly 250-800 ft. (80-250 m.) on the margins of the upland areas. Slope conditions here vary considerably and both directly and through their influence on the soil have an important effect on land use. Higher precipitation than on the lowlands and the frequently siliceous nature of the soil parent materials have given rise to the widespread development of Acid Brown soils, with podsolised soils and organic soils occurring locally. Despite their limitations, the Acid Brown soils are largely devoted to farming, in the absence of any strong competition from other uses.

The soils of the *uplands* reflect strongly the influence of climate.

247

High humidity and rainfall are largely responsible for the widespread development of podsolised and organic soils. These soils are particularly extensive in Scotland; farther south where the leaching is less extreme, as in some parts of Ireland and Wales, Acid Brown soils are more characteristic and have a higher capacity for both farming and forestry. Formerly, much of the upland was forested to a height of 1,500-2,000 ft. (450-600 m.) but it is now largely covered with biotic sub-climax vegetation of acidic grasses, sedges, and heather (with bog occupying the wetter sites). In general such land can be most profitably exploited by extensive and, where possible, multi-purpose uses. The difficulties in the way of achieving such utilisation present an important land-use problem in the British Isles.

Institutional controls. Apart from political measures, institutional controls find expression both in the attitudes of those who decide how land is used and in the way in which land is held.

Attitudes towards the use of land vary greatly from, for example, the paternal and possessive concern of an ageing Scottish crofter to the exploitive and detached view of a purely commercially-minded developer in metropolitan England. Similarly, the manner in which the land is held may range from that of an Irish peasant's small-holding, which is seldom put up for sale, through the common grazings of upland Wales, where use and ownership are divorced, to that of the estate, of perhaps a commercial organisation in London, which is withheld from the market only so long as it produces an appropriate return or shows a satisfactory appreciation in value. The form in which the land is held, in particular the size and disposition of its component parcels, also materially affects the way in which it is used. This is a matter of substantial concern and Denman (1958, p. 123) has urged an understanding of what '. . . the honey-comb of estates in land means for national planning . . .' He implies the dangers of an excessively abstract and mechanistic approach to land-use planning.

Location of the land. Much of the geographical order that is imparted to the arrangement of land uses (Fig. 36) is attributable to location. Thus, from a physical and, to some extent, an institutional standpoint, the greater part of the lowlands of the British Isles (in some instances only as a result of improved drainage) is suitable for the most intensive or most profitable uses, such as commerce and manufacture. Yet, such uses are highly localised in their distribution with reference to the pull of former or existing centres and arteries of economic activity and development. These are most

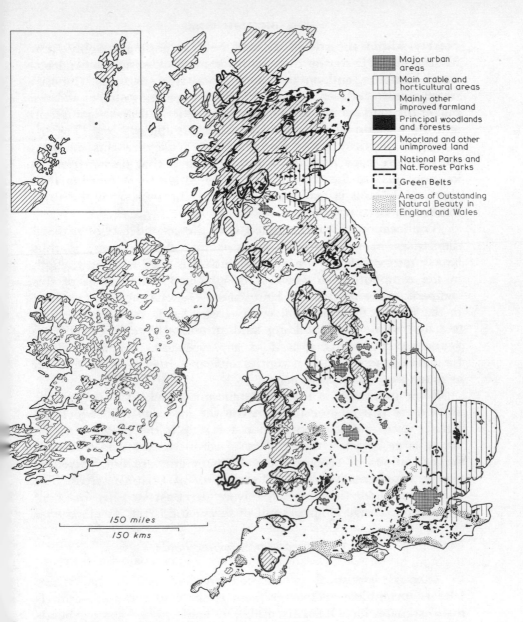

	Major urban areas
	Main arable and horticultural areas
	Mainly other improved farmland
	Principal woodlands and forests
	Moorland and other unimproved land
	National Parks and Nat. Forest Parks
	Green Belts
	Areas of Outstanding Natural Beauty in England and Wales

150 miles
150 kms

Fig. 36.   LAND USE AND PROTECTED LAND. Sources: Forestry Commission, Land Utilisation Survey, Ministry of Housing and Local Government, Ordnance Survey, Scottish Development Department. National Parks in Scotland are proposed and not statutory Parks. National Forest Parks are marked only where they lie outside National Parks; no boundary is shown for the Forest of Dean Forest Park. The Green Belts and Areas of Outstanding Natural Beauty shown include both statutory areas and those under consideration.

notably within the so-called 'axial belt' extending roughly from Merseyside to Dover, at the major ports and other accessible deep-water harbours, and on the more productive coalfields. Concentrated residential uses necessarily follow a similar pattern, and the pull of the markets so provided is exhibited in both the organisation and the location of the more intensive farming systems. The intensity of horticulture in London's Lea Valley reflects, in part, the high use capacity and value of the land that derive from its location; just as the comparatively low intensity of farming over much of Ireland is explicable partly by distance from the main markets in Britain.

The location of land, coupled with the related fact of regional differences in the intensity of economic development, is thus largely responsible for the way in which it is used and the strength of the competition to which it is subjected. The effects of this competition are revealed by land values. General purpose farmland in the English Midlands will often change hands for £250 per acre (0·4 ha.), while good building land around a large city may fetch £10,000–20,000 per acre; land of any type that becomes available for development within a central city area may well be sold for as much as £250,000 per acre.

Some indication of these differences is provided by Figure 36, since there is a relationship between the intensity with which the land is used and the competition for it. But the patterns shown are in large measure the product of competitive forces related to earlier periods of economic development and are not, therefore, always representative of the distribution of existing forces. The current situation is more effectively demonstrated by maps of population change (Fig. 44) and of recent industrial developments.

Competing uses for the land

Although statistical information on land use in the British Isles is incomplete and varies from country to country, approximate estimates have been assembled in Table 11 and some generalised distributions are shown in Figure 36.

Land for building purposes. Persistent demands for land for building and associated uses have been generated by the growth of population, by its increasing affluence and mobility, and by its progressive concentration, together with the manufacturing and service industries that provide employment, in certain parts of the British Isles. Between 1951 and 1961 the population increased by

**Table 11. Approximate extent of major land uses
within the British Isles, 1960**

	England	Wales	Scotland	Northern Ireland	Eire	British Isles
Acreage (000 acres)[1]						
Urban Land[2] acres	3,800	200	510	120	240	4,870
hectares	1,520	80	205	50	95	1,950
Forest Land ,,	2,100	460	1,610	80	420	4,670
	840	185	645	30	170	1,870
Improved Farmland ,,	21,790	2,610	4,310	1,940	11,270	41,980
	8,715	1,045	1,725	775	4,510	16,770
Unimproved Farmland ,,	3,290	1,670	11,000[3]	790	3,000[4]	19,830
	1,320	670	4,440	315	1,200	7,900
Other Land[5] ,,	1,060	160	1,640	420	2,090	5,400
	425	65	655	170	835	2,150
Total Land Area ,,	32,040	5,100	19,070	3,350	17,020	76,750
	12,820	2,040	7,630	1,340	6,810	30,640
Percentage						
Urban Land	11.8	3.9	2.7	3.6	1.4	6.4
Forest Land	6.5	9.0	8.5	2.4	2.5	6.1
Improved Farmland	68.0	51.1	22.6	57.9	66.2	54.7
Unimproved Land	10.2	32.7	57.6	23.6	17.6	25.8
Other Land	3.3	3.1	8.6	12.6	12.3	7.0
Total	100	100	100	100	100	100

[1] Rounded to nearest 10,000 acres; from official sources unless otherwise stated.
[2] Land under buildings, roads, railways, etc. These are estimates based on figures for 1950 calculated by R. H. Best. The Irish figures have been obtained by assuming the same proportions per thousand population as in Scotland.
[3] Excluding ungrazed deer forest (1958 estimate).
[4] Estimate by M. D. McCarthy, Central Statistics Office.
[5] A residual figure that may include land that ought to be returned under other heads.

4% and, according to the 1961 census, 76% of the population is urban (ranging from 37% in Eire to 80% in England and Wales), though such a figure understates the true position owing to the lag in the extension of the administrative boundaries of urban districts. The effects of this concentration have, however, been modified more recently by a process of dispersion to the periphery of the conurbations and towns. Such dispersion has been accentuated by re-development within the older central portions of the larger towns where population densities have fallen. The effect has been an increase of pressure upon the land available at the periphery of the urban areas; controlling this pressure has provided the outstanding land-use planning problem in the British Isles, especially in Britain.

There are no official data of the extent of land used for building and related purposes, but Best (1959) has estimated the urban area for Great Britain (including roads and railways) at over 7% of the total surface area. This proportion has approximately doubled since the beginning of the present century; and forecasts made on the basis of the local authority development plans suggest that between 1950 and 1970 as many as 700,000 additional acres (280,000 ha.) will be required in England and Wales alone (Wibberley, 1959). The increased demand for extensive sites for power stations, oil refineries, and other large-scale installations, notably on the navigable estuaries (Willatts, 1962), may be expected to add to this figure.

Not all urban land is built over. Best has shown that housing accounts for only 44% in large settlements, while as much as 20% is open space. Moreover, there are great variations in the intensity with which built-over land is used. Prior to the First World War, residential building in towns was often at a density of more than 40 houses per acre (100 per ha.) but the emphasis given to semi-detached and detached housing since 1919 has reduced densities in newer urban areas to 12 houses per acre (30 per ha.) or less. An understanding of these differences is important to any assessment of the social implications of suburban growth. The intensification of use of urban land by erecting multi-storey structures was not common in the British Isles before 1939, when few commercial buildings even in the city centres were higher than six stories and residential blocks seldom exceeded four stories. High building has increased with changes in techniques of construction and planned attempts to economise ground space and to improve the layout of urban developments; yet in residential development the economies of space from building high are not great, and the additional building costs are considerable (Denman, 1958).

Transport uses. The development of a close network of both roads and railways, particularly within Great Britain, has consumed a considerable amount of land. Such uses occupy approximately one million acres in Great Britain alone (Best, 1959) and will increase with the much-needed development of new trunk roads. The construction of M1, the first of a planned series of motorways in England, extending a distance of 70 miles (110 km.) from London to near Birmingham, required some 2,000 acres (800 ha.). The area occupied by airfields is not large, but they demand level, well-drained land that is accessible to major centres of population. London airport alone occupies nearly 3,000 acres (1,200 ha.) of river terrace that was formerly used principally for intensive market gardening. It has also increased the local demand for land for business and residential purposes.

Mineral extraction. The extraction of minerals and related activities represents an important use of the land, especially within Great Britain, and one that presents serious problems of restoration. Derelict land (mainly from mineral working, but including that related to former manufacturing uses) occupies some 150,000 acres (60,000 ha.) in Great Britain (Best, 1959), principally within the older industrial areas. There are extensive areas on the coalfields, and in the salt-mining district of east Cheshire, where subsidence has resulted, particularly from earlier working, and the capacity of the land is much reduced (Wallwork, 1960; James, et al., 1961). Additional areas have been made sterile with colliery and other waste.

The surface working of minerals presents very different problems (Beaver, 1955). At the present time, some 12,000 acres (4,800 ha.) are required annually in England and Wales alone, of which approximately three-quarters is restored for some other use. There are statutory obligations to restore land used for open-cast coal mining and ironstone quarrying, but restoration is not normally practicable when chalk, limestone, and road metal have been extracted from deep quarries, or where low-value minerals are worked in shallow pits. The restoration of sand and gravel pits presents special difficulties (Wooldridge and Beaver, 1950), particularly since their excavation is often followed by flooding. There are numerous disused gravel workings in Great Britain although 'dry pits' are now normally restored immediately (James, 1958) and increasing use is being made of 'wet pits' for waste disposal and recreational purposes.

In the Irish Republic, particular attention has been given to the large-scale exploitation of peat which is estimated to occupy roughly three million acres (1,200,000 ha.). A statutory corporation, Bord na Móna, has been established for the purpose and is concerned particularly with producing fuel for peat-fired power stations.

Farmland. Despite the substantial decrease in the importance of farming as an employer of labour and the sizeable loss of land to other uses, it still occupies 81% of the total area of the British Isles. There are, however, substantial variations in the intensity with which the land is farmed. Unimproved land, consisting mainly of upland moors and of lowland bog and heath, accounts for 32% of all farmland. In addition, part of the land that is recorded by farmers as being improved, under the heading of permanent grass-land, does not differ greatly in its feeding capacity from rough grazings, so that extensive grazing probably accounts for nearly half the farmland in the British Isles. In 1953 the hills and uplands were contributing only about 4% of the gross agricultural output of Great Britain (Davidson and Wibberley, 1956). On the basis of limited data available for Ireland, it seems doubtful whether the proportion for the British Isles as a whole is any higher.

The greater part of the agricultural output of the British Isles comes, therefore, from little more than half the farmland. Within the United Kingdom, this output is provided by only 4% of the working population and contributes about 50% of the country's food requirements, although a proportion of this is derived in-directly from other lands through the use of imported feeding stuffs. In Eire, the equivalent proportions are respectively 38% and 75%. This most productive part of the farmland is distributed principally over the lowlands and the more favoured portions of the dissected plateaux and lower upland slopes. Yet even within this improved land there are striking differences in the intensity of use. The highest intensity is found in the market gardening areas of the Fens and elsewhere, which provide a gross output of £200 or more per acre and justify a substantial use of both capital and labour. On land of low capacity, such as the poor clays of parts of the Weald, the gross output may well be less than £40 per acre, and in parts of Ireland it is less than £30. In general, the major regional differences in the intensity of use of farmland in the British Isles, especially in Great Britain, are tending to be exaggerated at the present time. This situation arises largely from the search for increased productivity and lower unit costs and the greater possibility of their achievement through investment at the intensive rather than the extensive margin.

This primary concern of farming with the lower lands of more favourable gradients and drainage has necessarily brought it into conflict with the increasing demands made by other competitors, notably residential, industrial, and commercial development. Be-tween 1900 and 1950, 7% of the total agricultural land of Great

Britain was lost to other major uses, much of it being land of high agricultural capacity in the Midlands and south of England (Best, 1959). In both Northern Ireland and the Irish Republic, the loss has been substantially less. The competitive pressure on farmland in Great Britain will increase; and it has been estimated that in the second half of the present century a further two to three million acres (0·8-1·2m. ha.) mainly of better quality land, will be lost to agriculture in Great Britain. Nevertheless, in the twenty years since the late 1930s net agricultural output rose by 60%, and there remains considerable scope for further intensification in the use of farmland. Wibberley (1959) suggested that an increase of $2\frac{1}{2}\%$ in agricultural productivity every ten years will compensate for the expected loss of farmland during the present century.

Forest land. Although the greater part of the British Isles has a climate suitable for the growth of trees, only about 7% of Great Britain is at present occupied by forests and woodland, and in Ireland only $2\frac{1}{2}\%$. Dependence on timber from overseas is, therefore, considerable, over 85% of that used being imported.

Woodland is widely distributed in Great Britain, only the high uplands, the exposed western coasts, parts of the low-lying clays, and the bog, fen, and alluvium being entirely without. In Britain, some two-thirds of the acreage is privately owned and consists largely of broadleaved trees; in Ireland, there is very little private woodland. State programmes of afforestation are principally concerned with planting conifers on poorer land in the uplands; in the United Kingdom a target of 5,150,000 acres (2,100,000 ha.) of productive woodland has been proposed, while in Eire it has been suggested that a million acres (400,000 ha.) could be afforested in the national interest. The progress of planting has, however, been hindered by difficulties of acquiring suitable land, most of which is in use for rough grazing; state forestry must generally yield to the agricultural interest and also to objections on amenity grounds. Nevertheless, since 1947 the acreage of woodland in Great Britain has increased by well over one eighth and the productive area has been more than doubled; in recent years, private land owners have become interested in afforestation, encouraged by planting grants and tax reliefs. In Ireland the woodland area has doubled since 1945.

Interesting data on the competitive strength of forestry for land in Britain has been provided by the Natural Resources (Technical) Committee (1957). Its findings suggest that on marginal farmland in the uplands, forestry is capable of providing a slightly greater return on capital, and that on light soils in the lowlands there is little difference in the returns from farming and forestry, provided that agriculture does not require investment in improved buildings.

Recreation and other uses. Among the other uses of land within the British Isles, particular importance attaches to recreation, to the gathering and storage of water, and to uses for military purposes, all of which are commonly not exclusive in their demands.

Large areas, particularly in the uplands, are used for both private and public recreation. In Scotland nearly a fifth of the rough grazings is also used for deer shooting, while there are some $1\frac{1}{2}$ million acres (600,000 ha.) of ungrazed deer forests; extensive areas, mainly of heather moor, also provide grouse shooting. Although there are few areas where the public has legal rights of access, much of the uplands is also used for walking and climbing. Nevertheless, the growth of large towns has emphasised the need for public open spaces and for access as of right, and this is being partly met by both private and statutory organisations. The National Trust for England, Wales, and Northern Ireland, an independent body founded in 1895, now administers over 250,000 acres (100,000 ha.), ranging from landscaped parks and small patches of woodland to large stretches of moorland. The National Trust for Scotland exercises similar responsibility for over 70,000 acres (28,000 ha.), while in the Irish Republic a National Trust has been recently founded. The National Parks Commission (now the Countryside Commission) has a duty to promote public access in the ten National Parks in England and Wales (Fig. 36); it also exercises general oversight on all questions of amenity in England and Wales, including the designation of Areas of Outstanding Natural Beauty. Proposals for the setting up of National Parks have also been made in Scotland, and development in the areas suggested is more strictly controlled than elsewhere. In Great Britain, the Forestry Commission has established a number of National Forest Parks in which facilities are provided for recreation, including camping; a small Forest Park has also been created in Northern Ireland. Purely recreational uses are largely confined to playing fields and golf courses; in the United Kingdom, the National Playing Fields Association is active in promoting the extension of public playing fields.

Many of the functions of the National Parks Commission relate to conservation. The National Trust and the Ministry of Works are directly concerned with the preservation of buildings and other items of historic interest. Likewise, the Nature Conservancy, founded in 1949, is authorised '. . . to provide scientific advice on the conservation and control of the natural fauna and flora of Great Britain, including the maintenance of physical features of scientific interest'. The Conservancy designates Nature Reserves and also Sites of Special Scientific Interest.

Many of the gathering areas for water, both for water supply and power generation, are in the uplands and provide suitable sites for afforestation, although only some 3% of the half million acres (200,000 ha.) used for water supply in Great Britain is under trees. Where the water is intended for consumption, certain controls are necessary on agricultural uses, and although an official report (Gathering Grounds, 1948) suggests that these need not always be too restrictive, large areas are used only for sheep grazing. Recreational uses, except possibly fishing and walking, are generally unacceptable.

Military uses of land in the United Kingdom have been declining and now occupy about 900,000 acres (370,000 ha.). Of this land over half is probably used for training purposes, principally on certain heaths, downs, and moors in England and Wales. Such use is often intermittent only and at other times grazing and even cultivation are possible. In Eire the extent of military land is quite small.

Problem areas and planning policies

Planning legislation relating to the use of the land developed in a largely *ad hoc* manner and has, therefore, proceeded furthest in Great Britain where the need has been most pressing. In Northern Ireland, the basic legislation bringing all land under planning regulation was passed in 1944; but only outline plans are at present in preparation and control is, therefore, of an interim nature. In the Irish Republic control is permissive under the Town and Regional Planning Acts of 1934 and 1939.

In Great Britain, the first planning measures were enacted as early as 1909 and were greatly strengthened after the First World War. Their effectiveness was, however, limited by the absence of adequate measures of control and by unsatisfactory provision for compensation to landowners whose property was required for planned development. In the late 1930s and early 1940s, three official bodies were set up to enquire into the basic problems relating to land use and planning. In 1940 the Barlow Commission advocated the establishment of a national planning authority to achieve, among other things, a more satisfactory geographical distribution of industrial employment. In 1942 the Scott Report stressed the need to conserve good agricultural land and rural amenities and also indicated the need for a central planning authority. In the same year the Uthwatt Committee went even further in arguing for the establishment of fully-effective machinery with which to implement land-use planning.

There followed a series of enactments, which culminated in the Town and Country Planning Acts of 1947. These provide the basis of existing planning in Great Britain under which local authorities are required to prepare development plans. The plans are made available for public scrutiny and are submitted for approval to the Minister of Housing and Local Government or Secretary of State for Scotland. Such approval is subject to the satisfactory conclusion of any necessary public enquiries, but once it is given the development proposals cannot be readily challenged. They are, however, intended to be revised every five years, and then require the same process for their approval.

Other planning legislation enacted during the post-war period includes measures relating to controlling the distribution of industry, creating National Parks, establishing New Towns, and restoring land after mineral extraction. In addition, some achievements have been made, both directly and indirectly, through fiscal measures, such as subsidies for encouraging hill farming, tax relief on private forestry, and support to industry in areas of economic difficulty. Government exhortation and persuasion, the pressure of public opinion, and routine consultations and co-operation between government departments have also contributed to a more rational and controlled approach to the use of the land.

It is important to recognise that fully-effective planning in Great Britain is largely confined to land involved in building development, to the location of medium and large-scale manufacturing industry, to mineral working, and to conservation. Neither forest land nor agricultural land is subject to development control; nor are the land-using activities of government departments. In addition, there is much land which, because of the manner in which it is held, is both beyond control and effectively insulated from competition; the land held by the Crown is a good example. Likewise, the use of common land in England and Wales, or of land in multiple ownership or occupation in Scotland and Ireland, cannot easily be changed. Nevertheless, planning legislation has made possible progress in dealing with the land-use problems presented by certain areas of the British Isles.

Conurbations and the axial belt. It has been suggested that the most critical problems of land use have arisen from the continuing concentration of population in certain restricted parts of the British Isles which possess the greatest comparative advantage for economic development. These are most notably the conurbations and larger individual towns of the lowlands of England, Wales, and Scotland, with special importance attaching to the region between London and Liverpool known as the axial belt.

The Barlow Commission was concerned with the general problem of concentration within Great Britain. Its more serious regional manifestations were studied by the West Midland Planning Group, and by Sir Patrick Abercrombie and his associates who formulated the Greater London Plan (1944). The Abercrombie proposals for London were of particular importance; they developed the notion of restricting the growth of conurbations and cities by circumscribing them with 'green belts' within which development would be limited; they also advocated the establishment of new towns beyond the green belts to absorb population from the city centres and to focus peripheral growth.

Green belts have been established around Greater London and four Scottish towns and similar belts have been provisionally agreed around other major concentrations of population (Fig. 36). London's green belt, though subject to increasing pressure, has been well maintained; but the strength of the continued pressure for growth has resulted in sharply-rising land values within the urban area, and has created problems within the urban peripheries that have not altogether been solved by the successful creation of New and Expanded Towns and by related measures (Powell, 1960). These problems point urgently to the need for a broader view of planning in Britain that will provide for the controlled growth of cities and city regions within a regional framework and pay due regard to the need for, and location of, improved road systems.

Coastal areas. The coastal areas of Great Britain are also subject to increasing competition for space, both for holiday and residential purposes, and for industrial development. The demand for holiday accommodation has grown rapidly with the now general provision of holidays with pay, improved standards of living, and increased family mobility. The demand for camping and caravan sites is especially striking and has raised serious problems of the preservation of coastal scenery and amenity. Residential development at the coast, particularly in southeast England, has also placed a heavy demand upon the land in localities readily accessible from London and other major centres.

The important recent industrial developments at coastal locations, notably on major estuaries, have in some instances also raised serious questions of amenity and conservation and point to the importance of co-ordination in land-use planning in the British Isles.

Depressed industrial areas. The loss of economic strength and the declining population that typify some of the older industrial areas of Great Britain have produced a situation of insufficient land competition. Here, therefore, the problem is whether the restoration of derelict land, the replacement of sub-standard housing and the provision of adequate amenities are justified. On economic grounds, the case for so doing is often weak, though there are strong social and political pressures for rehabilitation.

Poorly-developed rural areas. In upland areas that are not too remote there are competing uses of low intensity that often cannot individually provide an adequate return on capital but which are potentially compatible, given an appropriate multiple-use system of development. Such a system offers the greatest promise of a sufficient return on investment and thus of attracting such investment. Extensive farming, principally grazing, must be supported and where necessary replaced by a fuller development of forestry, improved water control and storage, and facilities for public recreation. As the mobility of the population increases, and as improved roads are provided from the expanding city regions, the demand made on such areas for recreation and tourism may be expected to increase substantially.

The more remote rural areas present a very different problem. Their economies are largely dependent on farming and experience no great competition for the land from alternative uses. They also suffer from the generally small size of farm holdings, frequent complications of tenure or of multiple ownership, the high average age of the population, and severe limitations in capital provision, management, and marketing. The areas involved, which include much of rural Ireland, particularly its western portions, and northern Scotland and the Isles, are poorly developed compared with the rest of the British Isles and have long been losing population. Some attempt is being made to meet their difficulties by the introduction or strengthening of alternative uses of the land, including small-scale manufacturing, forestry, and tourism, and also by agricultural

improvement. But the essential problem is one of transport provision and transport costs.

Conclusions

The problems presented by existing uses of land and the differing degrees of competition to which the land is subjected are by
no means peculiar to the British Isles. They arise in many instances
from regional differences in the level and strength of economic
development and because these differences tend to be exaggerated
rather than reduced with time. A recognition of this appears, however, to be vital to a proper understanding of the measures necessary
for the successful planning of land use. Hitherto such planning has
been necessarily somewhat experimental and piecemeal; it has also
tended to be restrictive in its conception, and generally localised
in its application. In particular, the growth of conurbations in
Great Britain has been constrained without perhaps sufficient
regard for the relevance, indeed necessity, of such growth to the
effective economic development of the United Kingdom as a whole.
The problems that the conurbations present, especially those of
the Midlands and Greater London, must be viewed more broadly
than in terms of urban sprawl, loss of farmland and rural amenity,
and conflict between economic and social values. Effective planning
must continuously recognise the need for growth through the most
intensive use of the land in those areas that currently enjoy the
greatest comparative advantage. It must also seek positive means
of achieving a geographically more equitable distribution of
economic advantages. This can be satisfactorily attained only by
regional, national and even supra-national approaches to planning.
Such planning would of necessity take note of the fact that, at its
greatest, the distance between the economically-favoured and less-
favoured parts of the British Isles is comparatively small and capable
of being bridged by rapid and substantial improvements in the
provision of roads and ferries. Such provision would not only greatly
reduce the economic handicaps of many areas, but would also lessen
the pressure at the intensive margin of land use, the breadth of
which, at least in England, is now unduly restricted.

The emphasis given to the economic aspects of land-use planning
need not and should not, at the present stage of planning in Britain,
imply a neglect of social values. Indeed, in many respects, the
economic and social considerations are inextricably linked. This is
particularly so in regard to the likely effects of the improvements

that have been urged in the provision of transport facilities. As has been noted, such improvements would do much to ensure a more balanced geographical distribution of economic growth and would, at the same time, greatly enhance the attractions of rural and small-town living. They would, likewise, not only reduce the pressure to grow that characterises some of the conurbations, but would also provide for those who live in them speedy access to open spaces that are now relatively inaccessible for brief visits, such as much of the uplands of Great Britain and the greater part of Ireland.

References

ABERCROMBIE, P., 1944. *Greater London Plan*. H.M.S.O., London.
BEAVER, S. H., 1955. Land reclamation after surface mineral workings. *J. Tn. Plann. Inst.*, **41**, 146-54.
BEST, R. H., 1959. The Major Land Uses of Great Britain. *Stud. Rur. Land Use*, **4**, Wye College.
DAVIDSON, B. R., and WIBBERLEY, G. P., 1956. The agricultural significance of the hills, *Stud. Rur. Land Use*, **3**, Wye College.
DENMAN, D. R. (Ed.), 1958. *Land Ownership and Resources*. Cambridge.
JAMES, J. R., 1958. Land planning in an expanding economy. *J. Roy. Soc. Arts.*, **106**, 589-604.
JAMES, J. R., SCOTT, S. F., and WILLATTS, E. C., 1961. Land use and the changing power industry in England and Wales. *Geogr. J.*, **127**, 286-309.
POWELL, A. G., 1960. The recent development of Greater London. *Advanc. Sci.*, **17**, 76-86.
Report of the Royal Commission on the Distribution of the Industrial Population (Barlow Report), 1940. *Cmd.* 6153, H.M.S.O., London.
Report of the Committee on Land Utilisation in Rural Areas (Scott Report), 1942. *Cmd.* 6378, H.M.S.O., London.
Report of the Expert Committee on Compensation and Betterment (Uthwatt Report), 1942. *Cmd.* 6386, H.M.S.O., London.
Report of the Natural Resources (Technical) Committee, 1957. *Forestry, agriculture and marginal land*. H.M.S.O., London.
STAMP, L. D., 1962. *The land of Britain—its use and misuse*. 3rd Ed., London.
SYMONS, L. (Ed.), 1963. *Land use in Northern Ireland*. London.
WALLWORK, K. L., 1960. Land-use problems and the evolution of industrial landscapes. *Geography*, **45**, 263-75.
West Midland Group, 1948. *Conurbation: a planning survey of Birmingham and the Black Country*. London.
WIBBERLEY, G. P., 1959. *Agriculture and Urban Growth*. London.
WILLATTS, E. C., 1962. Post-war developments. The location of major projects in England and Wales. *Chart. Surv.*, **94**, 356-63.
WOOLDRIDGE, S. W., and BEAVER, S. H., 1950. The working of sand and gravel in Britain—a problem in land use. *Geogr. J.*, **115**, 42-57.
WRIGHT, H. M., 1961. *Land use in an urban environment*. Liverpool.

14

AGRICULTURE AND FISHERIES

Facts and figures

IN spite of the overwhelmingly urban population, agricultural activity dominates the human landscape of the British Isles, and farm output is a primary national concern. About two-thirds (c. 31 m. acres, c. 12 m. ha.) of the United Kingdom is under crops and grass: Eire has 11·6 m. acres (4·4 m. ha.). For farming purposes this is divided into 387,000 holdings and 314,000 holdings (over 1 acre, 0·4 ha.) respectively. In Great Britain some 875,000 are employed in agriculture and horticulture (but their minority status in the employment structure is evident when it is observed that national and local government employees number half as many again). In Eire, farmers constitute about half of the labour force (independently of their wives who may be an important element on the farm): in Ulster, about a quarter of the employed males work on farms. Farming is one of the most heavily underwritten and one of the most carefully-protected sectors in the economy.

Facts and figures about agriculture have concerned the islanders since the days when John Bull became a national figure. The French Wars, the dismal prognostications of Thomas Malthus, the progressive founders of the Board of Agriculture (1795), and the example of the Statistical Survey of Scotland prompted an experimental survey of the agricultural resources of England and Wales in 1801 (Henderson, 1952). But despite Irish returns in 1847 and those undertaken by the Highland and Agricultural Society of Scotland in 1854, a precise collection of farm statistics for England and Wales was resisted until 1866 (Coppock, 1956). British farmland is not directly taxed so that land records of a public character are not available. A Land Register, initiated in 1925, only lists a minority of properties; but there are cartographic records of land which was still titheable in the 1840s. *The Farm Survey of England and Wales* of 1941-3 was the first thorough-going enquiry into land holding; but only a brief summary of it has been published. Land ownership and facts appertaining to it remain largely confidential. An annual return, comprising 148 items, is required on 4 June for all agricultural holdings of more than one acre. Irish agricultural statistics are taken annually on 1 June. Accordingly, basic facts are not uniform for the British Isles as a whole.

The British attitude to farm statistics and records has been in keeping with a traditionally *ad hoc* approach to farming enterprise and it accords with a system of agricultural education and research hitherto characterised by extemporisation. Yet this situation has bred plenty of privately-initiated schemes that have become renowned public institutions, e.g. John Lawes's Rothamsted farm, Wye College (Hall, 1913), the Royal Agricultural College at Cirencester, and Harpur Adams College in Shropshire. Such institutions have done much to counteract the pragmatic approach and to promote a more responsible attitude to agricultural education. State investment in agricultural research is now reflected in a multitude of experimental farms, the discoveries of which are behind many of the effects the geographer seeks to interpret.

There have been many interpretations of the British farming scene since Arthur Young and William Cobbett undertook their pilgrimages. The contemporary topographer will be struck by the persistent diversity of farm enterprise, the overriding importance of animal husbandry, the complexities of organisation, and the effects of national policy in modifying the course of development. And on his journeys, regularly confronted by the sea, he will be mindful of the ministerial marriage of convenience that in England and Wales places the harvest of the sea under the same cabinet office as that of the land.

The diversity of British agriculture

Diversity is the outstanding characteristic of agriculture in the British Isles. It is made possible by an oceanic climate, by the considerable variations in local climate resulting from differences in altitude, and by immensely varied rocks and soils. Diversity of stock and crop is matched by variety in farm type and form. The antiquity of settled husbandry has contributed its own legacy to the farm scene, while farm practice is inseparable from regional variations in social and technical evolution. Differences in the inherent qualities of land and climate are therefore complemented by great variations in size and structure of operating units. In addition, there can be few temperate latitude farmlands where juxtaposition of archaic practices and contemporary techniques is more pronounced.

The range of climatic opportunity may be measured by com-

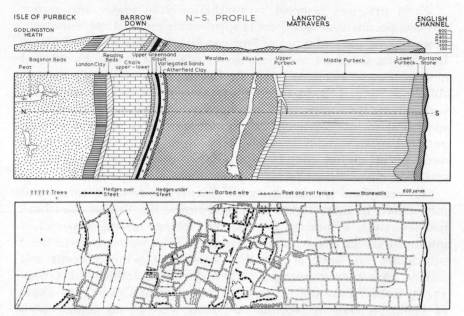

ISLE OF PURBECK BARROW N—S. PROFILE LANGTON ENGLISH
        DOWN   MATRAVERS   CHANNEL

GODLINGSTON
HEATH

Fig. 37.   TRANSVERSE SECTION THROUGH A PART OF DORSET: showing the close correlation between dry stone walls and limestone bedrock, the flourishing hedgerows in the clay vale and the barbed wire fencing which predominates on the thin soils of the chalk down-lands.

paring the farming of southwest Cornwall, the extreme growth conditions of which are reflected by the 'tropical gardens' of Tresco, with those of northeastern Scotland, where the number of frost-free days around Perth may be 70-80 less and the temperature range twice as great; or by comparing the humidity, precipitation, and cloudiness which conspire to foster the bogs of Eire or the saturated margins of Lough Neagh, with the light precipitation and drying winds that exaggerate the aridity of East Anglia.

The British Isles display a range of soil quality, mechanically and chemically. It is expressed visually in the rusty red soils of the Oolites, the milk-chocolate colours of the Shropshire Triassics, the creamy white of the dry chalk benchlands, or the nigger brown of Fenland peat. It may be detected in the depth of the furrow, felt in resistance to the ploughshare, and heard in the epithets applied to tenacious Midland clays or hungry Breckland sands. Stoniness is not uncommon: most chalk dip-slopes have their affliction of flints, disintegrating limestone gives rise to the distinctive brashy Cotswold soils, and the boulders of glacial plains such as those of the Solway lowlands may be abundant enough to permit construction of field boundaries.

Farm practices respond sympathetically to major and minor physical peculiarities and there is appreciable regional specialisation. Maps of land use and types of farming illustrate this in broad terms. In addition there are many narrower specialisations both old and new that, given available price conditions, reflect relatively favourable local costs. The degree of specialisation changes continuously, with resuscitation generally more apparent than decay. Yet, despite specialisation, exclusiveness in cropping is rare. For economic and personal reasons many crops will be common to areas markedly different in natural condition. Intense intermixture of enterprise and crop characterises farms in most areas (Jones, 1954).

Diversity and specialisation are inseparable from invention and innovation. In more recent historical times, the British Isles have had few rivals as hearths for the transformation and dispersal of improved stocks, crops, and techniques. Improvements have been principally the work of devoted enthusiasts, while precept and fashion have been important in their diffusion. Jethro Tull (1674-1741), Robert Bakewell (1725-95), and Thomas Coke (1754-1842) of Holkham Hall in Norfolk—all men who would concur with Francis Bacon that 'a plough in a field arable would be the most noble and ancient armes'—are outstanding examples of practical leaders whose methods were taken up by yeomen farmers (Fussell, 1947, 1950). A large company estate (cf. the 11,500 cultivated acres (4,650 ha.) of Iveagh estate in Norfolk) or 'hobby' farm (of which Great Britain has 50,000) may still perform the same function.

British invention and innovation were recognised throughout Europe by the mid-eighteenth century, and scientific husbandmen came from many lands to seek ideas. Two generations later, the regional names of improved British stock began to make their impact round the world. The hardier Ayrshire cattle were favoured by higher-latitude dairy-farmers; the more sensitive Jerseys and Guernseys left their Channel Island homes to enrich the milk of kindlier climes; the white-faced Hereford peopled New World rangelands; the hornless Aberdeen Angus 'blackskins' established prestige wherever beef was eaten. Pedigree stock sales, the prices of which have fascinated foreign newspaper editors for at least a century and a half, continue to establish new records.[1] Among regionally-distinctive varieties of sheep, of which there are fully thirty, the long-wooled Leicesters, hardy upland Cheviots (on the 'grass hills') or Scottish Blackface (on the heather), short-fleeced

[1] In 1963 an Aberdeen Angus bull sold for £63,000 at the Perth Sales to an American buyer.

Southdowns and Kent or Romney Marsh, have established world reputations. But there are many lesser-known breeds, such as the speckled Kerry of the Welsh border, that subtly reflect traditional adjustment to locality. Shire names are also recalled in fast-disappearing cart-horses such as the Clydesdale and Suffolk Punch. But the breeding of horses, principally for pleasure, retains a regional flavour—from Welsh cobs and Donegal or Shetland ponies, through race horses that train on chalkland 'gallops' at Newmarket, Newbury, or Goodwood, to hunters that follow the 200 packs of lowland Britain to be strengthened with a regular infusion of fresh blood from the four provinces of Ireland. County names, from Yorkshire whites to 'Wessex' saddlebacks, are attached to pigs; restaurateurs automatically announce turkeys as 'Norfolk' and ducks as 'Aylesbury'. Only the humble donkey, 100,000 strong in Eire, seems to have been omitted in the regional nomenclature of stock which is an integral part of the geography of British farming.

Overseas agriculturalists sought to acquire seeds for crops as well as stock for breeding and ideas about management. Seed material, disseminated throughout the British Isles, was also carried round the world in the wake of imperial expansion. Root crops were especially promoted, the turnip being inseparably associated with Lord Townshend (1774-1838) and the mangel wurzel with Dr John Lettsom (1744-1815). Although roots for fodder aided stock, roots for food were equally important—none more than the potato. Scottish seed potatoes, much concentrated in Ayrshire, are renowned abroad to the extent that a sedentary Lapp farmer may be able to talk with experience of 'King Edward' or 'Great Scot'. The identification of the potato with Ireland, especially with Galway and Donegal, is even more remarkable. The potato continues to be one of the cultural links along the Celtic fringes of Europe (Salaman, 1949). Descendants of tubers which probably first made their original entry to Eire from Iberia, are today returned as seed from Irish harbours. In the U.S. farm census all potatoes that are not 'sweet potatoes' are 'Irish potatoes'. Such a nationally distinguished vegetable naturally overshadows the very important British output of grass seed.

Changes in specialisation are inseparable from changes in demand. Cheese-making has been revived—industrially rather than domestically—to give new status to Cheddar, Cheshire, Gloucester, Caerphilly, Lancashire, Stilton, or Wensleydale cheeses. Horticulture responds with growing concentration upon single varieties of fruit—Victoria plums, Conference pears (which account for more than half of the acreage in Kent, Essex, and Worcestershire), Cox's Orange Pippins. Orchards of culinary apples, cider apples, and cherries (which are increasingly expensive to harvest) diminish. By contrast, the Scottish raspberry growers of Perth and Angus enter the export market with an effectively-delayed high-latitude harvest. Blackcurrants have proved as successful in Hereford and Worcestershire as in East Anglia. New varieties of strawberries may lift yields to 40 cwt. an acre (5,000 kg. per ha.) around Wisbech or extend the harvesting period so that October yields equal those of June in favoured seasons on favoured Kentish farms.

Market garden tracts, picking out climatic advantage (as in Cornwall or the Channel Islands), soil advantage (as in southwest Lancashire or the Sussex coastal plain), or market advantage (as in the Lea valley which claims a quarter of the British area under glasshouses) are matched by horticultural activities as developed as any in the world. The fashion of ornamental gardens, especially during the later eighteenth century, created a demand for flowering trees, shrubs and plants from homoclimes beyond the seas. It was a British enthusiast who purchased the collection of 'The King of Flowers' from the widow of Linnaeus, while private and public botanical gardens from unexpected Warrington to Royal Kew (founded 1759), have stimulated plant assembly, breeding, and dissemination. Surrey may be premier of the horticultural counties; though its nurseries may leave a less-lasting impression than Twyford's floral mile, the rose gardens of Portadown, or the 5,000 acres (2,000 ha.) of bulb fields that add a touch of the Netherlands to the Holland division of Lincolnshire.

The impact of all this upon a people who speak of cabbages in the same breath as kings, has been to encourage a wealth of agricultural lore, a farm vocabulary rich in regional differentiation, an irrepressible interest in phenological observation and a sophisticated annual shop window in the 120 year old Royal Agricultural Show.

A grazing kingdom

In his *Natural History of Selborne* (1788), Gilbert White called the British Isles 'a grazing kingdom'. The most rewarding crop for the greater part of the islands is grass, and their grasslands are very diverse. Semi-natural grasslands include meadows (or 'ings', as they may be identified along the Humber), salt marshes (e.g. along the Essex coasts), downlands, and the widespread grazings of the highland west. The degree of management of grasslands improved from their original estate is also varied. Many of the elaborately-controlled water meadows of Dorset, Hampshire, and Wiltshire that were the rich dairy lands of Thomas Hardy's *Tess of the D'Urbervilles*, are now sedge-infested, with overgrown irrigation channels and derelict sluices. Their neglect, in such a valley as the Frome, contrasts with the ingenious water-management of its tributary streams for the commercial cultivation of watercress.

Much of the British Isles that is under permanent grass has been undisturbed for centuries. A rich natural flora characterises it, though wartime conversion to arable has done much to reduce local displays of wild daffodils (in Worcestershire as well as in 'Wordsworth land') or fritillary lily (in south Oxfordshire). But the purple orchis and cowslip (still favoured for country wine-making) persist, and the buttercup (*Ranunculus spp.*) spreads its pleasing, if unpalatable, cloth of gold in early June to distinguish permanent from temporary grass.

As an element in rotation, temporary grass, including clover, is old established, but it has reached its maximum extent during the last generation. Its long-term yields generally, but not necessarily, exceed those of well-managed permanent grass. Temporary grass, distinguished officially from permanent grass since 1866, is a carefully-selected crop. There are 150-160 British grass species, but only about twenty of the native species are agriculturally significant (Hubbard, 1954). The identification and recommendation of grasses for husbandmen began in earnest with William Curtis, *Practical Observations on British Grasses* (London, 1790). Among principal grasses grown in leys are the indigenous cocksfoot (*Dactylis glomerata*) and perennial rye grass (*Lolium perenne*), Italian rye grass introduced in 1833 and Timothy (*Phleum pratense*) imported from New York State 200 years ago. From Aberystwyth and through the initiative of W. Davies and Sir George Stapledon, the first significant pasture surveys of Britain were made; at such centres as Jealot's Hill and Hurley there is regular experiment with seeding, fertilising, draining, and grazing practices.

Although much British and Irish stock remains out of doors throughout the year, winter keep is only sufficient to provide for a proportion of its sustenance. There is a continuous search for winter-hardy grasses and legumes (lucernes, sainfoin, beans, and vetches). Haymaking remains the principal way of conserving fodder, and mechanisation has introduced a new 'timeliness' to it. Tractors, tedders, and balers, replacing picturesque but arduous field opera-

tions that were especially sensitive to sunshine and shower, substantially reduce the risk of loss. The stock farmer is also being
won over to ensilage. Grass-drying machines are uneconomic save
for the largest holdings; their pellets are a civilisation away from the
seaweed that is still fed as a supplementary fodder along the maritime fringes of the west.

The purpose of grass farming is to produce stock and animal
products. Stock is ubiquitous in almost all types of farming region;
but some broad generalisations may be made about the British Isles'
increasing herd of 16 million cattle and diminishing flock of 29
million sheep. Stock breeding is widespread, but claims relatively
more attention in Ireland and upland Britain because of their more
restricted farming opportunities. Dublin, Belfast, Waterford,
Cork, and Londonderry are the principal exporters of store cattle
to be fattened in Britain and send an average of 375,000 a year.
Sheep predominate in Highland Britain, most of all in the Southern
Uplands. No less than in Cistercian times, they graze the northern
dales of Yorkshire. Professional shepherds are still found in W. H.
Hudson's downlands as well as in the highlands; nor has the
drover disappeared, though he no longer follows the green lanes
of the Midlands. At large and in detail, there is interdependence
between upland and lowland farmers, much hill stock being win-
tered or fattened on the plains. Even metropolitan England has
specialised breeding, and livestock fairs mark its rural calendars
no less than those of the rest of the country.

Milk and meat and their processed goods are the principal
British farm products. Dairying predominates and is widespread;
though there are distinct concentrations such as those of Ayrshire,
Limerick, the Cheshire/Shropshire plain and the vales of the West
Country (Simpson, 1959). Average yields for recorded dairy herds,
which account for a quarter of those of England and Wales, are 922
gallons (4,190 l.) per annum. Friesian (66%) and Ayrshire (14%) are
the principal breeds. Yields are sensitive to the natural flush of
grass in May and early June, and the growth of aftermath in July.
Given the prevailing economic milieu, beef production is generally
less profitable per acre than dairying, most cash crops, or even sheep
(James and Cayton, 1961). Beef cattle are kept for reasons individual to particular farms, but they are not commonly found on
land that will support cash crops. The small farmer, especially,
concentrates upon dairying with related pig production: there are
6 million pigs in the United Kingdom. Both activities guarantee a
regular return as against more irregular returns from store beasts.

Poultry and eggs derive increasingly from large-scale broiler and battery plants respectively. These are virtually rural factories and are usually located within a few tens of miles of the principal consuming markets. British broiler production stands at 125 million per annum. Many farms retain a horse despite the large number of tractors (c. 500,000 in the U.K.). The decline in farm horses, by 160,000 in Eire alone between 1921-61, may be regarded as releasing some 500,000 acres of land for the production of something other than fodder for motive power.

Much land under field crops in systems of rotational husbandry also yields animal foods. The British Isles have 2·3 million acres (0·9 ha.) under oats. Powys is the chief winter variety and Condor is the spring variety. Barley claims 5·6 million acres (2·3 ha.) with Procter as the principal variety cultivated: it is more important for fodder than for brewing. Wheat totals 2·3 million acres (0·9 m. ha.): Capelle is the favourite winter variety, and Jufy I the principal spring variety. Potato, turnip, and sugar beet are the leadings roots, with East Anglia as a region of specialisation, the Fenman favouring the potato and the Norfolkman the beet. Kale, for winter consumption by cattle and sheep, is a valuable 'environmental evader' because of its resistance to cool and humid conditions. Canning and deep freezing have called forth field crops such as peas in South Lincolnshire, which average 3 tons per acre plus ten tons of haulms (7·5 and 25 metric tons per ha.). All crop yields have been multiplied by plant breeding and the more scientific application of fertilisers. They have been steadied by weedkillers which have eliminated most of George Crabbe's deadly category of weeds, and by insecticides and poisons that have reduced the pests of tiny creatures caught in the clear gaze of the Northampton labourer and poet John Clare.

The organisation of British agriculture

Size, shape, and ownership conditions repeat the characteristic of diversity. They are features rooted in the historical evolution of the farm scene and in the local events that have made for differentiation within the more general framework of enclosure, emparking, 'plantation' (as in Ireland) and the later promotion of smallholdings. Because of the formal definition of an agricultural holding, more than half of the farms in both the United Kingdom and Eire are less than 50 acres (20 ha.) in size, and this might well create the impression that they are nations of smallholders. But the absolute range of farm size is great, with 10,000 acres (4,000 ha.) not un-usual in north Scotland. Holdings of all sizes are found in all areas; though there are considerable variations in the size of holding from county to county. Almost all farms are commercial enterprises; but the number that fall below the minimum desirable annual trading profit of £500 is considerable. As in other countries, income may be supplemented by 'off-farm' activities and there is a strong feeling that these should be promoted. Commonland rights often increase the effective size of the operating unit in the uplands; but there are many outlying areas along the Atlantic coasts and the offshore islands where the subsistence conditions of a virtual peasant farming prevail.

Given the classification of farm sizes and the nature of special-isation, it is evident that most holdings fall short of the optimum size for their pursuits. There is some agreement that a good family farm, engaged in mixed husbandry, should be about 120 acres (48 ha.) in size, divided into 12 fields of 10 acres (4 ha.) each (Stamp, 1962). Some farm economists would consider 150-250 acres (60-100 ha.) as the ideal size for a British dairy farm and that a holding specialising in cereal cultivation should approach 1,000 acres (400 ha.). Yet 'the stronghold of dairying' is the farm of less than 100 acres (40 ha.). A problem directly related to farm size is shape. In Britain, parliamentary enclosure did much to create unitary holdings. In Ireland, the Congested Districts Board (and after 1922, in Eire, the Irish Land Commission) promoted con-solidation (Freeman, 1960). But severance remains a common feature and relatively little is known about it in detail: amalgamation is a sensitive issue.

Conditions of land ownership also distinguish British farming from that of most countries. Most farmers are tenants, but knowledge about tenancy and ownership distributions is largely restricted to England and Wales, where about 38% of the farmers are owner-operators. The proportion of tenancy is highest in the north and lowest in southeast England. In Ulster 80% of the land is owner-occupied (Symons, 1959). There is relatively little correlation be-tween ownership and farm size, though farm ownership is slightly higher for the smallest and largest holdings.

Both the relationship between ownership and tenancy and that between farms of different sizes, having passed through considerable changes since the 1890s, incline towards stability. The break-up of large estates, principally as a result of death duties, has caused frequent transference to new landlords—often to commercial organisations. Complementarily, the Small Holdings Act of 1892 permits County Councils to provide loans for the sponsorship of small farmsteads, and the Land Settlement Association Ltd., founded in 1934, has created many units of 5 acres (2 ha.) with piggeries, poultry, and greenhouses on 25 estates throughout the country.

While Arthur Young's dictum that 'the magic of property turns sand into gold' may be valid, security of tenure has done much to produce the same results. Tenurial arrangements are very diverse. Scottish crofters combine the advantages of owner-occupiers and tenancy. On ordinary tenanted holdings, so many of the costs of maintenance are born by the landlord that operators frequently prefer to be tenants. On the other hand, the system of letting for short periods, e.g. conacre for 11 or 12 months in Ulster, has led to deterioration in farm fertility. In Great Britain, most tenants would probably have difficulty in finding sufficient capital to become owner-operators. With agricultural land of fair to good quality fetching £250-300 per acre (per 0·4 ha.), there are many apparently 'dirty boot' farmers in the British Isles who could sell out and live as *rentiers* on annual incomes of well over £2,000. Farming, indeed, is more than an exercise in economics: it is a way of life. Only in this light is it possible to understand the anomalies in its structure.

The landscape of the British Isles is rich in features that reflect former farm shapes, property conditions and operational procedures. Most prominent among these are field boundaries. In the lowlands of Britain and Ireland, they are dominated by hedgerows: in the uplands, by stone walls. Walls proliferate where stone is ready of access, e.g. in the Oolitic and Carboniferous limestone country. Parliamentary enclosure gave especial impetus to the spread of quickthorn hedgerow and stonewall, and a mosaic of four-sided fields was laid out largely in accordance with sketch plans in the husbandry books and encyclopaedias of an age when horse-drawn ploughs ruled the land. Thus, the new enclosures contrasted with the old 'closes' that surrounded the nucleated villages; but, like them, their principal purpose was animal control. Field boundaries also reflected intakes from waste and commonland (Robertson, 1949; Eyre, 1957). The construction of the great walls (Raistrick, 1952) across the sheep runs of the high Pennines is a saga, largely unrecorded, that speaks of the last decade of cheap man power. The existing pattern of boundaries, frequently ill-suited to contemporary practices, is superimposed upon earlier boundary systems, with some of which it accords and with others of which it is discordant. It is generally concordant with rundale or runrig pattern in

Ireland and there is notable continuity in the field boundary systems of the treens and quarterlands in the Isle of Man (Davies, 1956): but there is discordance with much of the furlong and ridge and furrow patterns of the open field system (Mead, 1954). Patterns of proto-British farms and farming operations may be detected more easily in uplands than on lowlands. Suites of cultivation terraces make a stronger visual impact than the garden-like patches that were Iron Age fields. Both are commonly preserved under permanent grass. Centuries of ploughing have usually destroyed most lowland evidence of earlier farm patterns; though air photographs may reveal much.

In field management, artificial drainage is a vital factor. Ditches or dykes, often closely associated with boundaries, are very persistent. Past epics of reclamation—seventeenth-century Fenland, the Isle of Axholme with the Humber lands, the Somerset levels, the bogs of Eire, the mosses of Lancashire, the Lough Foyle sloblands—have become twentieth-century problems of maintenance. But probably the most extensive network of drainage ditches is on the claylands, the ditch being absent from the more porous sands and calcareous soils. Ditch-digging and maintenance machines are more effective than hedge-cutting machines. Tile drains at a minimum depth of 2·2 feet (0·6 m.), which last perhaps a century, and mole draining, which may last a decade or more, are necessary for under-draining claylands. Since 1945, $1\frac{1}{2}$ million acres have been underdrained in England and Wales. Drainage can only be economically maintained when wages are low, prices are high, or aid is given. The problem makes its impact in human terms if it is remembered that a lowland farm of 200 acres (80 ha.) may have to maintain 5 miles (8 km.) of boundary and several miles of open ditch. Miles of field boundary per square mile of land area vary from as much as 20 (32 km.) in Devon to as little as 2 in Argyll. Britain alone has over 600,000 miles (970,000 km.) of hedgerow, accounting for 65% of its field boundaries.

Many rented small holdings, especially in the highland zone, have rights of common pasturage that are associated with tenancy of the infield or inbye land. A series of acts from 1886-1961 have legalised the situation in the so-called seven 'crofting counties' of northwest Scotland (Moisley, 1963). Contrasts between the extensive husbandry of the rough grazings and the intensive cultivation of the arable plots, down to the detail of the 'lazy bed' of Ireland or the Hebrides, are one of the distinctive features of crofting or of 'cottage farming', its Irish counterpart.

Nation-wide diversity in the organisation of British farms contrasts with the greater uniformity of farm size and character in many countries. Undoubtedly the range of differences, financial and human as well as physical, has inhibited the development in most localities of co-operative schemes for selling, purchasing, and employing jointly-owned equipment (though more than 200 machine syndicates exist). In England and Wales a system of centrally-organised marketing boards—for hops (1932), milk (1933), potatoes (1933, 1954), eggs (1957), wool (1950), and sugar beet (the British Sugar Corporation 1956)—has been initiated by legislation. Scotland and Ulster have their own parallel arrangements. They have not been born of the farmer: they have been imposed upon him.

The harvest of the sea

Fishing has become an increasingly professional, protected, and provocative pursuit. There is still a litter of relics from the time when fisheries made a more widespread impact—from the pock marks of monastic fishponds and eel traps or coghills which represent the 'licensed engines' of Eire's Board of Fishery Conservators, to sturdy quays that are more lively with the rods of Isaac Walton's week-end disciples than with the equipment and products of commercial fishermen. Inland, fisheries have become the preserve of the rich, with trout rights on the Wiltshire Avon, Sussex Rother, or Shropshire Teme selling for thousands of pounds a mile, and salmon beats on the Hereford Wye, Lancashire Lune, or Royal Dee fetching the equivalent of £200 a fish. It is a comforting piece of gustatory geography that the connoisseur should still apply regional standards to fish—Yarmouth bloaters, Dublin Bay prawns, Southport shrimps, Severn lampreys, and Whitstable 'natives'. For all the acres of oysters that may be planted on the Essex mudflats, the south side of the estuary remains supreme. The art of gathering small fry is still practised, while periwinkles enter the Irish fishery statistics as a separate item and 'Cockles and Mussels' are cried if not sung on the promenades of most seaside resorts.

Both genetics and economics account for changes in fishing activity. Coastal fisheries have suffered as a result of overfishing and of shifts in the breeding grounds. Diminution of North Sea resources was already evident seventy years ago, and Scottish and east coast English ports have experienced a declining seasonal catch of the familiar herring. Inshore and offshore fisheries have also diminished in the western Channel where, for example, Lowestoft drifters made regular visits before the Second World War. The industry has therefore looked increasingly to the distant, deep-sea fisheries, which with their accompanying international complications have been visited since the late Middle Ages. But the proportion of the catch coming from deep-sea sources was never so great as today and the accompanying organisation and competition was never so intense. Fishing—employing 21,000 full-time: 6,000 part-time— has been forced to concentrate regionally and nationally. The small-scale, diversified pursuit has become large-scale and capital demanding. The fleet's 300 distant-water trawlers, costing more than £50,000 each, engage in 3 or 4 week journeys to Barents Sea or West Greenland which yield variable cargoes that are marketed principally in Hull. The total wet fish landings in 1960 were c. 16 m. cwt. (800,000 metric tons) and of the 50 varieties of fish listed, cod accounted for two-fifths by weight. As a fishing port, Hull, with its mile-long fish quay, has few equals; Grimsby, Lowestoft, and Fleetwood are next in rank. Scotland looks to the string of fishing ports from Aberdeen to the harbours of Moray Firth; but Lord Leverhulme's attempts to resuscitate Hebridean fishing failed. Billingsgate remains the focus of distribution in the south (Bird, 1958). Whaling is more strictly hunting than fishing, but the declining Antarctic migration of factory ships such as *Southern Harvester* or *Balaena* recalls another marine harvest. Vessels are manned largely by professional Norwegian crews and bring their products chiefly to Merseyside.

The concept of the national heritage

The administrative structure of the British Isles complicates all attempts to generalise; but for all constituent units it might be said that the attitude to and appreciation of agriculture has been subject to marked change in the twentieth century, and that for all its natural advantages and rustic felicities, farming occupies a position that is both critical and artificial. Its economic position was weakened with the revolution in transport that brought late nineteenth-century competition from oversea, large-scale, pastoral and cereal producers. Many of these producers were, moreover, members of a British empire that was as conscious of the needs of its overseas farmers as it was of home producers. 'High Farming' was accordingly succeeded by depression, with marginal lands 'tumbling down' to rough grazing (Prothero, 1912). But the status of farming was swiftly raised when the First World War threatened supply lines between the British Isles and overseas food sources, a situation to be repeated and intensified during the Second World War. A complex system of aids and supports was implemented which substantially modified the distribution of farming activity and produced a great increase in returns from the land (Murray, 1956).

As a result, the farmer has acquired both a new stability and a new dependence. Technically, his activity has become increasingly dependent on industry, which provides mechanical equipment, refines oils to drive it, and produces fertilisers to maintain the soil. There is also an increased dependence on fodder imports. In 1953, Stamp estimated for the U.K. that there were ·48 acres (0·19 ha.) of improved land per stock unit (of 1 bullock, 1 cow in calf or 7 sheep) as distinct from the 2·5 acres (1 ha.) required to keep it (Stamp, 1954, 1958). The deficit underlines the continuing need for the assessment of the Emperor of Blefuscu that 'he is the Commonwealth's best man who can make two blades grow where one grew before'.

The farming position is maintained principally by subsidy, though horticulture is protected by quotas and tariffs. There are subsidies for land put under the plough (by an Act of 1952) and guaranteed prices for meat, milk, eggs, wool, cereals, potatoes, and sugar beet (of 16·5% sugar content). Financial grants may also be provided, e.g. under the Farm Improvement Scheme. The cost of agricultural support in Britain is c. £300 m. per annum and the widespread character of the adjustment that must accompany any association with the European Economic Community is evident.

It is equally evident that Britain's agricultural land has a great unused potential, and that Ireland's is probably greater. Yields in the United Kingdom could be increased on at least a tenth of the cultivated area. But while there exist technical facilities for achieving this, it is difficult to agree upon the most rewarding points of application. It is a paradox that so much good land is so much less developed than so much of Britain's poorer land. Lower investment of capital and labour on better land would frequently yield a higher return than heavier investment on poorer land (Wibberley, 1954, 1959). Thus, through the Hill Farming Act of 1946 and the Livestock Rearing Act of 1951, especially favouring the farmer of land marginal to hill country, much capital has been spent in promoting marginal farmsteads (Attwood and Evans, 1961). By contrast, well-organised systems of irrigation in lowland Britain west of a line from Hull to Weymouth, might increase returns two years in three with less effort and less investment than the attempt to conquer the margins of many upland areas. The comparative cost and effectiveness of rural services in these outlying areas and the increase of returns by employing their land for alternative uses must also be borne in mind. Yet such issues, having broader social implications, cannot be resolved exclusively along economic lines.

The British Isles have two ultimate natural assets—farmland and minerals, the former a renewable resource and the latter a wasting asset. There is a new realisation that farmland is a national heritage as well as being a source of wealth for private interests. 'The desire for the occupation of the land' (as an Irish M.P. put it a century ago) is an urge common to the neo-pioneers who buy their raw mountains or re-occupy deserted isles and to the estateless who seek to acquire the prestige that goes with mellowed acres. The agricultural scientist plans for more flexible management, more simplified operations, more effective specialisation and, thereby, a more viable husbandry (Duckham, 1958). These acquired skills are married with growing speed to the inherited green fingers that have made the islands a horticultural nursery and to the understanding of beasts that have made them a stud farm for so much of the world. Such skills also make possible a whole series of new rhythms to gear in with the caprice of the weather—

> to outwit the cunning of the land
> that will not yield . . .
> her due of food and wealth
> unless the moment's twisted to its use.

They inspire new Georgics in the poet, talk of a new agrarian revolution among technicians, a new approach among all sorts and conditions of farmers, and a new challenge for the agricultural geographers who would record the response on the face of the land.

References

AGRICULTURAL RESEARCH COUNCIL, *Report* of, H.M.S.O., annually.
ATTWOOD, E. A., and EVANS, H. G., 1961. *The economics of hill farming.* Cardiff.
BIRD, J., 1958. Billingsgate, a central metropolitan market. *Geogr. J.*, **124**, 464-75.
COPPOCK, J. T., 1956. The statistical assessment of British agriculture. *Agr. Hist. Rev.*, **4**, 4-21;
— 1964. Crop-livestock and enterprise combinations in England and Wales, *Econ. Geogr.* **40**, 1, 65-81
— 1964. *An agricultural atlas of England and Wales.* London.
— 1968. The geography of agriculture. *J. Agric. Econ.*, **xix**, 153-75.
DAVIES, E., 1956. Treens and quarterlands in the Isle of Man. *Trans. Inst. Brit. Geogrs.*, **22**, 97-116.

DUCKHAM, A. N. 1958. *The Fabric of Farming*. London; — 1963. *The Farming Year*. London.

EYRE, S. R., 1957. The upward limit of enclosure on the east moor of north Derbyshire. *Trans. Inst. Brit. Geogrs*, **23**, 61-74.

FREEMAN, T. W., 1960. *Ireland*. Manchester.

FUSSELL, G. E., 1947. *Old English farming books from Fitzherbert to Tull*. London.

— 1950. *More Old English farming books*. London.

GUIDES TO OFFICIAL SOURCES, No. 4, *Agricultural and Food Statistics*, 1958. H.M.S.O.

HALL, A. D., 1913. *A pilgrimage of British Farming*, 1911-12. London.

HENDERSON, H. C. K., 1952. Agricultural returns in England and Wales, in 1801, *Geogr. J.*, **118**, 338-45.

HUBBARD, C. E., 1954. *Grasses*. London.

JACKSON, B. G., et al., 1963. The pattern of farming in the Eastern Counties, *Occasional Papers, No. 8*, Farm Economics Branch, School of Agriculture, Cambridge.

JAMES, P. G., and CAYTON, R. J., 1961. *Beef on the arable farm*. Cambridge.

JONES, R. B., 1954. *The pattern of farming in the east Midlands*. Loughborough.

MEAD, W. R., 1954. Ridge and furrow in Buckinghamshire. *Geogr. J.*, **120**, 34-42.

— 1966. The study of field boundaries. *Geogr. Z.*, **54**, 101–17.

MOISLEY, H. A., 1963. The Highlands and islands, a crofting region. *Trans. Inst. Brit. Geogrs*.

MURRAY, K. A. H., 1956. *History of the second world war. Agriculture*. London.

PROTHERO, R. E., (Lord Ernle), 1912. *English farming, past and present*, London.

RAISTRICK, A., 1952. *The story of the Pennine walls*. Clapham.

REPORT OF COMMITTEE ON GRASSLAND UTILISATION, 1958. H.M.S.O.

ROBERTSON, I. M. L., 1949. The head-dyke; a fundamental line in Scottish geography. *Scot. Geog. Mag.*, **65**, 6-20.

SALAMAN, R. N., 1949. *The history and social influence of the potato*. Cambridge.

SIMPSON, E. S., 1959. Milk Production in England and Wales. *Geog. Rev.*, **59**, 95-111.

STAMP, L. D., 1954. *The under-developed lands of Britain*. London.

— 1958. The measurement of land resources. *Geog. Rev.*, **48**, 1-15.

— 1962. *The land of Britain, its use and misuse*. London.

SYMONS, L. J., 1959. Agricultural progress in Ulster. *Geography*, **44**, 157-70.

WIBBERLEY, G. P., 1954. Some aspects of problem rural areas in Great Britain. *Geogr., J.*, **120**, 43-61.

— 1959. *Agriculture and urban growth*. London.

15

MINERAL RESOURCES AND POWER

Introduction

THE intensive utilisation of Britain's mineral resources depends on two factors, first the immense geological variety and wide range of the resources, and secondly the enormous home market provided by British industries. Probably no other equivalent area has been blessed with such a rich assembly of mineral of all kinds, from coal and iron ore to non-ferrous metals and the raw materials of construction. And although some of the metal wealth, worked for 2,000 years, has now been exhausted, the industries that were based on it have been able to survive in many instances, simply through the insular position of the country which facilitates imports from abroad.

Table 12 indicates the relative importance of the main minerals.

Mineral resources

We may conveniently divide the mineral resources into five groups, as follows:

(i) non-ferrous metals (copper, tin, lead, zinc); (ii) iron ore; (iii) the rarer non-metalliferous minerals (e.g. salt, gypsum, china clay); (iv) the common minerals or 'rocks' (e.g. limestone, granite, clay, sandstone, gravel); (v) petroleum; (vi) coal.

(i) *Non-ferrous metals*

Though perhaps the Phoenicians may have visited Cornwall for its tin, and though the Romans, our medieval ancestors, and more particularly those of the nineteenth century, worked the rich resources of tin and copper, lead and zinc, in many parts of Britain, this is now mostly a matter of historical geography, and the great mining industries of the past are no more. Scarcely a handful of metalliferous mines remains, and the bulk of our needs of these metals has to be supplied by imports of concentrates for smelting, mostly at port localities, or of semi-refined and refined metal.

The decline and extinction of these industries has been due in part to their small scale of operation and to the economic impossi-

Table 12.   1965 Mineral output (million tons)

Mineral	tons	metric
Coal	178.9	181.8
Gravel and Sand	102.9	104.6
Limestone	58.8	59.7
Clay and Shale	35.6	36.2
Iron Ore	15.4	15.6
Chalk	18.7	19.0
Igneous Rocks	24.3	24.7
Rock Salt and Brine	6.9	7.0
Sandstone	7.4	7.5
Gypsum	4.4	4.5
Fireclay	1.8	1.8
China Clay	2.2	2.2
Crude Petroleum	0.08	0.08
Lead	0.000	0.000
Tin[1]	0.001	0.001

1 Recoverable metal content of concentrated ore

bility of competing with the larger and more accessible fields in other parts of the world. About 1800, Cornwall provided a high proportion of the world's copper ore, and Swansea smelted it; but as soon as Swansea began to get cheaper ores from as far afield as Chile and Cuba, Cornwall's eventual fate was assured. Similarly, the economic depression of the 1870's, coinciding with a great increase in lead imports from Spain, was followed by the rapid decline of lead mining in Britain.

(ii) *Iron ore*

For its size, Great Britain has been exceptionally well endowed with ores of iron of several different kinds. The ores occur in three main geological forms: (*a*) haematite veins and masses, in solution hollows in the Carboniferous Limestone, especially on the western fringe of the Lake District but also in the limestone rims of the Forest of Dean and south Wales coalfields; (*b*) thin bedded ores, occurring as beds of nodules or as continuous seams a few inches thick, in the shales of the Coal Measures, particularly in certain coalfields; (*c*) thick bedded ores, up to 30 ft. (9 m.) thick, in the Jurassic scarplands of the east Midlands. The Romans are known to have worked all three types in different scattered localities. In addition a fourth type, thin nodular seams occurring in the Wealden rocks of southeastern England, provided a great medieval iron-smelting industry which, using charcoal as its fuel, survived until the Industrial Revolution came to place the emphasis on the ores of the coalfields.

Table 13. Iron ore output, 1913 and 1965 (thousand tons)

Formation	1913		1965	
	tons	metric	tons	metric
Haematite				
Cumberland	1,361	1,383	261	265
Furness	406	412	0	0
total	1,767	1,795	261	265
Jurassic				
Lower Lias (N. Lincolnshire)	*	*	5,065	5,146
Middle Lias (Cleveland)	5,941	6,036	0	0
Middle Lias (Leics., Oxon.)	*	*	1,456	1,479
Inferior Oolite	*	*..	8,485	8,621
total	12,572	12,733	15,006	15,246
Coal Measures				
England and Wales	951	966	0	0
Scotland	591	601	0	0
total	1,542	1,567	0	0
Other occurrences	116	118	147	149
total	15,977	16,253	15,415	15,662

* Figures not available for geological formations

(a) Haematite. In west Cumberland and in the Furness peninsula, red haematite, averaging 48-54% iron, occurs in the Carboniferous Limestone, in irregular masses. The ore is non-phosphoric and its extraction therefore received a great fillip after 1860 with the introduction of the acid Bessemer and Siemens processes of steel-making, for which purpose almost all other British ores were unsuitable. The Furness deposits have been exhausted, but a few mines survive in the hinterland of Workington, where a large iron and steel works is still partly dependent on this local ore.

The haematites of the Forest of Dean were important in Roman and in medieval and later times, but the workings are long since extinct. A small occurrence of a similar nature at Llanharry, on the southern rim of the south Wales coalfield, is now the only contributor to the 'other occurrences' in Table 13.

(b) *Coal Measures ironstone*. The bedded ores occurring in the Coal measures are of exceptional historical interest, since the Industrial Revolution in Britain, in the late 18th and early 19th century, was founded upon them and upon the coking coals that were found in the same series of strata in several coalfields. But for this fortunate geological accident the vast industrial developments that took place during the period could hardly have occurred, and the history of Britain in the nineteenth century might have been a very different one. Yet they were not rich ores, nor were they very easy to obtain. Their iron content was no more than 30-35% and they occurred in thin seams or in beds of nodules, involving much excavation by hand labour. But they could often be obtained from the same mines as the coking coal, and that was the economic reason for their use. There are still millions of tons of this ore left, but it can never be mined in competition with the thickly-bedded Jurassic ores (which are mostly mass-produced by modern opencast methods) and with richer ores imported from abroad.

Two sorts of Coal Measures ores were used: the 'clayband' type, carbonate of iron in a clayey matrix, and the 'blackband' type, containing carbonaceous matter in addition, and so easier to smelt. The claybands were most abundant in the south Staffordshire and Shropshire coalfields, and in south Wales, Derbyshire and west and south Yorkshire, and the Scottish coalfields. Blackbands were chiefly found in Scotland and in north Staffordshire.

(c) *Jurassic ironstones*. Though they were known to the Romans and were worked in medieval times, these ores were forgotten, and were re-discovered about 1850. They differ from the haematites in being composed of iron carbonate (siderite) or iron-aluminosilicate (chamosite), often oxidised to limonite, and in being stratified; they differ from the Coal Measures ores in their occurrence in thick beds, between 6 and 30 feet (2-9 m.) thick, which over large areas either crop out at the surface or can be got beneath overburden of less than 100 ft. (30 m.). Like the Coal Measures ironstones, they are phosphoric; this hindered their use in the steel industry until after the Thomas-Gilchrist 'basic process' of 1879, and in this, as in their disposition and geological age, they resemble the 'minette' ores of Lorraine.

Three separate horizons in the Jurassic sequence yield iron ore:

(*a*) The Lower Lias, in north Lincolnshire, around Scunthorpe. Here a thick (20-30 ft., 6-9 m.) bed of lean ore (20-22% iron) is worked by opencast methods, and as the workings advance eastwards under thicker cover, mining is developed. The ore is calcareous, and a siliceous complement—usually ore from Northamptonshire—is added to give a more readily smeltable mixture.

(*b*) The Middle Lias, sometimes called 'Marlstone', is iron-bearing in two districts. In the Cleveland Hills of north Yorkshire it was discovered in 1850 on the scarp-face of the hills, and was quickly followed underground. A seam 6-10 feet (2-3 m.) in thickness was worked by shaft mines. The great iron and steel town of Middlesbrough grew up on the mouth of the Tees with the development of this iron-ore field, which reached its maximum output in 1913 and is now exhausted.

Farther south, in the scarplands between south Lincolnshire and north Oxfordshire, the Marlstone is worked in three separate areas by opencast methods—in south Lincolnshire (Grantham area) in Leicestershire (the Melton Mowbray area) and in Oxfordshire (the Banbury area). The bed varies between 6 and 12 feet (2-4 m.) thick, and carries about 25% iron.

(*c*) The Inferior Oolite (Northampton Sands) formation now provides about one-half of all the British iron ore output. The field extends discontinuously from the Grantham district of south Lincolnshire to near Northampton. The bed is 6 to 12 feet (2-4 m.) in thickness, yields about 32% iron, and is worked almost entirely by opencast methods, particularly around the great steel town of Corby.

The opencast working of these Jurassic iron ores has given rise to considerable land-use problems, but reclamation of the worked-out areas for agricultural purposes or forestry is now the rule and the considerable areas that became derelict in the 1930s are now largely restored to some economic use.

Iron ore imports. The home output of iron ore is insufficient, both in quantity, and in quality, to satisfy the British iron and steel industry, and almost as much again is imported; though the higher quality of the imported ore means that much more than half the smelted iron comes from imported ores. The sources are far flung, with Sweden heading the list, followed by North Africa, Canada, South America (Venezuela and Brazil) and West Africa.

(iii) *The rarer non-metallic minerals*

The most important of these are: *salt*, which is obtained almost entirely by brine-pumping from the thick rock-salt beds that occur in the Triassic rocks, particularly in mid-Cheshire (the Northwich district); *gypsum*, the raw material of plaster of Paris and plaster-board, which is quarried or mined from Triassic rocks at a few places in east Staffordshire and in Nottinghamshire; the anhydrous form, known as *anhydrite*, is mined at Billingham-on-Tees, where it gave rise to a large chemical industry; *china clay*, which is used in paper and linoleum manufacture as well as in the pottery industry, and is obtained from large, deep, open pits in the granite rocks of the St Austell district of Cornwall; *fireclay*, which is used for the manufacture of refractory goods, and is quarried or mined in several coalfields, but particularly in south Derbyshire (Swadlin-cote area), north Staffordshire, the Black Country, and Lanarkshire.

(iv) *The commoner minerals or 'rocks'*

The long and complex geological history of the British Isles has resulted in a wide variety of rock-types being found, of many different ages; whilst the density of the settlement pattern, and road and rail networks, ensure that relatively few rocks of technical value are economically inaccessible. The uplands yield igneous and metamorphic rocks, slates and hard varieties of limestone and sand-stone, together with shales for brick-making; the lowlands yield brick-clays, chalk and the softer limestones and sandstones, whilst sand and gravel from superficial deposits are found in very wide-spread localities, though especially in lowland valleys.

Igneous rocks. The coarser-grained granites are quarried for ornamental stone or for heavy constructional work (though increas-ingly now substituted by ferro-concrete structures), as in Devon and Cornwall and the Aberdeen-Peterhead district. The finer-grained granitic rocks are used for road-metal, as in Leicestershire, the Lleyn in north Wales, and Devon and Cornwall. Metamorphic rocks, such as gneiss, are quarried for road metal in the Malvern Hills and the Scottish Highlands. Fine-grained rocks of basaltic type are particularly favoured for road-making, and many are deeply quarried, as in Northumberland, the Rowley Hills of south Staffordshire, the Clee Hills of Shropshire, and the Scottish Lowlands.

Slate. Vast areas of the Southern Uplands of Scotland, the Lake District, north and central Wales, southwest England and south-eastern Ireland, are composed of slaty rocks, but in only a very few places is the slaty cleavage sufficiently well developed to make the quarrying of roofing slate a possibility. The outstanding areas are in north Wales, where slates of Cambrian age are quarried in enormous open pits in Caernarvonshire northwest of the Snowdon range, whilst slates of Ordovician age are mined to the east of that range at Blaenau Ffestiniog. Slate, however, has been largely replaced by clay tiles and more recently by concrete tiles as a roofing material, and the quarrying industry is but a shadow of what it was a hundred years ago. The quarries and their spoil-heaps (for 95% of what is quarried is either unsuitable for use or is wasted during the preparation of the slates) have left gigantic scars on the landscape.

Limestone. The main geological formations yielding limestone are the Carboniferous Limestone, the Magnesian Limestone (Permian) and the Jurassic series. The Carboniferous Limestone is quarried on an enormous scale in parts of the Pennines (especially the Buxton district and in Weardale), on the fringes of the south Wales and north Wales coalfields, and on the margins of the Lake District. It is used for the chemical industries (several train-loads of limestone are sent each day from the Buxton area to Northwich in Cheshire), as a flux in the iron and steel industries, as a source of lime, for road metal, and for cement manufacture. The Magnesian Limestone has been used as a building stone but is more commonly quarried now in those areas where it is dolomitic in character for use in the basic process of steel-making (as at Coxhoe in County Durham, and farther south on the Yorkshire-Derbyshire border). There are many different horizons in the Jurassic series yielding limestones, and some of these have been in use as building stones for a thousand years; the Bath stone of the Cotswolds, the white Portland stone from Dorset (so much used as a facing material in London and other cities), and other famous stones from Northamptonshire and Lincolnshire, have contributed much to the local architecture of the areas in which they occur, and over a much wider area for such great buildings as cathedrals. Some of the Jurassic limestones are also quarried for the cement industry, as in Warwickshire and near Cardiff.

Chalk is of course a form of limestone, but it has never been much used as a building material since it is soft and does not lend itself to the production of squared blocks or 'ashlar'. It is, however, the source of some three-quarters of the country's cement industry, and is quarried on a vast scale on both banks of the Thames estuary, in the Chiltern Hills and South Downs, and on the banks of the Humber.

Clay and Shale. These brick-making materials are fortunately widespread, and of a variety of geological ages from Ordovician to Pleistocene and Recent. Before the last war they were quarried in well over 1,200 brickworks scattered through almost every county of England and Wales and most Scottish counties outside the Highlands. Technical progress however has led to a reduction in this number by one-half, and there is an increasing concentration of mass-production brick-making on the Oxford Clay formation, notably in the vicinity of Peterborough, Bedford, and Bletchley, where over one-half of all the country's bricks are now made. Apart from this, the shales and clays of the Coal Measures are still very important (partly because their urban markets are so close at hand); and a large proportion of the clay roofing-tile industry is still concentrated in north and south Staffordshire.

Sand and Gravel. Special varieties of sand for the metallurgical industries and for glass-making are obtained from the Lower Greensand formation (Cretaceous) near Leighton Buzzard (Bedfordshire) and Kings Lynn (Norfolk), and from a superficial formation in the St Helens district of southwest Lancashire. Sand for the building industry comes mostly from sand and gravel pits. There are three major sources of gravel: (i) the 'solid' Bunter Pebble Beds (Lower Triassic) of the west Midlands (mainly north and south Staffordshire); (ii) the glacial gravels, deposited by meltwater from decaying ice-sheets, mainly in the Midlands, northern England, central Scotland and Ireland; and (iii) the river terraces, especially in the Midlands and southern England. The deposits are widespread and of very varied quality. Most of the worked deposits find local markets within a 20-mile (30-km.) radius, in the building and road-making trades, but some of the finer quartzite gravels move rather greater distances, normally by road. The most concentrated areas of production of the river gravels (the working of which leaves lagoons in place of often highly-productive agricultural land) are the Greater London area (the Thames terraces west and east of the metropolis) and the Trent Valley.

(v) *Petroleum*

The British Isles have not so far proved very productive in oil, and there is no reason to believe that they ever will be. Shale from which oil can be distilled occurs in the Coal Measures of the Scottish Lowlands, west of Edinburgh, and a few small oil-bearing structures in Carboniferous rocks have been tapped in Nottinghamshire, but that is almost all, and home production is but 0·2% of consumption. The bulk of our petroleum therefore must be imported. About three-quarters of it comes from the Middle East, notably Kuwait, and almost all the remainder from the Caribbean ar

(vi) *Coal*

For its size Great Britain is one of the richest countries in the world in coal, and indeed the country's industrial growth and prosperity were largely based on coal, which continues to play a vital though reduced role in the whole economy. In some areas coal has been dug for domestic heating since medieval times (it was exported from the Tyne to London in the fourteenth century) but it was during the Industrial Revolution of the late eighteenth and early nineteenth centuries that the use of coal in blast furnaces and as a fuel for steam engines, both stationary and locomotive, gave rise to a vast increase in output, which itself was dependent on the steam engine for pumping water out of the mines and for driving the winding machinery. One result of this early growth of coal mining, however, is that in many fields the best of the easily-accessible coal has already been worked out; moreover, many of the individual mines were old and uneconomic, so that an enormous task faced the National Coal Board in 1947 when the coal-mining industry was nationalised, and a vast programme of reorganisation has been carried through, involving the closing of several hundreds of the smaller and less productive mines and the spending of large sums on the modernisation of the more efficient pits and on sinking new ones. Compared with a maximum output of 287 million tons (292 m. metric tons) in 1914, when more than one million men were employed in coal mining, the output in recent years has been a little short of 200 million tons (203 m. metric tons), but the employment rate has shrunk to little more than 650,000.

Geologically and geographically the coalfields of Great Britain fall into three great provinces that were outlined during Carboniferous times; post-Carboniferous earth movements, by up-lifting some areas and depressing others, later subdivided these provinces and produced the eighteen major coalfields we recognise today. The three provinces were (i) The Scottish Lowlands, in the 'graben' between the Highlands and Southern Uplands; (ii) the central parts of Great Britain, between the Southern Uplands of Scotland and a formerly existing massif (known to geologists as 'St George's Land') which extended from central Wales across the English Midlands; (iii) south Wales and southern England, which lay south of St George's Land.

In the Scottish Lowlands subsequent uplift divided the coal-bearing formations into three major areas: (*a*) the Ayrshire basin, separated by the 'Cunningham' axis from (*b*) the Lanarkshire-Stirlingshire basin, this in turn being separated by the 'Pentland' axis from (*c*) the Fife-Midlothian basin (which still later events divided into two parts, separated by the Firth of Forth).

In central Great Britain, the Pennine and Lake District uplifts succeeded in effectively separating the coal outcrops into two groups, with the Cumberland, Lancashire-Cheshire, and north Staffordshire fields to the west and the Northumberland-Durham and Yorkshire-Derbyshire-Nottinghamshire fields to the east. Another uplift, at right angles to the Pennine axis, separated Cumberland from Lancashire and Durham from Yorkshire. Each of these fields (unlike the Scottish fields which are virtually closed basins) outcrops near to the uplands and dips underground to a concealed extension. In the Cumberland and Northumberland-Durham coalfields these extensions are largely submarine; in Lancashire-Cheshire the concealed extension is but narrow, because of extensive faulting that plunges the coal seams down to unworkable depths, but on the Yorkshire-Nottinghamshire side there is a very large concealed field, the boundaries of which are still imperfectly known. The remainder of the central province comprises the basins that lie between the Pennine uplift and the old massif of St George's Land. Under the Cheshire and mid-Staffordshire plains the coal, if present, lies at quite unworkable depths, but approaching the edges of the old massif the measures reappear at the surface, in a series of small basins which themselves have become separated by subsequent uplift and faulting. From west to east these are (*a*) the north Wales or Flintshire-Denbighshire field, dipping eastwards from the edge of the Welsh mountains; (*b*) the Shropshire fields; (*c*) the south Staffordshire fields; (*d*) the Warwickshire field; (*e*) the Leicestershire-south Derbyshire field. These last (*b* to *e*) lie on the northern edges of the old massif, which, except on the Welsh border, no longer forms a major upland area.

The third province extends from southwest Wales right into continental Europe. It has been divided by subsequent uplifts into four separate coalfields: (*a*) south Wales, which is by far the largest and forms an enclosed basin with no concealed extensions; (*b*) the Forest of Dean, a much smaller enclosed basin; (*c*) the Bristol-Somerset fields, forming a nearly-enclosed basin, (*d*) the Kent coalfield, which is unique in being entirely concealed beneath a cover of Mesozoic rocks.

Table 14. Output of coal 1965 from N.C.B. Divisions (million tons)

		tons	metric
Scotland		15·23	15·47
Northern	Northumberland, Cumberland, Durham	30·62	31.11
Northeastern	Yorkshire	42.46	43.14
Northwestern	Lancashire, Cheshire & N. Wales	12.13	12.33
East Midlands	Derbyshire-Nottinghamshire & S. Derbyshire-Leicestershire	45.29	46.02
West Midlands	Shropshire, N. & S. Staffordshire, Warwickshire	14.13	14.36
Southwestern	S. Wales, Forest of Dean, Bristol & Somerset	17.50	17.78
Southeastern	Kent	1.55	1.57
Opencast	several fields	7.30	7.42
	total	186.21	189.20

Quality of coal. The entire output being from rocks of Carboniferous age, all the coals are bituminous or of higher rank, and there are no lignites. Anthracite is produced, to the extent of between 3 and 4 million tons a year, in the western part of the south Wales field, and low-volatile steam coals (volatile matter 10-20%) come mainly from the middle part of the south Wales field, with some from Kent. Coals in the middle range (volatile matter 20-30%) are of two types, coking and non-coking. The non-coking varieties are found mainly in the Scottish fields, whilst the coking varieties produce the metallurgical coke of southwest Durham and eastern south Wales. Coals with a high content of volatile matter (over 30%) are also divisible into coking and non-coking varieties. The best coking coals, again used for metallurgical coke, come from the southern part of the Durham field, from south Yorkshire and from north Staffordshire. Altogether some 18-19 million tons of metallurgical coke, for use in blast-furnaces and foundries, are produced annually, together with 10 million tons for other purposes, and the total consumption of coking coal is about 28 million tons.

The other high-volatile coals comprise the gas coals, used to the extent of some 22 million tons a year in gas-works, and the ordinary industrial and domestic coals. These are much the most widely distributed varieties. Table 15 details the utilisation of British coal in a recent and a pre-war year.

Table 15. Coal consumption 1965 and 1938 (million tons)

	tons	metric	tons	metric
		1965		1938
Export and ships' bunkers	3.7	3.8	46.4	47.1
Electric power stations	69.3	70.4	15.2	15.4
Gas works	18.0	18.3	19.7	20.0
Coke ovens	25.7	26.1	19.7	20.0
Railways	2.8	2.8	13.6	13.8
Industry	23.1	23.5	47.1	47.9
Domestic	23.1	23.5	47.2	48.0
Collieries and miners' free coal	7.6	7.7	17.2	17.5
Miscellaneous	12.9	13.1	0.9	0.9
total	186.2	189.2	227.0	230.6

Remarkable changes have come about during the present century in the use of British coal, the most notable being the almost complete extinction of the coal export trade, which formerly provided such a large income and which was the basis of the prosperity of British tramp shipping. Before the First World War about one-third of the entire output was exported—amounting to 80-90 million tons a year. Other noteworthy features are the decline in the use of coal by railways (a result of the conversion to diesel and electric traction) and the very great increase in the use of coal for electricity generation, which in its turn has caused a decline in the use of coal for industrial and domestic purposes.

The following notes attempt to summarise briefly the present position and the prospects of the major coalfields.

Of the four major fields in Scotland, the two largest (Ayrshire and the Central or Lanarkshire-Stirlingshire field) are now in the most difficult position, with declining numbers of pits and poor outputs (below the national average of about 290 tons (296 metric tons) per man-year). The two easterly fields are better placed, with higher productivity rates and a greater potential development, particularly in Fife, though recent sinkings here have not proved as productive as had been hoped.

The Northumberland field is reasonably productive, though it has suffered from the much reduced demand for its steam coal, which was formerly an important export and bunker fuel. Its southward continuation in County Durham is also not far below the national average in productivity, but the western part of the field is becoming exhausted and the future lies with the concealed eastern part and its submarine extension.

The Cumberland field is a difficult one to work, and its productivity is low.

The Lancashire field is divided into two parts by the Rossendale upfold, which separates the small Burnley basin from the main south Lancashire mining area centred on Wigan and St Helens. In the former, drift-mining has proved successful in raising the general level of output; in the latter, there are many large and deep mines. But the field as a whole has been declining for several decades. The Yorkshire-Nottinghamshire-Derbyshire field is both the largest and the most productive of all the fields; with an output of some 80 million tons a year, it provides over 40% of the British total. The great majority of the pits are more productive than the national average, and some of the larger and newer ones in the concealed Nottinghamshire section considerably so. Mining conditions are on the whole easier than in most other fields, by reason of thicker seams and fewer faults. A great future still lies ahead for this field.

Amongst the smaller Midlands coalfields conditions are variable. The Leicestershire-south Derbyshire field has very high productivity rates, and so has Cannock Chase (the northern part of the south Staffordshire field). The north Staffordshire and Warwickshire fields have rather lower rates, but still in general above the national average.

In south Wales as a whole, where output is less than half what it was in the 1920s, productivity is low, largely owing to the difficult geological conditions. The output per man-shift in 1960 was only 2·68 tons (2·72 metric tons) compared with 5·96 tons (6·01 metric tons) in the east Midlands (Nottinghamshire) area, and it is lowest in the anthracite region of the northwest. South Wales, like the Northumberland-Durham field, has been very severely hit by the declining demand for its steam coal from the shipping industry.

Conditions in the Forest of Dean, Somerset, and Kent coalfields are also difficult, and productivity is below the national average.

The National Coal Board, continuing its policy of economic nationalisation, is expecting to close some 200 or more collieries in the early 1960s; the man-power deployed may well drop to 550,000, though without any reduction in output from the level of roughly 180-190 million tons.

Heat, light, and power

The direct consumption of coal by industry and domestic users for the provision of power (usually through the medium of the steam engine) and of heat has been noted in Table 15 (p. 291). The use of coal in gas-works results in the provision of gas for heat, light and occasionally for power, and also of coke for heat and power. The saleable output of gas in 1960 amounted to some 2,912 million therms, of which 2,243 million were supplied by gasworks and 504 million by coke ovens (this figure excludes the gas used in the integrated steelworks of which coke ovens form a constituent part). Of this output, some 49% was consumed by domestic users, 33% by industry, 16% by commercial users, and 1% by public lighting systems.

Electricity also provides heat, light, and power. Of the total output of 119,777 million Kwh in 1960, 117,083 million Kwh were generated by steam, 2,539 m. Kwh by water power, and 147 m. Kwh by oil engines. The coal consumption was 51·1 million tons (51·9 m. metric tons) and the oil consumption (to fire steam as well as oil engines) 5·3 million tons (5·4 m. metric tons). The current generated was consumed as follows: 49% by industry, 34% by domestic users, 13% by commercial users (shops and offices), 1·5% by traction systems (railways, trams, and trolley buses), and 1% for public lighting.

The Gas Industry. From its inception early in the nineteenth century, the gas industry has been market orientated, and a map of gasworks still bears a considerable resemblance to the map of urban population. Since the nationalisation of the industry in 1949, however, two tendencies have been apparent: (i) integration of regional supplies, with a vast increase in the mileage of pipelines and 'gas-grids'; (ii) the closing of many small local gasworks up and down the country (500 out of just over 1,000 works were closed between 1949 and 1958) and the increasing concentration of output in larger and more efficient plants. Three major locational features are now dominant: there is a great clustering of gasworks (i) in the major conurbations and (ii) especially in those conurbations which are situated in coalfield areas where coals of appropriate quality are available; (iii) at ports and other waterfront situations where coastwise coal supplies, especially from Durham, can be readily obtained.

In addition to ordinary gasworks supplies, considerable quantities of gas are piped into the local grids from coke ovens, especially in south Wales, County Durham, and the Yorkshire-Derbyshire coalfield; whilst coastal oil refineries, as on Southampton Water and the lower Thames, also contribute supplies.

Though it is still increasing, the expansion of gas consumption has been much less rapid than that of electricity, which in addition is now more widespread than gas by reason of its easier transmission.

The electricity industry

(a) *Thermal generation.* Appreciable changes have taken place since the First World War in the pattern of electricity generation and transmission. It was not until 1926, with the creation of the Central Electricity Board, that the many local supply systems were welded together into one national system, with a network of transmission lines, known as the 'Grid', connecting them. Geographically the pattern comprised six main groups of generating stations, a pattern, as with the gas industry, largely resembling the map of urban population: (i) the London area, based mainly on coastwise coal transport to riverside stations; (ii) south Wales and Bristol, again largely at coastal or riverine sites; (iii) the Midlands, with two separate concentrations, one in the west peripheral to the Birmingham-Black Country conurbation, and one in the east along the banks of the river Trent; (iv) Lancashire and Yorkshire, where again there is emphasis on riverside sites; (v) northeast England, especially Tyneside and Tees-side; (vi) central Scotland, especially on Clydeside and the Firth of Forth.

One of the major siting requirements of the power stations, apart from the accessibility of fuel supplies, was water in vast quantities for cooling purposes; the best sites were clearly those alongside large rivers (e.g. Trent, Severn) or tidal estuaries (Thames, Mersey, Southampton Water) where water could be taken in, and after use discharged back into the river. Elsewhere, large batteries of cooling towers were necessary, so as to use the same water over and over again.

Since the last war, certain technical factors have combined with a vast increase in the demand for electricity to produce a somewhat changed pattern. These factors are (i) the development of the 'super-Grid' using 275 KV transmission lines instead of the previous 132 KV (and future developments are likely to involve power lines at 400 KV); this has made possible the long-distance transmission of current from one region to another, at a lower cost than would have been incurred in transporting the required quantities of coal by rail; (ii) the concentration of new generating capacity on certain types of site and location where costs of fuel, transport, and water are at their lowest, e.g. coastal and riverside sites to which water-borne coal can be brought, and which are themselves on or adjacent to coalfields. By far the greatest development has taken place alongside the river Trent, for the river provides a large water supply (which, however, is still not sufficient to enable the power stations to dispense entirely with cooling towers), and is very close to the lowest-cost coalfield in the country, that of Nottinghamshire. High quality coal is not required, and the slack which is difficult for other users to employ can be used as pulverised fuel. So the middle Trent has become the focus of the 'super-grid' (which now extends for over 1,100 route-miles), with transmission lines extending southwards to London, southwestwards via the west Midlands to Bristol and south Wales, northwards to west Yorkshire and the Tees-Tyne area, and northwestwards to south Lancashire. Other lines of the super-grid are transverse, between Bristol and London, between Lancashire and Yorkshire and from Tyneside to Carlisle and Glasgow.

Ireland. In Ireland, in addition to normal thermal power stations using coal imports from Great Britain, several stations in the central plain have been established to use peat as their fuel.

Nuclear Power. Also feeding into the Grid are the nuclear power stations: these are coastal in situation, largely because of their enormous water demands, and in general are remote from centres of population, e.g. Sizewell and Bradwell on the East Anglian coast, Dungeness on the southeast coast, Hinkley Point and Berkeley on the Severn estuary, Hunterston on the Firth of Clyde, and Dounreay on the coast of Caithness. Only one, at Trawsfynydd in north Wales, is inland, and this is served by a large reservoir that is replenished by pumping the used water back into it.

Hydro-electricity. The British Isles are not well endowed with the physical possibilities of large-scale hydro-electric developments, for although there are mountainous areas with heavy and evenly-distributed rainfall, and steeply-graded rivers, the catchment areas are too small to provide much potential, and such areas are relatively remote from the main centres of population. Of the major rivers, only the Shannon in Ireland is used to generate hydro-electricity; for the rest, in the Scottish Highlands, the Southern Uplands and north Wales, it is a case of small catchments supplemented by dams, occasionally by pumped storage and sometimes by the diversion of water through watershed tunnels. The Shannon scheme, with a power station near Limerick, utilises an artificial fall of about 100 feet (30 m.) and sufficient current is generated to supply almost the whole of Eire. In the Scottish Highlands the principal schemes are those in the west, where the power is used at Lochaber, Kinlochleven, and Foyers for the aluminium industry, and the Grampian system based on the water resources of the great Rannoch upland; farther north there are several small developments, and in the Highlands as a whole there is now a fairly widespread distribution of electric current. In southern Scotland the Falls of Clyde have long been used, and the Galloway scheme uses rivers and lakes in the valleys of the Ken and Dee.

References

BEAVER, S. H., 1944. Minerals and planning. *Geogr. J.*, **194**, 166-93.

JAMES, J. R., SCOTT, S. F., and WILLATTS, E. C., 1961. Land use and the changing power industry in England and Wales. *Geogr. J.*, **126**, 286-309.

MANNERS, G., 1959. Recent changes in the British gas industry. *Trans. Inst. Brit. Geogrs.*, **26**, 153-86.

MOUNFIELD, P. R., 1961. The location of nuclear power stations in the United Kingdom. *Geography*, **46**, 139-55.

RAWSTRON, E. M., 1955. Changes in the geography of electricity production in Great Britain. *Geography*, **40**, 92-7.

— 1960. Power stations and the river Trent: a note on further developments. *E. Midl. Geogr.*, **14**, 27-32.

STAMP, L. D., and BEAVER, S. H., 1963. *The British Isles* (Chapters 14, 15 and 16). London.

THOMAS, T. M., 1961. Coal mining in Britain: a declining industry? *Tijdschr. v. Econ. Soci. Geogr.*, **52**, 267-75.

TRUEMAN, Sir A. (Ed.), 1954. *The coalfields of Great Britain*. London.

16

INDUSTRY

THE economic well-being of the British Isles is dependent primarily on the production and sale of manufactures. This group of small islands could not otherwise support its present high density of population. Although distinguished thus from many other parts of the world, the internal geography of the Isles is by no means everywhere dominated by manufacturing industry, the distribution of which is very uneven.

Full justice cannot be done in one short chapter to the data that are available. Perhaps the closest approach to objectivity is to be found in the statistics of employment published for local government areas in the industry tables of the decennial censuses of population. This is an indirect method since regional production cannot be conclusively measured in terms of only one of its factors: but statistics of employment are for various reasons more readily amenable than others to geographical analysis, and they do give a reasonably acceptable indication of the variation from place to place of industrial activity. Three maps from the 1951 tables, the latest published at the time of writing, must suffice here as the statistically descriptive foundation for this summary of the geography of manufacturing in the British Isles.

This chapter has three aims. The first is to show where manufacturing is more and where less important both absolutely and relatively. The second is to explain broadly these spatial variations; particularly in connection with the major features of regional specialisation and diversity today. The third is to discuss some current problems that relate to industrial location in the British Isles, and to offer some conclusions.

The variable spatial significance of manufacturing

Figure 38 shows the density by counties of employed population in the British Isles for 1951. A clear break in the intensity of shading has been contrived so that areas respectively above and below the average of 200 per square mile (80 per sq. km.) may be readily discerned. A county framework has been used because, whereas

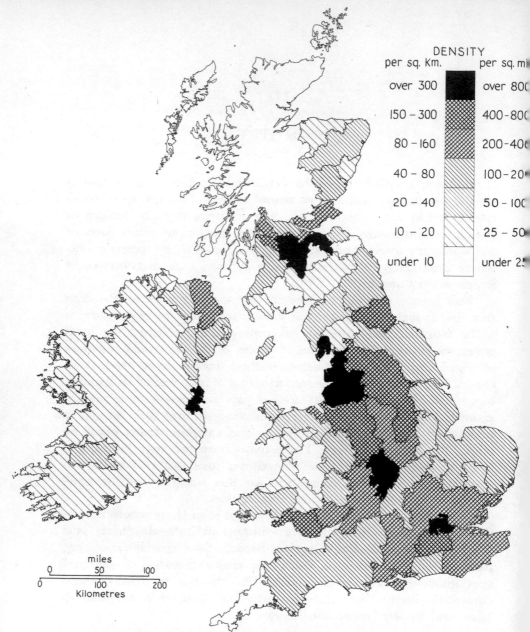

DENSITY

per sq. Km.		per sq. mi
over 300	███	over 800
150 – 300	▨	400 – 800
80 – 160	▨	200 – 400
40 – 80		100 – 200
20 – 40		50 – 100
10 – 20	⁄⁄⁄	25 – 50
under 10		under 25

miles
0   50   100
0   100   200
Kilometres

Fig. 38. DENSITY OF EMPLOYED POPULATION IN THE BRITISH ISLES, 1951.

the 1951 Census for England and Wales can be analysed by a finer framework (rural districts, urban districts, and county boroughs), the censuses of Eire, Northern Ireland, and Scotland cannot.

Within the limitations imposed by this framework the map shows three salient features. (i) The greater part of the British Isles has less than the average density of employment. (ii) There are two

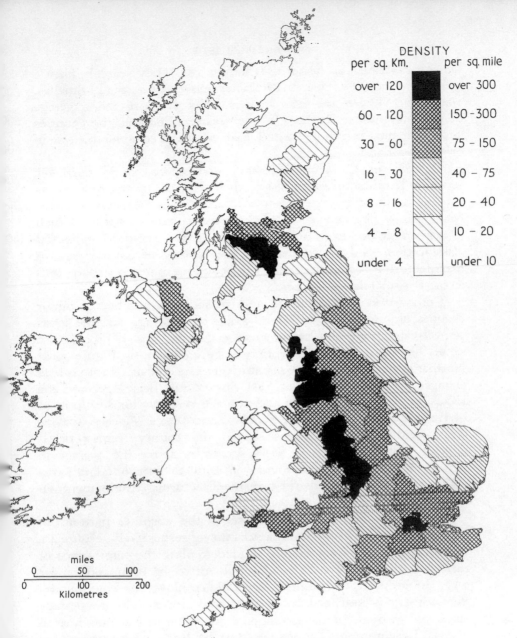

DENSITY

per sq. Km.		per sq. mile
over 120	▓	over 300
60 – 120	▦	150 – 300
30 – 60	▨	75 – 150
16 – 30	▨	40 – 75
8 – 16	▨	20 – 40
4 – 8	⁄	10 – 20
under 4	☐	under 10

miles
0   50   100
0   100   200
Kilometres

Fig. 39. DENSITY OF EMPLOYED POPULATION IN MANUFACTURING, 1951.

large areas of more than average density. The larger extends from Lancashire and the West Riding of Yorkshire through the Midlands into south Wales, in the form of a great 'crescent'. The smaller centres on London. These two areas are separated by a narrow strip of lower density comprising the counties of Northamptonshire and Oxfordshire, rather like the 'hour glass' pattern of population density described by Osborne (Chapter 18). They scarcely form a solid 'axial belt' (Taylor, 1938; Baker and Gilbert, 1944; Smailes, 1946). (iii) There are four smaller areas of more than average density comprising Durham in northeastern England, the counties of Dublin and Antrim in Ireland, and an area of considerable size in central Scotland.

If, however, the term 'industry' is considered in the narrower sense of 'manufacturing industry' then the map of employment as a whole needs to be supplemented. Figure 39 is introduced, there-fore, to show the density of employment in manufacturing, which is defined as orders 3 to 16 inclusive of the standard industrial classification used in the census. The density of employment in manufacturing is slightly under 75 per square mile (30 per sq. km.) in the British Isles as a whole.

Comparison of Figures 38 and 39 shows a number of minor changes among the counties in grade of shading, but the areas respectively above and below average density remain broadly the same. The most notable exception is the inclusion on Figure 39 of Northamptonshire in the area of above average density. Less notable changes are the exclusion of East Sussex and Berkshire, and the inclusion of Stirlingshire. In addition the very low density in most of Ireland and much of both Scotland and Wales is clearly shown. Thus, within the limitations set by the county framework, it appears that the two large areas shown as above the average in density of employment on Figure 38 unite to form one large area above the average in density of manufacturing employment on Figure 39.

Figures 38 and 39 approximate to the absolute patterns of employment in industry and manufacturing respectively. Figure 40, in contrast, shows by means of graded shading the significance of manufacturing relative to total employment in each county for 1951. In addition, the number of people employed by manufactur-ing industry is indicated by proportional circles. The percentage employed in manufacturing ranged from 58·68 in Renfrewshire to 3·57 in Roscommon. The average for the British Isles was 36·49, which in the key to the grades of shading has been rounded to 35%. (As a result Roxburgh is shown as being above the average when in fact it is 0·07% below it.) The county with the greatest total employed in manufacturing is Lancashire (1,202,671 in 1951). The smallest figure is for Nairn (322). The largest conurban total is that of Greater London (1,522,349): but, as Table 16 shows, manufacturing plays a smaller part in the employment structure of Greater London than it does in the employment structures of most other conurbations in England.

Table 16.

Conurbation	Employment in Manufacturing	
	Actual	As a percentage of total employment within each conurbation
Greater London	1,522,349	35.50
South East Lancashire (Manchester)	680,874	55.08
West Midlands (Birmingham)	691,430	61.61
West Yorkshire (Leeds-Bradford)	465,322	55.29
Merseyside (Liverpool)	206,021	34.55
Tyneside (Newcastle)	149,559	40.77

In view of what follows it is also worth noting that, among the counties around London and including London itself, Buckinghamshire, Middlesex, Essex, and Hertfordshire are above the average, while London, Surrey, and Kent are below it. Thus the major manufacturing region of Britain contracts in southeastern England on the evidence of Figure 40 in comparison with that of Figure 39. A similar contraction is apparent also towards the southwestern end of the industrial 'crescent', for both Monmouthshire and Glamorgan are slightly below the average for the British Isles. In addition, while Gloucestershire is only slightly above the average, the counties north of the Thames in the London region are above and well clear of the average (Table 17).

Table 17 and the evidence of Figure 40 thus place somewhat greater emphasis, so far as manufacturing industry is concerned, upon the existence of an 'axial belt' from Lancashire to London (but no farther southeastwards) than upon the 'crescent' from Liverpool to Swansea. The 'crescent' may be said to diminish in intensity towards its southwestern extremity, whereas in the 'axial belt' a high proportion of manufacturing to total employment is maintained from Leicestershire to the Thames estuary.

Differences may also be observed as between Figures 39 and 40 in the composition of the smaller manufacturing regions. Like south Wales and for a very similar reason, namely the high proportion of workers engaged in mining, Durham (23·95% employed in manufacturing) falls below average. Thus it does not appear as a manufacturing county on Figure 40. Antrim (44·72%) is clearly

301

Table 17.

| County | Employment in Manufacturing | |
	Actual	Percentage of total employment
Gloucestershire	158,347	38.22
Monmouthshire	159,503	34.25
Glamorgan	152,100	31.26
London	787,973	30.77
Middlesex	398,602	46.10
Essex	262,538	48.02
Hertfordshire	104,716	41.99
Buckinghamshire	74,617	43.20
Bedfordshire	73,050	48.67
Northamptonshire and Peterborough	94,735	48.52
Leicestershire	161,919	52.18

a manufacturing county on both maps: but Dublin (28·08%) fails to satisfy the criteria of Figure 40. In Scotland there are several differences. The counties flanking the Firth of Forth (Fife, Midlothian and West Lothian, respectively 30·71, 30·11, and 28·35%) are excluded from the manufacturing region of central Scotland on Figure 40, and Ayrshire (36·53%) is just included. In addition, Angus (44·53%) lies well above average on account of the importance of manufacturing in the employment structure of Dundee. In Roxburgh (36·42%), employment in manufacturing virtually equals the average on Figure 40 but falls well below the average density on Figure 39.

In sum, therefore, there are one large and several smaller regions of manufacturing in the British Isles. The status and shape of these regions vary according to the methods of representation adopted. Most of the British Isles is, however, below average in manufacturing employment whatever method is adopted. Much is very considerably below average, and in very few counties is manufacturing so dominant a feature of the employment structure as to exceed 50%.

Explanation of the regional form

The reasons for the present regional form of manufacturing in the British Isles are to be found first among those facts that have or have had a bearing on the location of manufacturing industry in general, and secondly among those facts whose influence has been applicable specifically to certain industries. Additionally the effect of successful local enterprise, leading in some cases to local special-isation selected from among the alternatives that might otherwise have been economically feasible, cannot be ignored.

The general facts have been (a) the location of the traditional populous area of greatest size in Britain, namely lowland England; (b) the location of the coalfields, and (c) the location of the market. Each of these has played a part in moulding the present pattern of manufacturing industry. Each has been relatively more important during certain periods of time and less important during others.

Before the industrial revolution manufacturing industry was very largely to be found in agricultural lowland England where most of the population lived and where London was already the most concentrated market in the British Isles. A smaller area of manufacturing existed in lowland Scotland in conjunction with Scottish agriculture. There was little development of manufacturing in Ireland, in Wales or in highland Britain in general. It should not therefore be assumed that the present patterns of population and manufacturing industry in the British Isles are either long-established or necessarily largely permanent. The twentieth-century trend is for lowland England to reassert its influence as the area in which people prefer to live and work. The location of the tra-ditional populous area of greatest size in Britain is not, therefore, without relevance today.

The influence of this fact diminished, however, with the in-creasing use of coal for fuel and power, from the industrial revolution to the early twentieth century. The exposed coalfields had previously been largely shunned by agriculture and population, because they were mainly within highland Britain or on its fringes. But now manufacturing industry expanded along with mining, and both activities resulted in a rapid increase in population on the coalfields. Thus the exploitation of the latter greatly modified the pattern of manufacturing in the British Isles. Nevertheless, while manu-facturing industry tended generally to stagnate or decline away from the coalfields in lowland England during the nineteenth century, population density remained high there and its growth continued. The effect of the influx of population and industry to the coalfields of Lancashire, Yorkshire, Derbyshire and Notting-hamshire, the Midlands, and south Wales was, therefore, to extend northwards and westwards the already populous area of lowland England. This enlarged area remains the dominant region today in the economic geography of the British Isles. As Figure 39 shows, however, not all of it is above average in density of manufacturing employment and the area is reduced still further on Figure 40 where the relative proportion engaged in manufacturing is shown. It seems, therefore, that neither the location of the traditional populous area (lowland England), nor the location of the coalfields, can together account for the present regional form of manufacturing in the southern half of Britain. The straightforward superimposition of the two cannot alone explain the proportionately low level of employment in manufacturing present today either in much of lowland England or on the south Wales coalfield. Likewise the proportionately low level of manufacturing on the coalfield of Northumberland and Durham and the high level in Antrim cannot be accounted for in terms of the general facts so far presented.

During the twentieth century the direct use of coal in manufacturing industry has been increasingly replaced by electricity from the mains. The cost of fuel and power, and the cost of transport have risen less than many other costs, and both form a smaller proportion of total costs now than they did during the nineteenth century. Proximity to market rather than to fuel has thus increased in importance, while proximity to raw materials has in general become less important.

Since transport costs have declined relative to costs of labour, and since lavish use is now made of road transport for distribution, it is not clear at first sight how proximity to market may have reduced costs of production in industry generally. It would seem, however, that proximity to market affects the attainment of increasing economies of scale, in concert with the psychological easing of the task of management. Given a large potential market close at hand the chance of growth taking place is greater because opportunities are more readily discernible. Thus a large town gives greater scope than a small town for economies of scale in the production of consumer goods especially. The task of management in planning where and how to market the product is made easier. Far more careful consideration must be given to problems of marketing from a plant located in, say, Northern Ireland than from a plant located near London, although the extra costs of transport incurred in coping with the extra distance may not be large.

London has always been the largest compact market in the British Isles. It stimulated production in lowland England and within its own bounds before the industrial revolution. In the twentieth century it has resumed this role with renewed force, and

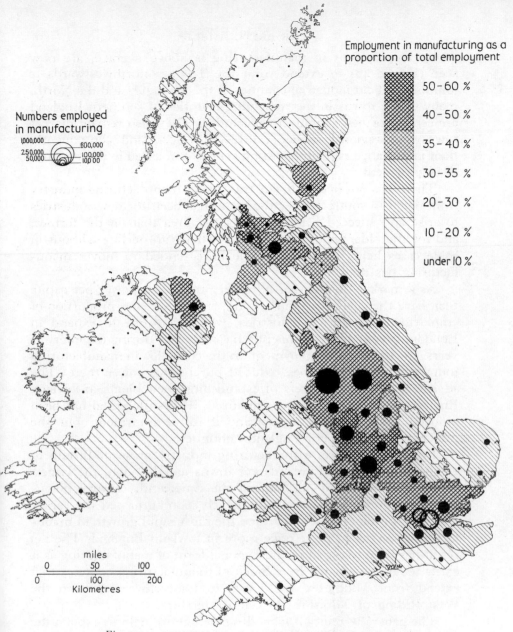

Employment in manufacturing as a proportion of total employment

50 - 60 %
40 - 50 %
35 - 40 %
30 - 35 %
20 - 30 %
10 - 20 %
under 10 %

Numbers employed in manufacturing

1,000,000
600,000
250,000
100,000
50,000
100'00

miles
0   50   100
0   100   200
Kilometres

Fig. 40.   NUMBERS EMPLOYED IN MANUFACTURING, 1951.

many industries, newly developed during the past fifty years, have been set up not only in and around London but also in the towns of lowland England in preference to those of most of the coalfields. This latter trend is more clearly apparent between London and the Midlands, but towns elsewhere in lowland England have also expanded as centres of manufacturing. Thus although the counties,

305

whose employment in manufacturing is above average, are now seen (Figure 40) to extend from the Thames northwestwards to join the coalfield industrial counties of the Midlands and the North, many of the towns in the remaining counties of southern England are centres of new manufacturing today. They also remain market towns and regional service centres, however, and consequently their importance as manufacturing centres is masked in the statistics of employment.

There has not been a major transfer of manufacturing industry from north to south. Rather the trend has been for new industries to arise and succeed better in the latter area than in the former, and for the older industries of the coalfields to decline without in some cases being replaced. People have tended to move: manufacturing has not.

As a market London has a higher purchasing power per capita than have the coalfield conurbations; and the greater proportion of employment in service industries, which continue to expand in London, gave stability to this purchasing power during the interwar years. In contrast unemployment on the coalfields in manufacturing industry and in the mines reduced purchasing power there. The advantage to manufacturers of establishing their plants in lowland England was thereby further enhanced. This differential has been reduced since the war by continued full employment, but the preference for southern England continues.

In sum, therefore, manufacturing industry arose in Britain in company with agriculture, market towns and London, the largest commercial centre of all. During the nineteenth century manufacturing spread to the coalfields which soon surpassed the earlier .·rea in importance. But since 1900 the most rapid growth of manufacturing has taken place once more in lowland England. The net result has been to establish the regional form of manufacturing as it exists today, dominated by a block of manufacturing counties that extend from Middlesex and Essex to Lancashire and from the West Riding of Yorkshire to Gloucestershire.

The generally-relevant facts discussed above help to explain the regional form of manufacturing in the British Isles today. They do not so readily explain the smaller regions, notably in south Wales, Antrim, and Northumberland and Durham, and they throw little light on the detailed regional composition of the structure of manufacturing industry in the British Isles as a whole. Specifically-relevant facts are needed, therefore, to add depth to the description so far presented.

Regional *specialisation* of manufacturing is the dominant fact to emerge from a study of the nineteenth century industrial geography of Britain. Regional *diversity* of manufacturing has in contrast been the dominant evolutionary development during the twentieth century. Thus no large specialised regions have come into being during the last sixty years, although a number of towns in lowland England have become specialised. Diversification has not made equal progress everywhere, however, and much regional specialisation remains as a legacy from the nineteenth century.

Heavy industry including iron and steel is still outstanding in central Scotland, on the northeast coast of England, and in south Wales. Steel, cutlery, and tools characterise the Sheffield district. Textiles are highly significant in west Yorkshire and to a smaller degree in the east Midlands (Nottingham and Leicester); and, notwithstanding a rapid decline in recent years, cotton is still the leading trade of Lancashire. Footwear manufacture, dominant in Northamptonshire, overlaps the textile region of the east Midlands around Leicester. The 'Potteries' district is synonymous with Stoke-on-Trent and the north Staffordshire coalfield. In contrast, however, the 'Black Country' of the west Midlands no longer specialises in heavy industry as it did until the third quarter of the nineteenth century. It has become instead a highly-varied metalware, engineering, and vehicle manufacturing region, and is now more akin to lowland England in the structure of its manufacturing economy than to the coalfield industrial regions of highland Britain.

Given the technological circumstances of the time, regional specialisation of industry in Britain during the nineteenth century seems to some extent to obey the law of comparative advantage. Coalfields were the best areas in which to undertake manufacturing: but some coalfields were clearly more suited to certain industries than to others. Furthermore certain industries (e.g. footwear) had less need of a coalfield location than others. Thus regional specialisation ranged from heavy industry in central Scotland and south Wales, and on the northeast coast, for which access to tidewater for receipt of raw materials and more significantly for despatch to overseas markets was as important as the local availability of coal, to footwear manufacture which needed simply to concentrate in order to achieve locational economies, and did so at first in Northamptonshire where there is no local coalfield. Textile manufacture was obliged to seek interior locations: cotton on the Lancashire coalfield; wool on the west Yorkshire coalfield, and knitwear in the east Midlands. All three could have succeeded equally well on coastal coalfields: but there they would have had to compete with the heavy industries for resources especially of capital, management and labour. The need of the heavy industries for coastal location was greater than that of textiles, and as long as the former remained profitable they seem to have had the power to shut out or strangle other industries competing for resources. The decline of the cotton industry of the Glasgow district after about 1860 is clear evidence of inability to compete within the local economy.

It would appear therefore, that, while regional specialisation was necessary during the nineteenth century in order to achieve external economies, the heavy industries were able to pre-empt the use of the coastal coalfields. As long as the heavy industries remained highly profitable few other major productive activities were feasible save the export of raw coal. During the interwar period, however, heavy industry and coalmining declined markedly in profitability. Meanwhile technology of power and transport had advanced so far that lighter industries no longer found coal-field locations economically advantageous. The possibility of introducing a new specialisation, as took place for example on Clydeside during the nineteenth century, had greatly declined. The age of coalfield specialisation had passed, and in the age of diversification not only did proximity to coal seem unnecessary but also many of the coalfields and their associated industrial areas seemed highly unattractive environments in which to establish new plants.

Since the coastal coalfields were pre-occupied with heavy in-dustry and coal exports during the nineteenth century, lighter industries had to make do with the interior fields. Comparative advantage for industrial location declined from the coastal fields inland. Similarly, however, it declined among the interior fields themselves to some extent. Thus Lancashire came to specialise in cotton textiles because of its superior accessibility to overseas supplies and markets. Cotton was primarily an export industry and the overseas market for cloth was expanding rapidly. Wool in contrast was expanding less quickly and primarily supplying the home market. The exposed coalfield of west Yorkshire was, there-fore, a good enough location for wool manufacture and better in respect of water supply than some other interior fields. What confirmed its specialised development was, however, that among the earlier, major, handloom-weaving districts it was the only one situated on a coalfield. Knitwear and footwear, both of which also supplied mainly the home market, had little need of coalfield locations, nor could they hope to compete for resources on coalfields or in other areas where concentrations of other locationally more demanding industries were expanding. But they stood to gain themselves through concentration, and any otherwise largely disengaged area with appropriate urban nuclei and surplus rural labour could have served their purpose. Somewhere in lowland England was, therefore, indicated. In the event knitwear came to concentrate near the 'spare' coalfields of Derbyshire, Nottingham-shire and Leicestershire, while footwear first chose central North-amptonshire where there is no local coalfield. The subsequent development of footwear around Leicester was a function of expansion and the need for labour rather than coal.

Textiles were excluded from south Yorkshire (Sheffield), the Potteries, and the west Midlands (Birmingham and the Black Country) because these areas were already engaged in developing successful specialisms simultaneously with the expansion of the cotton industry of Lancashire. Neither north Staffordshire nor Sheffield was exclusively well endowed by nature to become a centre of pottery and steel manufacture respectively, though certain favourable physical conditions can be adduced to help explain their early development. But neither area is wholly unique in these res-pects and physical determinism will not adequately serve as the basis for a causal analysis. Both industries were, however, similar in their need for large amounts of coal and also in the high value in relation to the weight of their products and to the value of their raw materials. Sheffield steel is much more costly than run-of-the-mill steel made for example at Scunthorpe. The manufacture of pottery at Stoke is not so demanding of the physical environment as is the manufacture of cheap bricks at Bedford or cement along the Thames estuary. Why the north Staffordshire coalfield came to be chosen from among those possible for specialisation on pottery manufacture, and the south Yorkshire coalfield for fine steel is very largely a matter of economic history and individual enterprise rather than physical geography. While these industries could have succeeded on certain other interior coalfields or even have changed places, their success would probably have been neither greater nor less as a result.

The existence and prosperity of the west Midlands industrial region is less difficult to explain. Its early development was depend-ent on three facts. (i) The region possessed a coalfield containing a thick seam (30 ft.; 9 m.) of easily won coal. (ii) It was situated well towards the centre of lowland England. (iii) As a small, agricul-turally-unattractive upland it was sparsely peopled and so had much room to develop once industry arose.

There were, therefore, few man-made restrictions to limit the enterprise of those who came to develop the coalfield and to live there, while progress in transport raised the value of its natural resources in relation to the major market and populous area of Britain at that time. Men of enterprise and initiative found it easier to seek opportunity and refuge on the Birmingham plateau than to go to south Wales or the northeast coast, or to emigrate; and natural resources and scope for freedom of action were superior on the south Staffordshire coalfield than in the other two midland coalfields (Mid-Warwickshire, and Leicestershire and south Derby-shire). Perhaps a similar black country could also have arisen in the Erewash valley between Nottinghamshire and Derbyshire, but the restrictive influence of the nearby towns of Nottingham and Derby seems to have been too great to have allowed the growth of a Birmingham or a Manchester to give commercial cohesion and impetus to the Erewash valley.

Thus close contact with lowland England and restrictions on the development of other midland coalfields gave the west Midlands an early advantage so far as manufacturing was concerned. The re-gion came to serve as the workshop of Britain before Britain became the workshop of the world.

Great enterprise, the ability to innovate, and the readiness to seek and accept changes in products enabled the west Midlands to survive and expand when competition arose from the coastal coal-fields in heavy industry during the nineteenth century. Continued enterprise and versatility coupled with its position within lowland England have likewise enabled the region to participate fully in the new 'prosperity through diversity' of the twentieth century.

It appears, therefore, that comparative advantage for manu-facturing has operated in a variable fashion in the history of indus-trial location in the British Isles. Before the industrial revolution, London and certain parts of lowland England were the best-endowed areas. During the eighteenth and early nineteenth centuries the west Midland region rose to prominence as a manufacturing area and its coalfield specialised on heavy industry. Its resources and its position relative to the major markets in Britain gave it an unrivalled ad-vantage over other coalfield regions. In the nineteenth century, however, as overseas markets rapidly expanded, the coastal coal-fields became the best areas for industry. But heavy industry took precedence; and because these areas were also the best from which to export coal, manufacturing did not expand sufficiently in south Wales and in Northumberland and Durham to become dominant in the employment structure. (Hence these regions do not stand out as manufacturing areas on Figure 40.) In central Scotland, where the export of coal was not so prominent a feature of the economy, manufacturing industry and especially heavy industry did, however, become dominant in the employment structure. As a result the west Midland region lost its advantage for specialisation in heavy industry, but it retained advantages for industry in general and so was able to develop new enterprises and to diversify.

Between these advantageous extremes, namely, the coastal coalfields of highland Britain and the west Midland coalfield of lowland England, were the less advantageous but nevertheless specialised manufacturing regions mainly located on interior coalfields. Which coalfield came to be chosen probably mattered little; and it would not be possible in purely economic and geographic terms to account, for example, both for the great and highly-specialised development of manufacturing on the north Staffordshire coalfield and for the comparative neglect of manufacturing on the Leicestershire and south Derbyshire coalfield. It is impossible to know whether Sheffield and Stoke were the most profitable places respectively for steel and pottery manufacture in Great Britain, or what difference in profit would now result if their roles had been reversed. It seems unlikely that the difference would be great.

One major specialised region, Antrim, remains to be discussed. Antrim is the only county in Ireland where employment in manufacturing exceeds the average for the British Isles (Fig. 40). Dublin county has a density of employment in manufacturing that exceeds the average (Fig. 39), but as in London the proportion employed in service industries is well above average. Elsewhere in Ireland manufacturing is little in evidence. Its absence is not hard to explain. No coalfields of consequence, a low standard of living and of purchasing power giving rise to a poor home market, general economic neglect for centuries, mass migration and a declining population for much of the period since 1850, have all combined to discourage the development of manufacturing except in Protestant Ulster and especially County Antrim. Two industries have dominated the employment structure, shipbuilding at Belfast and linen manufacture there and in other towns in Antrim and elsewhere in Ulster.

Shipbuilding at Belfast is in effect an extension of shipbuilding

311

on Clydeside: that is, of part of the industrial structure of central Scotland. Water transport makes this industry more feasible than any other heavy industry for Northern Ireland.

Linen antedates cotton as a textile industry and was formerly more widespread in the British Isles. Its development was actively discouraged in Britain in favour of wool before the industrial revolution, and subsequently it was ousted from Lancashire and much of central Scotland by the more profitable and rapidly-expanding cotton industry. Only in Northern Ireland was it able to compete effectively on a considerable scale for local resources, and its success there once more illustrates the operation of the law of comparative advantage in the context of nineteenth-century regional specialisation in manufacturing.

Present-day problems

The problems of industrial location in the British Isles today are twofold. First is the regional one. Industry is unequally concentrated in (a) one large region consisting of the counties extending from London to Lancashire and from west Yorkshire to Gloucestershire, which if density (Fig. 39) is taken as the criterion reaches also into south Wales and beyond London to the south coast of England; and (b) several smaller regions in highland Britain. It should be noted, however, that all these regions whether large or small are essentially political and statistical entities. They do not imply a landscape choked everywhere with industrial buildings and settlement. The intensity of incidence of manufacturing varies within them as a feature of the landscape and each region, whether large or small, can be further subdivided. Secondly there is a developmental problem, with the division of the British Isles into (a) a diversified southeastern area comprising London, the Midlands conurbations, and other towns of much of lowland England; and (b) the remainder of the British Isles, characterised so far as manufacturing is concerned by regional specialisation. The populous area of medieval times has reasserted itself as the diversified area in the twentieth century. The specialised manufacturing and coalfield regions tend in contrast to remain specialised and to find new industry hard to attract when replacement of a declining specialisation is needed. The efficient location of industrial expansion in relation to the distribution of population and of invested capital is the outstanding issue of British economic geography today.

This is well shown in the London region and in Northern Ireland.

Whereas in the former, population, industry and the number of jobs continue to grow and labour is scarce, in the latter region, population and industry expand more slowly, and unemployment is well above the national level. In a slump the situation in Northern Ireland, south Wales, central Scotland and on the northeast coast of England would rapidly deteriorate. But a slump of the 1930 order of magnitude is not now envisaged and therefore the problem of regional profitability for manufacturing in the regional social context is the dominant one.

Three questions arise. Should expanding industries be allowed to seek their own locations? Should they be directed to locate more evenly in relation to the existing distribution of population? What are the econo-geographic bases upon which a reasonably adequate compromise can be reached between these two opposing views?

The last question is the crucial one; and it is impossible to answer it wholly objectively because many of the facts are unknown if not unknowable. The paramount fact is that in times of full employment and expanding economy almost any sizeable settlement in the British Isles could serve as a profitable location for well-managed manufacturing industry. What range of industries would be suitable in any particular place still remains in doubt as does the degree to which profitability may vary from industry to industry and from place to place. In times of economic contraction it seems likely that the area of profitability would contract southeastwards and narrow about the London-Birmingham-Nottingham triangle which seems to have been the most viable area for industry in all conditions during the present century. This may, however, be a spurious judgment because the assumed reduced viability of the outlying regions may in part be due to their high degree of specialisation. If in times of expansion diversification could be introduced to the outlying regions, economic contraction might have far less dire effects.

The evidence of the systematic geographical analysis of particular types of industry favours this view. Plants engaged in light engineering, light chemicals, electrical equipment, plastics, rubber, hosiery, footwear, clothing, food, drink and tobacco and many other expanding light industries are functioning quite satisfactorily in most parts of the British Isles. They are not exclusively found only in lowland England. So the tendency of many managements in these industries to prefer locations in lowland England and especially in the London region does not conclusively establish the greater profitability of that area. The preference may in part be

313

personal and social in the popular sense rather than narrowly economic. Proximity to a large market was important in the growth of many firms that are now well established, and it remains helpful to the managements of many small firms that are striving to expand: but the wish of expanding large and medium-sized firms to stay near London can no longer be so readily justified in terms either of the cost of transport to market or of the executive need for proximity between the factory and the hub of the market. To leave lowland England altogether or to set up a second factory in central Scotland, for example, is undoubtedly somewhat irksome to management: it need not be uneconomic to the firm. Lower costs resulting from cheaper labour and freedom from congestion may more than compensate for the adverse effect of greater distance either upon the tasks of management or upon the cost of transporting materials and products. Indeed one may wonder at times whether the choice of location for expansion depends more upon the desire to minimise managerial effort and inconvenience than upon the urge to maximise profit.

In recent years the automobile industry has been encouraged to set up new plants in northern England and in Scotland, areas from which this industry was virtually absent formerly. If these enterprises succeed, the case for the direction of many other expanding industries will have been strengthened. But the automobile industry is made up of large firms and large plants; and it is easier and safer to urge new and distant locations upon large firms than upon smaller ones. Many more large-scale plants have found, or have been found, sites outside the London-Birmingham-Nottingham triangle than within it since the war (Willatts, 1962). The reverse has been truer of smaller firms, though some of these have set up factories in country towns and in the older coalfield industrial regions (Johnston, 1955; Weekley, 1957). To resuscitate the latter far more rapid development along these lines is needed.

Resuscitation is probably not everywhere desirable, however. The congested industrial towns of the coalfield conurbations contain much old property and much drabness. Some of them lack the space to rebuild because they are almost surrounded by other similar settlements. To help the population to remain in these conditions by bringing in new industry might be less socially desirable than to encourage gradual migration to towns in lowland England. Resuscitation must imply improvement in living conditions as well as the introduction of new industry. The limit is set by the former rather than by the latter.

Conclusion

It seems that London, the west and east Midlands and most of the towns of lowland England will continue to thrive and expand as centres of manufacturing. However restrictive a policy is adopted there towards large firms, small firms will arise in their place. The major problems in this area are those of London, but since they derive more from the expansion of service industries in central locations than from the expansion of manufacturing, they cannot appropriately be discussed here. Large-scale manufacturing industry would gain little real advantage through being nearer to the European mainland than it is today. It is already being actively discouraged from expanding in London. How far it should be increasingly discouraged from expanding in southeastern England generally must depend partly on the degree to which resuscitation of the coalfield industrial areas is deemed necessary. Small-scale industry must be allowed free rein, however, for proximity to London at first, and subsequently the maximum scope for small-scale salesmanship in Europe through location in southeastern England may well prove the key factor in stimulating growth. But once these small firms have reached the size at which field sales representatives can be employed, expansion near London need not continue.

Great anxiety need not be felt for the future prosperity of Lancashire and the West Riding of Yorkshire which together form the northern component of the large manufacturing region of England (Fig. 40). The cotton industry is declining but diverse industries are replacing it. Older skilled workers suffer more than the young from changes of this kind. The Yorkshire woollen and worsted trades are declining less rapidly than cotton because they have always been largely dependent on the home market, and potential competition from imports is less severe. Should a more rapid decline ensue, however, there is no reason to suppose that diversification would not be as successful in west Yorkshire as it is in Lancashire. The highly-specialised steel district centred upon Sheffield in south Yorkshire could present more serious problems of re-development if the demand for special steels, cutlery, tools and 'bespoke' steel articles declined, but the likelihood of a marked and permanent decline taking place seems remote at present.

Apart, therefore, from problems of rehousing, re-adjustment to new trades in some places, and a number of local 'black spots' in which new industries seem reluctant to settle, the viability of Lancashire and the West Riding is not greatly in doubt. Some settlements will doubtless decline but the prospect for the area as a whole is reasonably secure.

South Wales and the northeast coast, as Figure 40 shows, are not preponderantly manufacturing regions. Coalmining is still a very large employer of labour, and many places are still highly dependent upon it. Employment in manufacturing is largely concerned with heavy industry, and furthermore the areal patterns of coalmining and manufacturing do not coincide. At present heavy industry, save for some anxiety over shipbuilding, is prosperous. Coalmining in some places is not. Thus the need for new industries is felt more today in the mining valleys and uplands than in the coastal and estuarine urban areas. Local shifts of population seem an inevitable prospect for the future: but there is space on the coastal lowlands both of south Wales and of Northumberland, Durham and north Yorkshire for new manufacturing communities to arise. Both areas are as well placed for overseas trade today as in the past and, if the replacement by new industries of coalmining and such industries as are declining is deemed socially appropriate, such a policy could be promoted with benefit to the national economy. There is no economic need to allow these regions to run down in favour of a shift of population back into lowland England.

Central Scotland also has problems that derive from the decline of coalmining but it is primarily a manufacturing region as gauged by statistics of employment. As a whole the region is well represented in a wide range of industries. Locally, however, specialisation is more nearly the rule. Furthermore many of the industries represented are either heavy ones or diminished remnants of activities that were formerly more widespread; and problems of rehousing occur that are similar to those of the coalfield industrial areas farther south. It appears that, if the Scottish economy is to be reactivated, importation and resurgence of managerial enterprise is needed mainly to innovate but also to cope with the minor inconveniences of relative isolation and distance from the large market in the southern half of Britain. It is not a problem of higher costs of transport that besets Scottish industry. Distance to market is unimportant in this respect for most light manufactures. Costs might indeed be lower in Scotland because labour is probably cheaper there; and one can hardly credit that productivity would be less than in the south if modern methods of production and management were adopted to the full.

Northern Ireland is the only sizeable area in the United Kingdom where unemployment has been a consistently serious problem since the war. Even in times of over-full employment elsewhere in the United Kingdom, industrialists have been reluctant to go to Northern Ireland to establish new plants. Some have of course gone either independently or in response to the advertising campaign sponsored by the Northern Ireland Government, but not enough. In addition, the shipbuilding, textile and aircraft industries are not expanding at present and the home market of Northern Ireland is small. As well as distance from southern Britain the region suffers the additional inconvenience of the Irish Sea crossing with no likelihood there of a tunnel or a bridge because the demand is too small.

These difficulties are not insuperable. Many industries can succeed just as well in Northern Ireland as elsewhere in the United Kingdom. Belfast is no more inaccessible from the major markets of Europe and the world than are parts of Scandinavia. Perhaps a population of one and a third millions is not large enough to produce an adequate amount of enterprise. Certainly, however, though aid and enterprise from without may always be helpful it is neither so dependable nor so helpful as enterprise and initiative born at home.

In Eire manufacturing industry is poorly developed and amounts to only about 15% of total employment as against 40% in agriculture and fishing. Food, drink and tobacco, clothing, transport equipment and textiles comprised 117,000 out of 184,000 employed in manufacturing in 1951. Since then a certain amount of new industry has been developed, especially by European firms. But here too home enterprise in both manufacturing industry and agriculture is essential to economic progress.

The British Isles today have no greater, perhaps no other, resources than enterprise, skill, a high standard of education, a great amount of invested capital, and goodwill in the free world. These are the foundations upon which further economic development must be built. It is perhaps easier or more convenient and socially acceptable now to be enterprising in southern Britain than elsewhere in the British Isles. But for enterprise to be successful it is not necessarily restricted to choosing locations in southern Britain. As great or even greater economic success can possibly be achieved in the traditional manufacturing regions and elsewhere. But the hard facts of accountancy are lacking to prove this contention. The only real evidence for its validity is that of new enterprises that have succeeded in the traditional manufacturing regions. This evidence is, however, an inadequate basis upon which to formulate a policy for industrial location. Until truly objective data relevant to costs, prices and profits are made available and analysed geographically with the aid of modern computing equipment and techniques, a convincing objective view will be lacking. It is sadly needed for both social and economic reasons. But one should remember always that the maintenance of an expanding economy is the need above all else, if a gradual and beneficent solution to the social and economic problems of location is to be found.

References

CENSUS, ENGLAND AND WALES, 1957. *Census 1951, England and Wales*. Industry Tables.

CENSUS, SCOTLAND, 1956. *Census 1951, Scotland*, Vol. IV. Occupations and Industries.

CENSUS, NORTHERN IRELAND, 1953-5. *Census of Population of Northern Ireland, 1951*.

CENSUS, IRELAND, 1954. *Census of Population of Ireland*, 1951, Vol. III, Part 2, Industries and Industrial Status.

BAKER, J. N. L., and GILBERT, E. W., 1944. The doctrine of an axial belt of industry in England. *Geogr. J.*, **103-4**, 49-73.

HILL, C., 1954. Some aspects of industrial location. *J. Industr. Econ.*, **2**, 184-92.

JOHNSTON, W. B., 1955. The East Midlands and post-war development in manufacturing. *East Midl. Geogr.*, **1**, pt. 4, 3-18.

SCOTTISH COUNCIL (Development and Industry), 1961. *Inquiry into the Scottish Economy*, 1960-61.

SMAILES, A. E., 1946. The urban mesh of England and Wales. *Trans. Inst. Brit. Geogr.*, **11**, 85-101.

TAYLOR, E. G. R., (and others), 1938. Discussion on the geographical distribution of industry. *Geogr. J.*, **92**, 22-39.

WEEKLEY, I. G., 1957. Industry in the small country towns of Lincolnshire, Northamptonshire and Rutland. *East Midl. Geogr.*, **1**, 21-30.

WILLATTS, E. C., 1962. Post-war developments: the location of major projects in England and Wales. *Chart. Surv.*, **94**, 356-63 and 436-8.

17

TRANSPORTATION

TRANSPORTATION in Britain is at a parting of ways for the direction of future developments. In the sister island of Ireland, with comparatively little traffic potential, trains have been withdrawn from much of the railway network. Britain, more heavily industrialised and populated, longer retained traffic on the railway routes. Laissez-faire policies lay behind the provision of canals, of railways and of road services. However, new appraisals have been made, and decisions in the early 1960s will determine transport facilities for the rest of the century.

Waterways

Coastal shipping has varied greatly with technology. When craft were small they could safely lie on the ground at low water. Harbours and creeks, now considered useless, once carried a coastal traffic of significance: Lothian coal shipments from Port Seton, and Cornish kaolin from Newquay can serve as examples. As vessels became larger, approach channels had to be dredged, quays with deep water alongside constructed, and more elaborate shore equipment provided and thus traffic became concentrated on ports better situated in relation to seaways or populated districts.

Physical conditions for coastal shipping are not always easy: shallows narrow apparently broad estuaries such as the Thames and the Tay; services can be delayed by gales and strong tidal currents; crowded east coast estuaries are difficult to navigate in the fogs prevalent in summer. The considerable tidal rise is a handicap to providing cross-Channel train ferries; it must be remembered that the difference of gauge between railways in Ireland and Britain prevented their use across the Irish Sea.

While the tonnage of coastal shipping arrivals and departures has increased since 1938, there is a change in the services. Passenger services demand a fixed departure time and this often means that vessels have to sail before the cargo offering is fully loaded, and after 1945 the passenger service on the London-Leith run was not restored because of this drawback. The Dundee-London shipping

319

service, started in the days of sailing vessels, was withdrawn recently and the cargoes sent instead by special trains three times a week; the 'shipping company' continues but merely functions as a forwarding agency. In the case of services to the northern and western isles the number of ports of call has been reduced and road vehicles are used to distribute from main ports such as Lerwick. Commercial interests are tending to concentrate on a few regional ports for distribution of their product; e.g., cement carried from the Thames estuary to a bulk store in Aberdeen for distribution in northern Scotland.

The heavy capital cost of a modern ship is leading to the absorption of local companies by the larger unit; in 1961 the North of Scotland, Orkney and Shetland Shipping Company was acquired by Coast Lines Limited. Rising labour costs on the ships and at docks make the economical operation more difficult and so marginal services will be withdrawn unless a subsidy is obtained. The North Isles service in the Shetland Islands is threatened, the North Isles service in Orkney is now with a vessel built by government funds and the shipping firm of MacBrayne, serving the Western Isles, has long had a heavy government subsidy. As long as island groups are populated, coastal services are needed to 'bridge' the sea gap. As regards the Channel ferry services, they are within sight of the end if a tunnel or bridge is constructed between Dover and Calais; military fears no longer stand in the way since long range weapons and aircraft have now largely nullified the moat-value of the Straits of Dover.

Inland navigation. Many rivers, not now regarded as navigable, were used in medieval times by small boats and when trade increased rivers were deepened to the new industrial areas. Rivers meander and are subject to seasonal floods and low water and so attention was turned to the artificial 'navigation cut'. The first modern British canal of this type was that sanctioned in 1755 to allow coal to be sent from the Wigan coalfield. Many miles of canal were cut by the navvies before 1815, but unfortunately they were nearly all planned by small local concerns with limited perspective; dimensions were varied and small, locks were small and numerous, and tunnels confined, but these canals did allow mass movement for the first time in inland areas such as Birmingham. Canals were dug in many parts of the British Isles. The Royal Commission on Canals and Waterways reported in 1909 that attention should be concentrated on the cross-canals of Mersey-Thames and Humber-Severn and since then there has been improvement by the Grand Union

Canal Company (an amalgamation of minor companies in 1930), of the route between London and the Midlands.

British canals suffer from their narrow cross-section, which results in small-capacity craft and means wash from boats damages the banks unless they are concreted; from the need to cross frequent hills (across the scarplands between London and Avonmouth, 125 locks in 178 miles (285 km.)); from the difficulty of providing adequate catchment basins at the various summits to replace the loss of water by seepage and at locks; and from the subsidence in the mining districts. Canals helped to create the eighteenth century industrialisation but, from the building congestion of Victorian industrial towns, cannot be readily extended to meet changing needs.

A canal could create traffic but lost it rapidly to a railway when a line was constructed to serve the same area, because the rail did not close with frost or summer drought, was speedy, and could readily enter a factory by a siding. Only occasionally, with special circumstances, did a canal hold appreciable traffic against rail competition. Nowadays the reduced traffic does not cover the cost of maintenance, let alone the interest charges, and powers are being sought to abandon more canals; e.g., in 1962 for the Forth and Clyde Canal. An advantage of closing a canal to navigation is that swing and hump-back bridges can be removed and road conditions thereby improved, but there is often a claim made by riparian owners for maintenance of the water for either farm or industrial needs.

The two government-sponsored canals in Britain, the Crinan and Caledonian, have never been a commercial success. The only British ship canal for large vessels is the Manchester Ship Canal opened in 1894. It was not a financial success for twenty years but from the start it allowed Manchester to function as a port and there is a developed waterfront along part of the 35 miles (55 km.) between the city and the open sea.

Traffic on the narrow-section canals is now negligible. In the early days fly-boats carried passengers along some of the canals and the modern version of this is the holiday cruise. The canal service can rarely compete with the railway and still less with the road, but perhaps a more vigorous life might have been displayed if the companies had acted as carriers and not just provided the routeway.

Railways

It is over two hundred years since the first railway was constructed in Britain and over 130 years since the first steam locomo-

tive pulled a passenger train on the Liverpool and Manchester
Railway. The spectacular financial success of this company led to
the first trunk railway (the London and Birmingham opened in
1838), and its success triggered off a speculators' mania for railway
schemes. Competitive lines were encouraged by a Parliament
frightened of monopoly, a real fear because railway companies not
only provided the track but also acted as the sole carrier along
the route. Into towns too small to provide much traffic, two companies ran lines: Ayr (population 9,308 in 1861) was the largest
burgh in Scotland served by only one railway company. Today
many of these competitive links and stations have been removed
but in times of flood, blizzard, and war there has been some value
in having alternative routes.

Railways in Britain were probably the most expensive per mile
in the world because of their massive engineering works and
heavy legal costs, although it must be remembered that many rural
lines, regarded as feeders, were cheaply built. Originally, these
minor lines were also cheaply worked but now the shorter working
week means either more staffing or overtime rates and so the running
costs rise without any more traffic.

In recent years the railway operators have won the right to make
more competitive contracts for services rendered and can strike
separate bargains with large users instead of having to treat all alike.
The basis of charging for most purposes is distance run and this
can add materially to the cost with circuitous routes: an extreme
example is the journey between Bristol and Wick which is 495
miles (800 km.) in a direct line, 652 miles (1,050 km.) by the shortest
practical roads and 701 miles (1,130 km.) by rail: this is equivalent
to Wick being as far as the Faeroes in direct distance from Bristol.

The rail services developed against a background of an expanding Victorian industrialisation based on coal. Twentieth-century
industry turning from coal to oil and to electricity has led to a
decline in the transport of coal, as also has the change in space
heating: Blair Castle in Perthshire used to burn 350 tons of coal
a year but now it needs just a minute fraction of that tonnage.
Heavy industry is declining and, apart from this, technological
improvements in smelting have greatly reduced the coal consumption to produce a ton of steel. There is a change too in industrial

Fig. 41 (*opposite*). PASSENGER FACILITIES 1899-1962 (SUMMER TIME-TABLES). The pecked
lines represent steamship routes that offered passenger-carrying facilities in 1899 but did
not do so in 1962. The dots represent stations that were open for passengers in 1899 but
were not in 1962. The Channel Islands are ignored in this map and in Figures 42 and
43, as their services are regarded as outwith the normal services of the country.

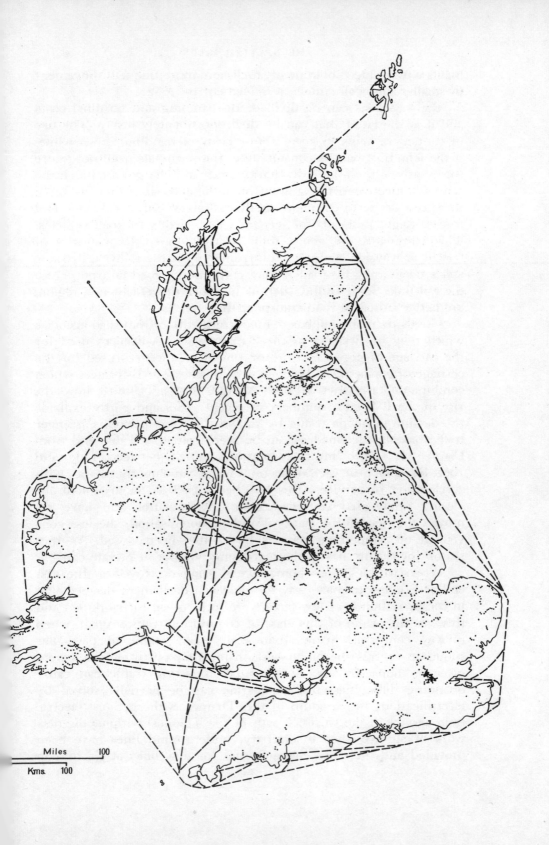

Miles 100
Kms. 100

habits with reduced holding of stocks and more frequent movement in smaller lots well suited to movement by road.

Railway costs can be divided into running and terminal costs and it is the latter that can be disproportionately heavy. The use of containers helps to keep labour costs of handling down while, if the length of haul is considerable, the terminals need not figure too greatly in the total cost. Station and yard charges are much the same irrespective of the amount of traffic and, since they are high, there is a desire to eliminate small stations of only local value and to use freight railheads for serving a wide area with road vehicles. This eliminates the goods train picking up small quantities of freight at wayside stations. Unfortunately for the railway, if traffic starts its journey by road it may continue by road and never use the rail link. Some traffic, such as livestock movement in a region, are better suited to road transport than rail.

Goods traffic by rail has to meet competition from road agencies which may be licensed in three main ways: A-licences used for the carriage of goods for hire or reward; C-licences used for the carriage of goods in the holder's own business, or B-licences which combine under restrictions both A and C forms. Table 18 shows the rise in the C-licence numbers in recent years and partly explains the decline in goods traffic by rail in the same period. Passenger traffic has also declined as can be seen from this Table and from Figure 41, which indicates stations closed between 1899 and 1962. Stations near each other on a route can slow trains and, with acceleration of services, this has been used as an argument for closing rarely-used stations. Again, depopulation can have removed the need for a station. With nationalisation, the less convenient of competitive stations have often been closed. Another reason for closure lies in the increasing number of private cars.

When working-class homes were being destroyed in the east end of London to make way for railways, Parliament decreed that in compensation very low fares were to be given for workmen and this was the origin of this class of commuting traffic. Again, when railway companies were anxious to create traffic at particular suburban centres special concession rates for up to ten years were given to house-buyers. Successful commuting traffic can cause operating difficulties, but congestion can be partially solved by electrification; hence south of the Thames is the greatest electric train service in the world. North of the Thames, without the network of surface lines to electrify, underground lines have been provided and there are clamant cries for new links at £5 million

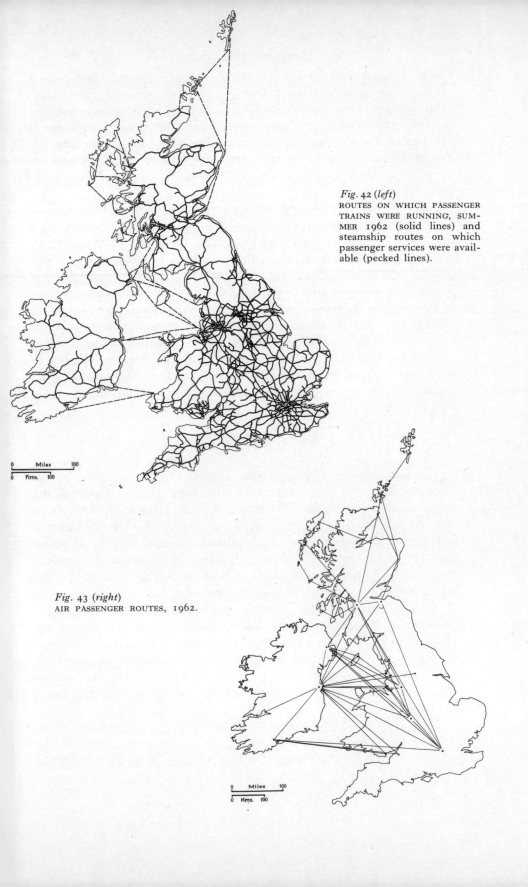

Fig. 42 (*left*)
ROUTES ON WHICH PASSENGER
TRAINS WERE RUNNING, SUM-
MER 1962 (solid lines) and
steamship routes on which
passenger services were available (pecked lines).

Fig. 43 (*right*)
AIR PASSENGER ROUTES, 1962.

a mile. London and Glasgow, with their underground lines, have a valuable means of dispersion from terminal points of surface lines. Many commuters, unable to park in central areas, now travel by car from their homes to a convenient suburban station and there is often need for car parking facilities. The size of London and the magnitude of passenger movements by road and rail demanded some co-ordination and London Transport exists to run integrated services.

Railway services are contracting over many areas of the British Isles mainly because the charges are high compared with road services. Charges are high largely because of labour costs and these can only be reduced by changing to methods needing less manpower: automatic signalling, uncontrolled level crossings, less porterage, only one man on a footplate, guards undertaking issue of tickets, less frequent track inspection, are all ways in which this reduction could be implemented. Again, if road licence charges were more closely approximated to cost of road repairs and to the interest on capital expenditure, there could be greater equality of transport charges and more traffic would pass to the railway, particularly if its latent advantage of speedy, mass movement could be realised.

Roads

The road pattern of southern Britain still bears traces of its Roman origin and it is interesting that, with the exception of the government roads in the Scottish Highlands, fifteen hundred years were to elapse before the State again controlled road developments. During this period the roads had either been ignored or been under manorial or ecclesiastical power. During the eighteenth century the need for improvement after centuries of neglect was met by the institution of turnpike trusts. These were a typically British approach of allowing local efforts, without government aid, to remedy a situation. It is significant that among the earliest trusts were those created to deal with crossing the clay vales. Fortunately, there is an abundance of road metal in Britain. Nowadays concrete for road construction makes demands on alluvial gravels and cement and the ballast supply for concrete can be obtained from many river valleys.

The altitude of some districts is high but steep gradients occur even in areas where the absolute height is not great. Scarp slopes are responsible for gradients such as 1 in 6 at Titsey Hill in Surrey

Table 18.   Traffic Features in Britain

	1935	1952	1960
Road			
Current licences (million)			
Total	2.58	4.90	9.38
Private cars	1.48	2.51	5.53
Public conveyance	0.10	0.14	0.10
Goods vehicles	0.44	0.97	1.40
A-licence	—	0.05	0.09
C-licence	—	0.80	1.20
Accidents (thousands)			
Total	228.2	208.0	347.6
Deaths	6.5	4.7	7.0
Deaths under 15 years of age	—	0.7	0.6
Passenger journeys, public vehicles			
('000 million)	—	16.3	13.7
Railway			
Loaded wagon-miles: ('000 million)	3.00	3.18	2.39
Passenger journeys: ('000 million)	1.23	0.99	1.04
Goods traffic (million tons)			
Total	270.8	284.9	248.5
Coal	174.8	170.8	148.1
Air (domestic services)			
Passengers arrived (million)	—	0.67	2.24
Freight carried ('000 short tons)	—	2.66	16.10
Mail carried ('000 short tons)	—	2.42	3.04
Tourism			
Passengers inward (million):			
by sea	—	2.68	3.80
by air	—	0.92	3.31
Air from Channel Isles	—	0.12	0.32
Air from Eire	—	0.14	0.36

Based on: Central Statistical Office, Annual Abstract of Statistics
No. 84 (1948) and No. 98 (1961).

or 1 in 4 at Cudham Hill in Kent, and thus rival the 1 in $3\frac{1}{4}$ of Hard Knot Pass in Cumberland or the 1 in 5 of the Devil's Elbow in Perthshire. Obstacles more potent than height are the broad estuaries of the Thames, Severn, Forth, and Tay which have led to demands for bridges or tunnels. Such works are beyond local resources and require substantial State aid.

When the railway companies became carriers, there were already on the scene public carriers such as Pickford and Chaplin. These firms co-operated with the railways but the new rival was so big that the older concerns had to play a subsidiary role. After the First World War surplus lorries encouraged a mushroom growth of small road carrier firms and the more efficient, or ruthless, grew into large concerns that took much freight from the older organisations. Not until just before the Second World War were the railway companies permitted by Parliament to purchase a share in the bus and lorry transport firms. After the war nationalisation of transport involved the large road transport firms. Later, with change of government, units of British Road Services were returned to independent operators and the virtual monopoly broken.

Since 1938 conditions have changed more radically than just a change of ownership of public carriers. The C-Licence and the private car have become more common, and as a result the public carriers, whether by rail or road, freight or passenger, are finding a reduction of traffic. When passengers were first carried by rail on the main lines, some of the aristocracy rode in their own coaches set on flat rail-trucks, and a modern device is to tempt people back to the rail by conveying their cars in a van and so saving them the fatigue and time of driving from, say, London to Newcastle or Perth. In other words the railway operator is trying to exploit the rail advantage for long journeys and to leave the local journey for car.

Theoretically, rail and road services are integrated as never before but every user of public transport can point to examples where there is no real cohesion of timings despite appeals from the public. In 1962, planned connections between outer suburban bus services and electric trains were introduced as an experiment in the Glasgow area.

One of the social problems facing traffic increases on the roads is the accident rate. Faster vehicles and greater density of traffic result in more accidents, which rouse public concern. Too often roads in Britain are inadequate for their traffic but even on motorways speeding vehicles have breakdowns and together with

328

human error bring death and destruction. There is a limit to the major road improvements possible in a landscape so intricately utilised as the lowlands of Britain.

Air

The First World War resulted in the introduction of commercial air services and the Second World War saw a great increase in comfort and speed. Many parts of the British Isles are subject to interruption of traffic by fog. The urban sprawl characteristic of British conurbations causes airports to be far from the central business districts and the time taken for the land links adds materially to the journey times between city centres; for this reason helicopters are being considered to reduce the time. Jet aircraft cause considerable disturbance from noise which affects many people in urban areas. Airport charges are high and unless there is a considerable use made of the facilities, the real cost per passenger is excessive.

The geography of the British Isles does suggest districts where air services are more attractive than the alternatives: most noteworthy are the cross-channel routes, to islands, and areas separated by difficult land journeys such as Aberdeen to Wick. The estuary of the Cheshire Dee was crossed in 1962 by a pilot scheme using the semi-airborne hovercraft.

Conclusion

Transportation in the British Isles is in a phase of transition. Developed originally, as all routeways are, by the needs of a time, tempered by geographical phenomena, it has now become so complex and congested in and around the great urban centres, that bold and imaginative government action must be taken before a smooth and integrated system can evolve. Without removing all choice of method of transport from users, it would nevertheless be reasonable to direct the heavy or cumbersome loads to rail or water services wherever possible, thus clearing some congestion from the roads. Travellers from abroad are amazed to see the processions of heavily-laden vehicles rumbling through towns such as Morpeth and York, damaging by vibration ancient structures that are part of the national heritage, while nearby the expensive steel track which could well carry the loads is not working to capacity.

329

Coastal shipping is also passing through a difficult phase and just as it would seem that major rail links should be fostered, so should the coastal services. With European trade links being increased, coastal locations may well become an asset in industrial location and routes. A situation beside the narrow seas could assume a greater importance since suitable craft could carry products economically between Britain and the ports of Europe, through the canals of many continental countries and by the Rhine artery into the heart of Europe. Transportation problems, while to some extent conditioned by geographical factors, are tending to become increasingly governed by economic trends.

18

POPULATION

Evolution up to 1801

THE distribution of population within the British Isles has altered considerably over the centuries, reflecting changes in the evaluation of natural endowment and geographical position, related in turn to economic, social, and technological changes. At the same time total numbers have greatly increased, especially in the last two hundred years.

The situation prior to the nineteenth century helps one to appreciate the vast changes in numbers and distribution that have taken place since. Twenty years after the Norman Conquest the great Domesday Survey of 1086 suggests a total population in England and Wales of over one million but under two. Just before the Black Death of 1348 the population may have been about 3·75 millions (Russell, 1948). This and later visitations of the plague led to a great fall in population, and it is possible that more than two centuries elapsed before the level of 1348 was regained. Thereafter there was a period of further steady growth, so that by 1700 the population was probably over 5½ but under 6 millions, while by 1750 it was perhaps 6 to 6½ millions. At this time the population of Scotland was recorded as 1·3 millions according to Dr Webster's census, carried out under semi-official auspices in 1755. Hitherto population growth had been relatively slow; birth rates and death rates were both high by modern standards (maybe over 35 per thousand per year) and the margin of births over deaths was precarious in many years.

The general distribution of population in England and Wales in Medieval, Tudor, and Stuart times, that is, until the eighteenth century, showed a fairly close relationship to agricultural productivity. The greater part of the population thus lay in Lowland England, and especially south of a line from the Wash to the middle Severn valley. Craft industries, such as the woollen manufactures of East Anglia and the West Country, further enhanced local densities, while important lacunae would no doubt correspond to unreclaimed woodlands, heathlands, and marshes, to the high chalk plateaux, and to the bleak moorlands of the southwest peninsula.

Two salients of this populous zone projected northwards from the Midlands on either side of the Pennines, one to the Lancashire-Cheshire Plain, and the other to the Vale of York and the northeast coastlands. In Scotland the lowland areas, especially those on the eastern side of the country, where also urban development was greatest, had the highest densities.

Dominating the populous areas of England were many small market towns and some important regional centres, such as Bristol, Coventry, Exeter, Hull, Newcastle, Norwich, Nottingham, Plymouth, and York, although the order of importance of the chief provincial cities naturally varied over the years. London was always by far the largest city and also the largest port. Bristol and Norwich were considered to be second to London in the seventeenth century, Bristol also being regarded as the second port of the country. In Ireland, with its widely-distributed rural population, Dublin was always the leading town and port.

In the second half of the eighteenth century there was a marked acceleration in the rate of population growth. It is still not clear whether the dominant factor was a rise in the birth-rate (possibly due to earlier marriages) or a fall in the death-rate (due to the reduced frequency of epidemics and to improvements in nutrition and hygiene). It is certain, however, that the maintenance of a high rate of natural increase between 1837 (when civil registration of births and deaths was introduced) and the early years of the twentieth century was due to a high birth-rate and a gradually falling death-rate. By the end of the eighteenth century the rapid increase in the rate of population growth and its economic implications were attracting the attention of various writers, of whom Malthus, with his prophecy of disaster, was the most notable. The first census, of 1801, revealed a population of 10·5 millions in Great Britain, a figure which, it is generally agreed, should probably be raised to at least 10·75 millions to take account of under-enumeration. The increase between 1750 and 1801 was thus about 40%.

These demographic changes, as Lawton has already indicated, broadly coincided with the earlier years of the Industrial Revolution, conventionally dated from the middle of the eighteenth century. The cotton industry of Lancashire, the woollen industry of west Yorkshire, the knitwear industry of the east Midlands and the mining and metallurgical activities of the coalfields of the Midlands and north of England were indeed already important before 1750 (although operated on a domestic or small-scale basis), and represented either industrial migration in the literal sense or else differential regional growth compared with the south. These changes were to be powerfully reinforced in the nineteenth century and, in fact, as early as 1851 the main outlines of the present population pattern were already becoming clear. Half the population was already living in towns, and the former populous zone stretching in broad fashion across the southern half of England, and related to a largely rural society, had now been superseded by the new 'axial belt' from London to Liverpool related essentially to an industrial and urban society. London retained and even increased its national pre-eminence, and its population, with suburbs, was nearly one million by 1801. On the other hand, eastern, southern, and south-western England declined in relative importance, although at the same time showing substantial population growth. At the western end of the old populous zone Bristol and its West Country hinterland were eclipsed in importance by Liverpool, the new second port of the country, and its industrial hinterland of Lancashire. By 1801 Bristol had been surpassed in population by Birmingham, Liverpool and Manchester-Salford, although none as yet contained over 100,000 persons. The populous zone had thus swung northwards, as it were, on its London pivot.

Industrialisation and urbanisation likewise proceeded in other parts of the British Isles. Coal mining and industry developed in south Wales, and also in the Central Lowlands of Scotland, where emphasis gradually shifted from the east to the west, as expressed in the very rapid growth of Glasgow and surrounding district. In Ireland, too, population grew rapidly in the second half of the eighteenth century onwards, sustained by widespread cultivation of the potato by her peasantry. Here, however, urbanisation and industrialisation were weak, this being chiefly due, no doubt, to the poor endowment of coal, iron ore and other industrial raw materials and to the low purchasing power and capital resources of the Irish.

Evolution between 1801 and 1921

In the nineteenth century geographical variations in employment opportunities and wage levels, along with rapid population growth, resulted in a high volume of internal migration that typically took the form of a townward movement. It can be assumed that the bulk of the migrants came from the younger, active age-groups, and this helps to explain why so many expanding industrial and mining

333

districts showed a higher rate of natural increase than country areas.

While economic 'pull' was important, economic 'push' should not be overlooked; underlying the townward movement was the fact that rural employment opportunities failed to keep pace with local population growth. As has been seen the enclosures of the eighteenth and early nineteenth centuries had led to a system of medium and large scale commercial farming which in turn produced sharp distinctions between owners or tenants, on the one hand, and landless labourers on the other. Only a small part of the agricultural population thus had a direct personal stake in the land, in contrast to most parts of Continental Europe. Outside the agricultural sector there was severe contraction of employment in small rural industries and crafts, due either to regional locational changes or to centralisation of production in urban factories.

Before the 1830s migration does not seem to have been on a sufficiently large scale to cause really wide disparities in regional rates of population growth, nor to have led to widespread local declines. From the 1830s onwards, however, the rural exodus increased in importance and inter-regional differences in rate of population growth became sharper as a result. Village population declines became more frequent and many villages that have not subsequently become affected by suburban or industrial development recorded their peak population figure somewhere between 1821 and 1851. The first instance of a decline of the population of an entire English county between two census dates is that of Wiltshire, for the period 1841-51. In Wales Merioneth, Montgomery, and Radnor also declined in this period; in Scotland, however, eight counties had declined between 1831 and 1841. Some authorities assert that the reform of the English Poor Law in 1834 (which abolished assistance given outside workhouse institutions) was an important factor in increasing the flight from the countryside. The role of the railways as a factor facilitating movement of the population was undoubtedly important after the 1830s.

Migration movements were predominantly local and regional rather than national in character, 'surplus' rural population generally moving to the nearest urban centres offering superior employment advantages, as Ravenstein (1885) showed in his classic study based on the census of 1881. What may be called 'rippling' or 'shunting' movements also occurred. For example, while the central industrial counties of the English Midlands drew population from the less industrialised ones to the east, west, and south, these central counties were in turn net losers of population to the north of England and the London area (Smith, 1951). In Scotland the Forth basin counties drew population from the north and south, but lost on balance to Clydeside (Osborne, 1958). The overall net movements between counties and broad regions of the country thus resulted from a multitude of complicated currents of migration.

In Ireland industrial development, except in the Belfast area, was meagre and offered less stimulus to internal population movements. The precarious structure of Ireland's largely subsistence peasant economy was tragically revealed by the Great Famine of 1845-46 and subsequent years, resulting from potato disease. The Irish Famine was one of the greatest human disasters of modern times not attributable to warfare. The population declined from an estimated $8\frac{1}{2}$ millions in 1845 to $6\frac{1}{2}$ millions in 1851. Enormous numbers perished from starvation or disease or took ship for England or Scotland, where they were absorbed into the lower sections of the urban working-class, notably in Lancashire, London, and Clydeside. Some went to America or Australia, often from British ports. The Irish immigration into Great Britain, already important before the Great Famine, continued into the second half of the nineteenth century, but diminished thereafter as most Irish emigrants turned to the United States. However, since the First World War Great Britain has again become the main destination.

While the inflow of the Irish thus contributed to population growth in Great Britain there was at the same time a considerable overseas migration of English, Scots, and Welsh, notably to the British Empire and the United States, while within Great Britain there was movement from Scotland to England. Emigration to North America had been taking place in the seventeenth and eighteenth centuries also, but quantitative information does not exist. Even for the nineteenth century there is no information about the external migration balance for England and Wales until the 1840s and for Scotland and Ireland until the 1860s. Between 1841 and 1861 England and Wales had a net loss of population by external migration of 408,000 (i.e. the difference between total population increase and natural increase). For the whole period 1861 to 1911 England and Wales lost on balance 1,541,000 persons, Scotland 737,000, and Ireland 3,137,000 (Carrier and Jeffery, 1953). In comparison with their total populations Scotland and Ireland thus lost much more heavily than England and Wales, which, in fact, received part of their outward flows. Overseas losses from Great

Britain were greatest in the 1880s and between 1900 and the First World War. High rates of outward migration were often related to a surge of economic activity in the receiving countries and to a complementary fall in Great Britain. This was particularly true of migration to the United States (Thomas, 1954).

By the eve of the First World War a gradual fall in the birth-rate had for some years been apparent (25 per thousand in 1910-12, compared with 35 in 1870-2), but since the death-rate was also falling (14 in 1910-12, compared with 22 in 1870-2), the rate of natural increase was largely maintained. Despite the high level of overseas migration the decennial rate of population growth in Great Britain for 1901-11 thus fell only slightly, to 10·4%. Earlier decennial rates were as follows:

1801-11	14·0	1851-61	11·1
1811-21	17·7	1861-71	12·7
1821-31	15·4	1871-81	14·0
1831-41	14·0	1881-91	11·2
1841-51	12·3	1891-1901	12·0

Emigration from Great Britain continued at a high rate in the years immediately before and after the War and was particularly directed to Canada and Australasia. The War itself led to the loss of 650,000 men on the battlefields and to a lowering of the birth-rate. Despite the immediate post-war rise in the birth-rate the decennial rate of population increase for 1911-21 was, therefore, only 4·7%, or less than one half of the 1901-11 rate and only one third of some nineteenth-century rates. Net outward migration was 859,000, after deducting overseas war deaths from home natural increase.

Within Great Britain the rural exodus was greatly reduced in scale after the beginning of the twentieth century. The cumulative effect of the loss of so many young persons in previous decades was now being severely felt in some rural areas in the form of a reduced rate of natural increase. Agriculture was, temporarily at least, in a more prosperous condition than it had been since the 1870s, when poor harvests and the unrestricted inflow of cheap foreign grain, followed by a decline of the arable area, heralded a long period of depression. Rural areas as a whole in England and Wales surprisingly increased in population by 10% between 1901 and 1911, compared with an increase of 11% in urban areas, although it must be remembered that many expanding suburbs and mining villages were technically 'rural'. After the War new inter-regional migration flows began to assert themselves when several of the major industrial and mining districts that had been attracting population in the nineteenth century lost their economic momentum and suffered severe unemployment, with a resultant loss of population. All these various changes, including the fall in the rate of national population growth, justify us in regarding the early part of the twentieth century as a period of transition from one demographic epoch to another.

Figure 44 illustrates two aspects of population change. In order to show shifts in the distribution of population the percentage increase for each area in each period was converted into a 'growth index', whereby the local rate of increase is expressed as a proportion of the contemporary rate of growth for Great Britain as a whole (not the entire British Isles), the national rate being taken as 100 in each period. Areas experiencing an increase of population are shaded in accordance with the growth index achieved, while areas experiencing a decline remain unshaded. It must be stressed that the categories of shading relate to different percentage ranges in each period. Circular symbols, corresponding to the associated absolute increases or decreases, are superimposed.

The maps show that, while most of the counties or county groupings in Great Britain had a population increase in each of the four thirty-year periods, the rates of growth varied very greatly compared with the national average. Within their territories, of course, there were also wide local differences. The first period, 1801-31, shows an interesting contrast with the three later periods, when regional disparities in rates of growth in Great Britain became much more pronounced and when Ireland showed a progressive decline of population. In all four periods the Clydeside counties and south Wales grew in population at well over the national rate, while, with the exception of one or two periods when growth was at about the national rate, the same was true for Lancashire-Cheshire, Durham-Northumberland, Yorkshire, and the industrial west

KEY TO FIGURE 44h

1 Cornwall	16 Leicester, Northampton, and Rutland	26 Cumberland and Westmorland
2 Devon		
3 Gloucester and Somerset	17 Derby and Nottingham	27 Berwick, Dumfries, Kirkcudbright, Peebles, Roxburgh, Selkirk, Wigtown
4 Dorset and Wiltshire	18 Stafford, Warwick, and Worcester	
5 Berkshire, Buckingham, and Oxford	19 Hereford and Shropshire	28 Ayr and Bute
6 Hampshire	20 Glamorgan and Monmouth	29 Dunbarton, Lanark, and Renfrew
7 Sussex	21 Brecknock, Cardigan, Carmarthen, Montgomery, Pembroke, Radnor	
8 Surrey		30 Clackmannan, Fife, Kinross, East, Mid-, and West Lothian, Stirling
9 Kent		
10 London and Middlesex	22 Anglesey, Caernarvon, Denbigh, Flint, Merioneth	31 Angus and Perth
11 Bedford and Hertford		32 Aberdeen, Banff, Kincardine, Moray, Nairn
12 Essex	23 Lancashire and Cheshire	
13 Norfolk and Suffolk	24 Yorkshire	33 Argyll, Caithness, Inverness, Orkney, Ross and Cromarty, Sutherland, Zetland
14 Cambridge and Huntingdon	25 Northumberland and Durham	
15 Lincoln		

337

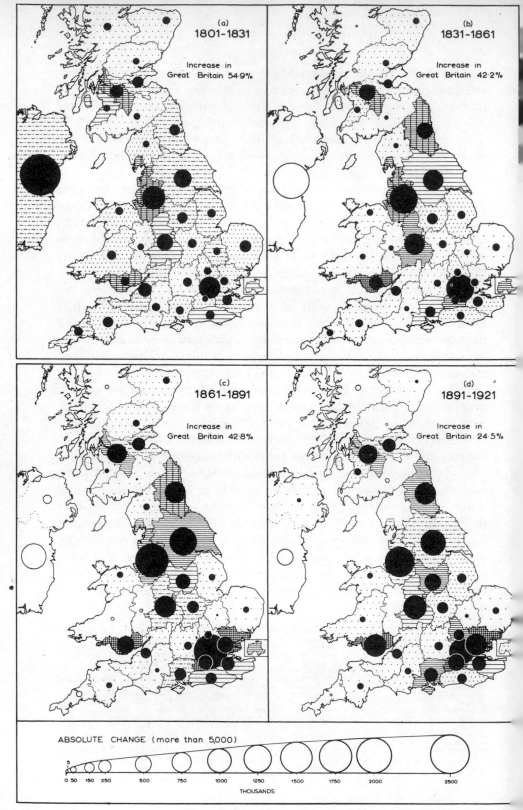

Fig. 44. POPULATION CHANGES IN THE BRITISH ISLES, 1801-1961.

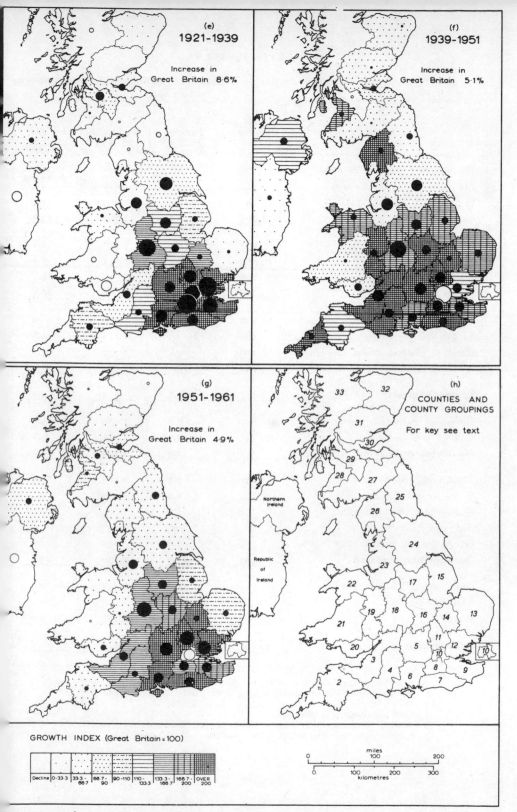

(e) 1921–1939

Increase in
Great Britain 8·6%

(f) 1939–1951

Increase in
Great Britain 5·1%

(g) 1951–1961

Increase in
Great Britain 4·9%

(h) COUNTIES AND
COUNTY GROUPINGS

For key see text

Northern
Ireland

Republic
of
Ireland

GROWTH INDEX (Great Britain = 100)

Decline	0–33.3	33.3–66.7	66.7–90	90–110	110–133.3	133.3–166.7	166.7–200	OVER 200

miles
0   100   200

0   100   200   300
kilometres

e of Man and Channel Is. excluded. (For key to Fig. 44h, see p. 337.)

Table 19.   Regional Population Changes

Area	1801		1861	
	Population (thous.)	Per cent of G.B.	Population (thous.)	Per cent of G.B.
Northern and Southern Scotland	708	6.7	1,022	4.4
Industrial W. Central Lowlands[1]	343	3.3	1,076	4.6
Industrial E. Central Lowlands[2]	557	5.3	964	4.2
Scotland	**1,608**	**15.3**	**3,062**	**13.2**
Northern England[3]	475	4.5	1,118	4.8
Yorkshire	859	8.2	2,034	8.8
Lancashire and Cheshire	866	8.2	2,935	12.7
North of England	**2,200**	**21.0**	**6,086**	**26.3**
Industrial W. Midlands[4]	596	5.7	1,616	7.0
Industrial E. Midlands[5]	580	5.5	1,120	4.8
Hereford, Shropshire and Lincoln	466	4.4	777	3.4
Midland England	**1,642**	**15.6**	**3,513**	**15.2**
Eastern England[6]	**615**	**5.9**	**1,012**	**4.4**
Gloucester, Somerset, Dorset, Wilts.	822	7.8	1,369	5.9
Cornwall and Devon	533	5.1	954	4.1
Southwestern England	**1,355**	**12.9**	**2,322**	**10.0**
London and Middlesex	1,031	9.8	2,984	12.9
Essex, Kent and Surrey	593	5.6	1,197	5.2
Beds., Herts., Berks., Bucks., and Oxford	491	4.7	824	3.6
Hampshire and Sussex	379	3.6	845	3.6
'Metropolitan' England	**2,493**	**23.7**	**5,850**	**25.3**
Glamorgan and Monmouth	116	1.1	492	2.1
Rest of Wales	471	4.5	794	3.4
Wales	**587**	**5.6**	**1,286**	**5.6**
Great Britain	**10,501**	**100.0**	**23,129**	**100.0**

1   Ayr, Bute, Dunbarton, Lanark, Renfrew
2   Angus, Perth, Clackmannan, Fife, Kinross, the Lothians, Stirling
3   Cumberland, Westmorland, Durham, Northumberland
4   Stafford, Warwick, Worcester
5   Derby, Nottingham, Leicester, Northampton, Rutland
6   Cambridge, Huntingdon, Norfolk, Suffolk

in Great Britain, 1801-1961

1801-61	1921		1861-1921	1961		1921-61
Per cent increase	Population (thous.)	Per cent of G.B.	Per cent increase	Population (thous.)	Per cent of G.B.	Per cent increase
44.2	1,023	2.4	0.1	976	1.9	—4.6
213.9	2,296	5.4	113.3	2,508	4.9	9.2
73.1	1,529	3.6	58.6	1,695	3.3	10.8
90.4	4,882[7]	11.4	59.4	5,178	10.1	6.1
135.1	2,569	6.0	129.9	2,697·	5.3	5.0
136.7	4,204	9.8	106.7	4,723	9.2	12.3
239.0	6,003	14.0	104.5	6,500	12.7	8.3
176.6	12,776	29.9	109.9	13,920	27.2	9.0
171.2	3,190	7.5	97.4	4,326	8.4	35.6
93.1	2,240	5.2	99.9	2,959	5.8	32.1
66.6	950	2.2	22.3	1,172	2.3	23.3
113.9	6,380	14.9	81.6	8,457	16.5	32.6
64.6	1,149	2.7	13.5	1,394	2.7	21.3
66.4	1,732	4.0	26.5	2,331	4.5	34.6
79.1	1,004	2.3	5.3	1,165	2.3	16.0
71.4	2,736	6.4	17.8	3,496	6.8	27.8
189.5	5,784	13.5	93.8	5,425	10.6	—6.2
102.0	3,482	8.1	190.9	5,721	11.2	64.3
67.7	1,254	2.9	52.2	2,512	4.9	100.3
123.3	1,667	3.9	97.2	2,507	4.9	50.4
134.6	12,187	28.5	108.3	16,166	31.5	32.6
322.8	1,729	4.0	251.2	1,672	3.3	—3.3
68.7	928	2.2	16.9	969	1.9	4.4
119.1	2,658	6.2	106.6	2,641	5.2	—0.6
120.3	42,769	100.0	84.9	51,250	100.0	19.8

7 Including 34,000 summer visitors subtracted from Argyll, Ayr, and Bute, but not redistributed.

Sources: Census of 1951, County Reports; Annual Reports for 1921 of the Registrars-General for England and Wales and Scotland; Census of 1961, Preliminary Reports for England and Wales and Scotland.

Midlands. Other areas showing more than the national average in at least two periods were Derby-Nottingham, in the industrial east Midlands, and London-Middlesex, Essex, Hampshire, Kent, Surrey, and Sussex in the southeast. Those areas in Great Britain that showed declines or very low rates of growth were, in general, the less industrialised parts of the country. Non-agricultural activities nevertheless expanded in such areas, but apparently at an insufficient rate to support parity of population growth with the country as a whole. In one county population decline was related to the contraction of non-agricultural employment. This was Cornwall, where tin and copper mining and fishing declined in the nineteenth century.

Table 19 shows changes in the regional distribution of Great Britain's population since 1801. While the population of the country as a whole increased from 10·5 millions in 1801 to 42·8 in 1921 the rate of growth varied considerably from one part of the country to another, as Figure 44 has already demonstrated. By 1921 Scotland, the English Midlands, eastern England, and southwestern England all had smaller proportionate holdings of the national population than they had in 1801, although within these broad areas the industrial west-central Lowlands of Scotland and the industrial west Midlands of England both showed considerable increases, and the industrial east Midlands showed only a slight fall. By contrast the north of England, Wales, and the group of counties here called 'Metropolitan England' increased their holdings, although within the two latter areas there were falls in the Rest of Wales and in the block of counties stretching from Bedford to Berkshire.

Evolution between 1921 and 1961

Between 1921 and the outbreak of the Second World War in 1939 Great Britain underwent important economic and demographic changes. High unemployment rates with associated outward migration flows characterised some of the major industrial areas, notably Clydeside, northeastern England, south Wales, and parts of Lancashire and Yorkshire. In all these areas leading industries, such as iron and steel, shipbuilding, heavy engineering, coal-mining, and cotton textiles were frequently in a declining or stagnating condition. While some loss of population from the countryside to the towns continued, against a background of agricultural depression, the associated migration movements were overshadowed by the so-called 'drift south' from the depressed industrial areas to the relatively prosperous Midlands and the south of England, especially the latter. Here consumer goods and light and medium engineering industries were expanding. Overseas migration continued to be important in the 1920s, and Great Britain suffered a net loss of 564,000 between 1921 and 1931. This, combined with a falling birth-rate, led to another decennial increase of only 4·7%. The population of Scotland and Wales declined for the first time and there were also declines in the two parts of newly-partitioned Ireland.

In the 1930s the 'drift south' continued, and although government assistance was given for the establishment of new industries in the so-called Special Areas, the employment thus generated had little impact before the outbreak of war in 1939. Unfavourable economic conditions in the Empire and the United States discouraged overseas migration and, in fact, led to a reflux of former emigrants. This feature, in conjunction with the arrival of refugees from the European Continent in the late 1930s, produced a net inward movement of about 500,000 to Great Britain for the years 1931-9—a striking reversal of pre-existing trends. The depressed economic conditions in many parts of the country and the now wide diffusion of birth-control led to a further fall in the birth-rate (to under 15 per thousand in 1933 for the United Kingdom) and to gloomy prognostications of a declining population with implications almost as alarming in their way as those envisaged by Malthus and others at the beginning of the nineteenth century.

The 1939-45 war, with its strategic dispersal of industry and full employment conditions, did something to arrest the drift south, as well as to invigorate many medium and small-size towns and country areas. After 1945 the housing shortage and the greatly-expanded policy of stimulating new industrial employment in the Development Areas, formerly the Special Areas, also acted as checks to some extent. In the 1950s, however, it was becoming plain that although the pre-war scale of the drift south had been reduced, it was still a continuing feature of British economic life. Renewed stresses in the coal-mining, shipbuilding and cotton textile industries have shown themselves since the late 1950s, after a long period of post-war prosperity, while at the same time, despite a high degree of government control over industrial location, the industries of the Midlands and the south of England, geared to the needs of an 'affluent society', have shown no signs of losing their buoyancy. For Great Britain as a whole the unemployment percentage varied between only 1 and 2% throughout the 1950s, compared with a range of 10 to 22% in the inter-war period.

The volume of both inward and outward migration has been high since the war. There has been a renewal of emigration to the British Commonwealth and to a lesser extent to the United States. On the other hand there has been a considerable inflow of population to Great Britain, although one of changing composition. Immediately after the war, for instance, many Polish ex-servicemen elected to remain in Great Britain, while since the late 1950s there has been a very great inflow of coloured persons from the Commonwealth, especially the West Indies and India and Pakistan. Immigration to Great Britain from Ireland has also continued, and within Great Britain the movement from Scotland and Wales into England has also persisted. The outcome of such opposing trends was that the net migration balance for Great Britain with the rest of the world was virtually nil for 1939-51 (after deducting from home natural increase 275,000 war deaths overseas) and about plus 100,000 for 1951-61. The post-war rise in the birth-rate (to 21 per thousand for the United Kingdom in 1947) was followed by a decline, but to a level above that of the 1930s, while since 1955 there has been a further rise in the birth-rate (to 18 per thousand in 1961), largely associated with a trend towards earlier marriage. The rate of total population growth in Great Britain for the years 1951-61 (4·9%) showed a slight rise above that for the preceding twenty-year inter-censal period, 1931-51, when the rate was 9·1. The two parts of Ireland suffered a net loss by migration of 1,115,000 in the years 1911-51 and 504,000 in the years 1951-61, with the Republic showing the heavier rate of loss. As a result the population of the Republic has tended to decline, despite its fairly high rate of natural increase.

Figures 44 (e), (f), and (g) show population changes for the three periods 1921-39, 1939-51, and 1951-61. The drift of population to the Midlands and south of England in the inter-war period is readily apparent from Figure 44 (e). South Wales and Northumberland-Durham experienced a substantial decline of population, while rates of growth in Clydeside, Lancashire-Cheshire, and Yorkshire were below the national average. In the English Midlands and in England south of a line from the Wash to the Bristol Channel the area of territory with population growing faster than the national average increased greatly compared with the previous period, 1891-1921. Some of the more rural counties situated at a distance from the London-Lancashire populous zone showed declines, while the same was also true of northern and southern Scotland.

Wartime and post-war conditions are reflected in Figure 44 (f) for the years 1939-51. London-Middlesex, which had been losing population to the outer suburban areas for several decades, now suffered a large decline of population, chiefly as a result of the effects of war-time dispersal. Apart from the crofting counties of northern Scotland, the only other area showing a decline was Clydeside, but south Wales, Lancashire-Cheshire, Yorkshire, and Northumberland-Durham still grew at rates below the national average. With the exception of London-Middlesex all the counties south of a line from the Humber to the Dee showed above-average increases, together with north Wales, Cumberland-Westmorland, and Ayr-Bute. The chief causes were the development of wartime industry, much of which persisted, frequently with adaptation, into the immediate post-war period, together with the maintenance of higher military forces at home than in 1931. These tended to be disproportionately located in the more rural counties. Figure 44 (g), illustrating the latest period, 1951-61, indicates some reassertion of inter-war tendencies, although south Wales and Northumberland-Durham show a marked improvement compared with the years 1921-39. London-Middlesex and some of the more remote rural areas all suffered declines.

Table 19 shows how these changes are reflected in the proportionate holdings of the national population for the various parts of the country in 1961 compared with 1921. Scotland experienced a further fall, in which the industrial west-central Lowlands now participated. All three sub-divisions of the north of England showed smaller holdings, Lancashire-Cheshire falling back to the 1861 level. Further increases occurred in the industrial Midlands and there were also increases in Gloucester-Somerset-Dorset-Wiltshire and in all parts of metropolitan England, except London-Middlesex, where there was a decline. Declines also occurred in south Wales and the rest of Wales. An interesting feature is the way in which certain of the more rural parts of the country that suffered relative decline in the nineteenth century successfully maintained their 1921 holdings, such as Hereford-Shropshire-Lincoln, eastern England, and Cornwall-Devon. The final column of the table, giving percentage increases for 1921-61, shows that Scotland and the north of England increased by only 6 and 9% respectively, while Wales experienced a very slight decline (concealing recuperation since 1939). On the other hand

345

Table 20. Population of the British Isles, 1801-1961
(thousands)

	1801	1831	1861	1891	1921	1939	1951	1961
England	8,305	12,992	18,780	27,231	35,230	38,995	41,159	43,431
Wales (incl. Monmouth)	587	904	1,286	1,771	2,656	2,465	2,599	2,641
England & Wales	**8,893**	**13,897**	**20,066**	**29,003**	**37,887**	**41,460**	**43,758**	**46,072**
Scotland	1,608	2,364	3,062	4,026	4,882	5,007	5,096	5,178
Great Britain	**10,501** **(c. 10,750?)**	**16,261**	**23,129**	**33,028**	**42,769**	**46,467**	**48,854**	**51,250**
Northern Ireland	—	—	(1,396)	(1,236)	1,258	1,295	1,371	1,425
Great Britain & **Northern Ireland**	—	—	**(24,525)**	**(34,264)**	**44,027**	**47,762**	**50,225**	**52,676**
Republic of Ireland	—	—	(4,402)	(3,469)	3,096	2,934	2,961	2,815
Ireland	**c. 5,200?**	**7,767**	**5,799**	**4,705**	**4,354**	**4,229**	**4,332**	**4,240**
Isle of Man	?	41	52	56	60	52	55	48
Channel Islands	?	63	91	92	90	97	103	104
British Isles	**c. 16,000?**	**24,132**	**29,071**	**37,881**	**47,274**	**50,845**	**53,344**	**55,643**

Sources: Census of England and Wales, 1931 and 1961, Preliminary Reports (for 1961 and earlier census figures and 1939 estimates for the various parts of the British Isles, and for 1921 estimates for Ireland). Census of Scotland, Northern Ireland and Ireland (Republic), 1961, Preliminary Reports. Connell, K. H., *The population of Ireland, 1750-1845* (1950) (estimate for Ireland in 1801 interpolated from data on pp. 4-5 and 25).

midland, eastern, southwestern and metropolitan England grew
by percentages ranging from 21 to 33. The national rate of growth
in the period was 20%.

The present distribution of the population

The British Isles are now (1965) inhabited by some 57 million
persons, of whom more than 54 millions live in the United Kingdom
of Great Britain and Northern Ireland, and about 2·8 millions
in the Republic of Ireland. From Table 20 it will be seen that as
far as England is concerned the population is more than five times
as large as that of 1801, for Wales more than four times as large, and
for Scotland more than three times as large. The present population
of Ireland, on the other hand, is nearly one-fifth lower than the
estimated total for 1801, and is, moreover, only about half the size
of the probable peak figure of about $8\frac{1}{2}$ millions in 1845, on the eve
of the great Irish famine. As a result of these changes England now
contains 85% of the population of Great Britain and 78% of the
population of the British Isles, compared with 79% and perhaps
about 53% respectively in 1801.

The average population density of England (863 per sq. mile,
333 per sq. km.) is one of the highest for any country in the world,
being exceeded in Europe only by that of the Netherlands (886
per sq. mile, 342 per sq. km., in 1960). Densities in other parts of
the British Isles are as follows: Wales 330 per sq. mile (127 per
sq. km.), Scotland 174 per sq. mile (67 per sq. km.), Northern
Ireland 272 per sq. mile (105 per sq. km.), and the Republic of
Ireland 106 per sq. mile (41 per sq. km.). England and Wales have
a combined density of 790 per sq. mile (305 per sq. km.). These
averages for the various parts of the British Isles conceal very wide
local contrasts; at the one extreme are the thickly-populated
working-class districts in the older parts of the great industrial
cities, while at the other extreme are large areas of virtually uninhabited mountain and hill country, especially in northern England, Wales, and Scotland (Fig. 45).

The high density of population in England and Wales, as has
been shown, is related to a high degree of urbanisation, 80% of the
population living in places with urban status in 1961. Even this
figure is a conservative one, however, and excludes many suburban
areas and small mining towns and country towns. Well over one
third of the total population of England and Wales (37%), forming
nearly one half of the urban population, lives in the six officially-

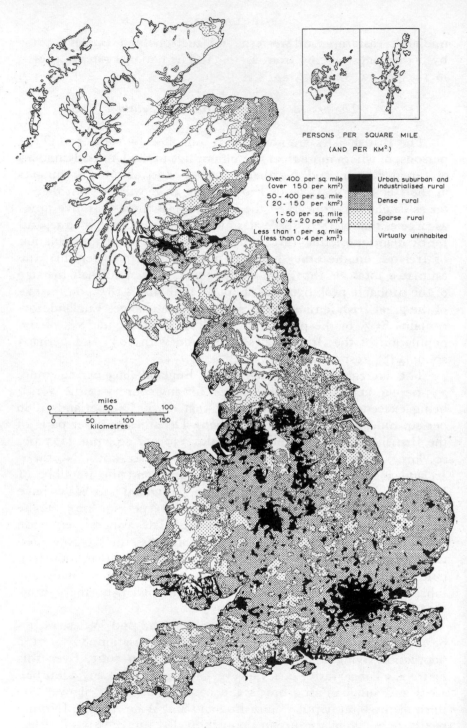

PERSONS PER SQUARE MILE

(AND PER KM²)

Over 400 per sq. mile
(over 150 per km²)

50 - 400 per sq. mile
(20 - 150 per km²)

1 - 50 per sq. mile
(0·4 - 20 per km²)

Less than 1 per sq. mile
(less than 0·4 per km²)

Urban, suburban and
industrialised rural

Dense rural

Sparse rural

Virtually uninhabited

miles
0   50   100

0   50   100   150
kilometres

Fig. 45.   DENSITY OF POPULATION, 1951. Based upon the Ordnance Survey 'Ten mile map'
of Great Britain (1 : 625,000), Population Density (1951), published 1961.

defined 'conurbations': Greater London (8·17 millions), Southeast Lancashire (Manchester) (2·43), West Midlands (Birmingham) (2·34), West Yorkshire (Leeds-Bradford) (1·70), Merseyside (Liverpool) (1·39) and Tyneside (Newcastle) (0·85). In Scotland towns contain 70% of the total population, 35% living in the central Clydeside (Glasgow) official conurbation (population 1·80 millions). Ireland is much less urbanised than Great Britain, the percentage living in towns being 54 in the Six Counties constituting Northern Ireland, and 37 in the Republic of Ireland, a proportion that rises to 42% if suburbs are included. Although there are no official conurbations as such in Ireland the statistical authorities for the two parts of the country give special population totals for Dublin and suburbs with Dún Laoghaire (661,000 in 1961) and Belfast and suburbs (529,000).

'Conurbations' or 'urban clusters' are such an important element in the population geography of Great Britain that they merit a short discussion. The term 'conurbation' was first introduced by Geddes (1915), who was thinking of major concentrations of urban population—'these city regions, these town aggregates', as he called them. Fawcett (1922, 1932) used the term in the narrower sense of towns linked together by continuous urban landscape, and he drew up a list of conurbations on this basis, with minimum populations of 50,000. Some of Geddes's conurbations, such as central Scotland, south Wales, and south Lancashire, were thus broken down into smaller components. The seven large official conurbations, which are statistical units consisting of complete local government areas, are, with the exception of Greater London, innovations of the 1951 census. They were delimited with close regard to the 'bricks and mortar' approach, although economic and social factors were also given consideration.

The contributions of Robinson (1953 and 1956) and Freeman (1959) have extended the literature on British conurbations. Freeman's contribution is a major work dealing with the genesis and anatomy of the conurbations. Figure 46, showing conurbations and large towns with more than 50,000 inhabitants in 1951, is based largely on Robinson's list. About two thirds of Great Britain's population were living in such urban concentrations in that year. Dominating the population pattern is the belt of high density and large-scale urban development extending northwestwards from Greater London to Liverpool and the Lancashire coast. Attention has been drawn to this populous zone by a number of geographers, and various names have been used for it, the best

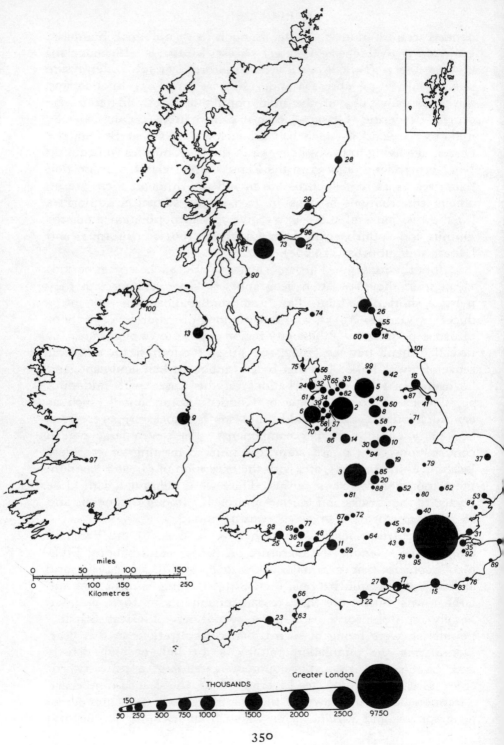

miles
0   50   100   150
0   100   150   250
Kilometres

THOUSANDS   Greater London

150
50 250 500 750 1000 1500 2000 2500 9750

350

known being the 'axial belt' (Taylor, 1938) and the 'hour-glass' (Smailes, 1946). The latter term has the merit of recognising the fact that the populous zone has two distinct portions. The southern one consists of the relatively-compact Greater London region, comprising the official conurbation and neighbouring large towns, such as Reading, Luton, Southend, and the Medway conurbation, together with numerous smaller towns, including the eight New Towns being built to receive London's 'overspill'. The limits of 'the contemporary London region'—'an embryonic conurbation a hundred miles wide'—have recently been discussed by Powell (1960-1), who suggests a radius of 40-50 miles (65-80 km.). Within such an area there is a population of about 12 millions. For the purpose of Figure 46 the official Greater London conurbation is extended to include all the population (about 9·75 millions) within a radius of about 25 miles (40 km.).

The Greater London region is closely linked by road and rail communications to the chain of towns that stud the south coast of

KEY TO FIGURE 46

1 Greater London (official Greater London conurbation plus other population within ca. 25 miles radius)	27 Southampton	64 Swindon
2 Southeast Lancashire (Manchester) official conurbation	28 Aberdeen	65 Accrington
	29 Dundee	66 Exeter
	30 Derby	67 Gloucester
3 West Midlands (Birmingham) official conurbation	31 Southend-on-Sea	68 Widnes, Runcorn
	32 Preston	69 Aberdare, Mountain Ash
4 Central Clydeside (Glasgow) official conurbation	33 Burnley, Colne, Nelson	70 Chester
	34 Wigan	71 Lincoln
5 West Yorkshire (Leeds) official conurbation	35 Chatham, Gillingham, Rochester (Medway towns)	72 Cheltenham
	36 Rhondda, Pontypridd	73 Falkirk, Grangemouth
6 Merseyside (Liverpool) official conurbation	37 Norwich	74 Carlisle
	38 Blackburn, Darwen	75 Barrow-in-Furness
7 Tyneside (Newcastle upon Tyne) official conurbation	39 St Helens	76 Hastings
	40 Luton	77 Merthyr Tydfil
8 Sheffield, Rotherham	41 Grimsby, Cleethorpes	78 Aldershot, Farnborough
9 Dublin, Dún Laoghaire	42 York	79 Peterborough
10 Nottingham, lower Erewash valley	43 Reading	80 Bedford
	44 Warrington	81 Worcester
11 Bristol	45 Oxford	82 Bacup, Haslingden, Rawtenstall
12 Edinburgh	46 Cork	
13 Belfast	47 Mansfield, Sutton-in-Ashfield	83 Eastbourne
14 Stoke-on-Trent, Newcastle-under-Lyme	48 Newport	84 Colchester
	49 Barnsley	85 Nuneaton
15 Brighton, Hove, Worthing	50 Doncaster	86 Crewe
16 Hull, Haltemprice	51 Greenock, Gourock, Port Glasgow	87 Scunthorpe
17 Portsmouth, Gosport, Fareham		88 Warwick, Leamington
	52 Northampton	89 Folkestone
18 Middlesbrough, Stockton on Tees	53 Ipswich	90 Ayr
	54 Margate (Thanet)	91 Great Yarmouth
19 Leicester	55 Hartlepools	92 Maidstone
20 Coventry	56 Lancaster, Morecambe	93 High Wycombe
21 Cardiff	57 Leigh	94 Burton upon Trent
22 Bournemouth, Poole	58 Chesterfield, Staveley	95 Guildford
23 Plymouth	59 Bath	96 Kirkcaldy
24 Blackpool, Fylde coast	60 Darlington	97 Limerick
25 Swansea, Neath	61 Southport	98 Llanelly
26 Sunderland	62 Cambridge	99 Harrogate
	63 Torquay, Paignton	100 Londonderry
		101 Scarborough

Fig. 46 (*opposite*). POPULATIONS OF CONURBATIONS AND LARGE TOWNS WITH MORE THAN 50,000 INHABITANTS (1951). Based on Robinson (1956) with the following alterations. (*a*) The official conurbations have been reinstated, with the exception of Greater London (see text above). (*b*) The following have been added: Bacup-Haslingden-Rawtenstall, Guildford, Leigh, St Helens, Wigan, Dublin-Dún Laoghaire, Cork and Limerick.

England from Bournemouth-Poole in the west to the south shore of the Thames estuary in the east, and it is becoming increasingly realistic to consider this coastal zone as a maritime appendage of the Greater London region, although separated from it by considerable tracts of rural country. Here Southampton in some measure fulfils the rôle of an outport for London, especially for passengers, while the resorts and residential towns, of which the largest is the Brighton conurbation, offer facilities for recreation and retirement, the latter function being reflected in elderly age-structures.

Northwestwards from the Greater London region a broad band of road and rail communications reaches out to the cities and conurbations of the inner Midlands, southern Lancashire-northern Cheshire, and the West Riding of Yorkshire. These constitute the loosely-knit northern component of the populous zone. While towns situated along, or close to, these connecting routeways (of which the largest are Northampton and Oxford) have often shown vigorous growth in recent decades, much rural country still separates the two components. The northern component has, curiously enough, no recognised name, although Edwards and Rawstron (1959) have suggested the useful term 'Central Urban Region'. This northern component of the populous zone consists of a discontinuous girdle of large towns encircling an inner zone of rural country, the northern portion of which corresponds to part of the thinly-populated Pennine uplands. Urban development is particularly intense in southern Lancashire and the northern parts of adjoining Cheshire. Here the two large conurbations centred on Liverpool and Manchester are almost physically linked to each other by smaller intervening urban clusters, such as Wigan, St. Helens, Warrington, and Runcorn-Widnes. This great urbanised zone, considered as one entity by Geddes fifty years ago, is continued northwards by the resort towns of the Lancashire coast (Southport and Blackpool) and by Preston and the cotton-weaving towns (Blackburn, Burnley, etc.). To the south and west of the Liverpool conurbation patches of high population density extend into north Wales and correspond to minor industrial and resort towns. To the east of Manchester lies a narrow tract of moorland, beyond which are the industrial towns of the West Riding of Yorkshire. These consist of two chief groups, both located on the western margin of the Yorkshire coalfield: the West Yorkshire (Leeds-Bradford) conurbation and the smaller urban grouping of Sheffield-Rotherham.

South of the Cheshire and Yorkshire county boundaries are the Midland conurbations, forming the southern portions of the Central Urban Region. With the exception of Stoke-on-Trent they form a discontinuous arc extending from Chesterfield, south of Sheffield, to Birmingham. By far the largest Midland conurbation is that of Birmingham and the towns of the south Staffordshire 'Black Country' lying to the northwest. The closely-related clusters of Derby and Nottingham, located in the east Midlands near the southern limits of the thickly-populated Derbyshire-Nottinghamshire coalfield, together form the next largest urban grouping, with a combined population of over 750,000, followed by Stoke-on-Trent, Leicester, and Coventry. It should be stressed that the Central Urban Region does not possess the high degree of functional cohesion shown by the Greater London region, although certain neighbouring conurbations and large towns often show close relationships with each other.

To the northeast and southwest of the Central Urban Region are two lesser population groupings—the Tyne-Tees industrial region of the northeast coast of England and the South Wales-Bristol area. The Tyne-Tees grouping embraces the Tyneside (Newcastle) conurbation, the adjoining town of Sunderland on the lower Wear, the lower Tees valley from Darlington to the Hartlepools and including Middlesbrough, and the mining districts of the Northumberland and Durham coalfield. The South Wales-Bristol area embraces the mining towns of the narrow valleys cut into the uplands of south Wales, the populous coastal lowland adjoining them, stretching from Llanelly and Swansea in the west to Cardiff and Newport in the east, and then, beyond the Severn estuary, the city and port of Bristol and its hinterland, including Bath. This population grouping is more extensive in area than the Tyne-Tees grouping, but is of a less concentrated nature, being fragmented by the moorlands separating the south Wales valleys and by the intervention of the wide Severn estuary.

Few urban concentrations of over 100,000 inhabitants lie outside these four great population groupings: 'Metropolitan England' (i.e. the Greater London region and the south coast), the 'Central Urban Region', Tyne-Tees, and South Wales-Bristol—or away from the communication lines that link these zones together. The exceptions are Plymouth in the far southwest, Hull and Grimsby-Cleethorpes on the Humber estuary, and Norwich and Ipswich in eastern England.

The populous, urbanised areas of the Scottish Central Lowlands are insulated from the English concentrations by a wide zone of only moderately- to thinly-populated country, where settlement is localised in valleys and coastal plains, separated by almost uninhabited hill ranges. Four-fifths of the Scottish population live in a quadrilateral with its four corners located approximately at Dundee, Edinburgh, Ayr, and Greenock. A tenuous extension of this quadrilateral stretches along the fertile coastal lowlands of northeastern Scotland and includes Aberdeen.

Forming a back-cloth upon which these urban patterns have been superimposed are the rural areas of Great Britain, containing only about one-fifth of the population. Rural densities are generally very low in upland districts, especially in 'Highland Britain', but in lowland areas, with their fairly close network of villages, densities are moderately high, despite the absence of any large class of small-scale farmers, such as is typical of much of western Europe. Indeed, less than 5% of the total occupied population of Great Britain is engaged in agriculture and horticulture. The introduction of piped water-supplies, electricity, motor-bus services, and radio and television to large parts of the British countryside in the twentieth century has removed many of the former drawbacks of rural life, and these facilities, together with the gradual extension of private car-ownership, have often led to profound changes in the functions and population structure of villages having reasonable access to towns. Many of them have attracted what has been called 'adventitious' population (Vince, 1953) and they have thus become little more than residential outposts of nearby cities, with a subsidiary agricultural function.

The population geography of Ireland offers marked contrasts to that of Great Britain. As has been seen above, the percentage living in towns is very much lower, and although the average density of Northern Ireland is higher than that for Scotland, the figure for all-Ireland (133 per sq. mile, 51 per sq. km.) is somewhat lower than that for Scotland. Ireland, however, has a much more even distribution of population than Scotland and has nothing to compare with Scotland's densely-populated central industrial belt. The greater part of Ireland shows moderate to low rural densities of between 50 and 200 per sq. mile (20-80 per sq. km.). Areas with more than 400 per sq. mile (150 per sq. km.) mainly occur in and near the five largest towns of Dublin, Belfast, Cork, Limerick, and Londonderry. The largest uninhabited or sparsely-populated tracts are chiefly found in the upland fringes of the country, especially in the northwest and the west. In the latter areas there is often a striking contrast with adjacent lowlands and coastal margins, where some of the highest rural densities are to be found (200-400 per sq. mile, 80-150 per sq. km.). Ireland's rural population characteristics also differ from those of Great Britain in that settlement tends to be dispersed rather than nucleated in character.

Trends and prospects

Forecasts of the future population of the British Isles and its internal distribution can only be very tentative. The latest official projections of the total population of the United Kingdom are 57 millions in 1970, 61 in 1980 and 75 in 2000, i.e. an increase of nearly 40% between 1965 and 2000. The current rate of natural increase of over 6 per thousand (based on a birth rate of over 18 per thousand and a death rate of under 12) is double the very low rate of 3 experienced for a time in the 1930s, and is expected to rise still further by the end of the century. The infant mortality rate of about 20 per thousand live births compares with rates of over 60 in the 1930s and 150 in the 1870s. The expectation of life for a male child at birth is now 68 years and for a female 74. The character of the future migration balance is particularly difficult to foresee. The Commonwealth Immigrants Act of 1962, under which the government has the power to restrict the entry of Commonwealth citizens (although not citizens of the Irish Republic) may obviously be an important factor, but as long as there are acute labour shortages in the less congenial types of employment some inflow is likely to continue from the West Indies and India-Pakistan. The official population projections given above assume an annual net inward migration balance of 10,000 up to 1970 and no net migration after 1975.

Within the British Isles it seems likely that some drift of population to the Midlands and south of England will continue, especially if economic association with the Continent should become closer. Even if new employment were stimulated on a really massive scale in the 'older' industrial areas and in Ireland, London would still exert a very considerable pull, while the increase in the number of retired persons (and of their financial resources compared with those of previous generations) makes inevitable the further growth of towns on the south coast. While the 'drift south' could, if unrestricted, lead to undesirable congestion, especially in the Greater London and Greater Birmingham regions, there are, admittedly, many parts of eastern, midland and southwestern England where

355

the urban overlay could be greatly expanded (see *note,* p. 357) without leading to the dreaded nemesis of endless 'subtopia'. Moderation rather than elimination of the southward drift is thus becoming accepted planning policy for the future. To a certain extent, it might be claimed, the tremendous rehousing problems of areas such as Clydeside and south Lancashire are mitigated by a loss of population. Again, it must be pointed out that the man-made environments of the older industrial areas may be themselves both a repellent to natives and a deterrent to potential incomers. The operation of what may be called 'amenity differentials' probably plays some part in the southward drift of professional persons, despite the operation of national salary scales in many instances and indirect attempts by the government at the geographical rationing of teachers and doctors.

Local decentralisation of urban populations, always a spontaneous concomitant of city expansion, now takes place largely on a planned basis, accompanied, however, by longer-range dispersal, made possible under the New Towns Act and the Town Development Act. London has its eight thriving New Towns, all with a considerable provision of industry, although they undoubtedly form part of the Greater London urban region. Liverpool has its New Towns at Skelmersdale and Runcorn, and Birmingham at Redditch and Dawley. In Scotland part of Glasgow's overspill is being attracted to the New Towns of East Kilbride, Cumbernauld, Glenrothes, and Livingston, all in the central lowlands. In northeast England Newton Aycliffe, Peterlee and Washington offer facilities for some population relocation in Durham, while Cwmbran fulfils a similar role in south Wales. In Northamptonshire, on the other hand, the iron- and steel-producing New Town of Corby has drawn its population from a wide area, but especially Scotland, from where the firm concerned partially migrated in the 1930s—one of the few instances of literal southward migration of industry. In contrast to these State-initiated New Towns, Northumberland has sponsored its own New Towns at Cramlington and Killingworth, chiefly for the receipt of overspill from Tyneside.

Somewhat analogous to the New Towns are the Expanded Towns, that is existing towns that have made an agreement with a larger one to receive population and industry. A number of towns within a radius of about 100 miles (160 km.) have made such an arrangement with London, including King's Lynn, Wellingborough, Swindon, Basingstoke, Andover, and Ashford, to name only a few, while Birmingham and Glasgow also have similar schemes.

Suburbanisation of rural villages, although often severely restricted by planning regulations, continues and is, ironically, often pre-cociously induced by the rigidity of the official 'green belts' surrounding the larger towns. The penetration of new 'adventitious' population into the countryside does, however, partially offset the continued decline of the agricultural population. In the more thinly-populated and remoter rural areas declining populations, often due to an excess of deaths over births as much as to outward migration, are sometimes associated with problems of reduced transport facilities and other essential services. The defining of the most socially desirable and yet most economically efficient, distribution of population is, indeed, one of the most complex problems facing British planners in the second half of the twentieth century. But the attainment of any such ideal pattern, would, no doubt, prove even more difficult a task than its formulation.

References

CARRIER, N. H., and JEFFERY, J. R., 1953. External migration: a study of the available statistics, 1815-1950. *Stud. Med. Popul. Subj.*, **6.**

EDWARDS, K. C., and RAWSTRON, E. M., 1959. De wereld waarin wij wonen en werken, *Vol.* 1, *Part* 3, *De Britse Eilanden.* Zeist.

FAWCETT, C. B., 1922. British conurbations in 1921. *Sociol. Rev.*, **14,** 111-22.

— 1932. Distribution of the urban population in Great Britain, 1931. *Geogr. J.*, **79,** 100-116.

FREEMAN, T. W., 1959 (2nd ed. 1966). *The conurbations of Great Britain.* Manchester.

GEDDES, P., 1915. *Cities in evolution.* London (new edition, 1949).

OSBORNE, R. H., 1958. The movements of people in Scotland, 1851-1951. *Scot. Stud.*, **2,** 1-46.

POWELL, A. G., 1960-61. The recent development of Greater London. *Advanc. Sci.*, **17,** 76-86.

RAVENSTEIN, E. G., 1885. The laws of migration. *J. R. Statist. Soc.*, **48,** 167-235.

ROBINSON, G. W. S., 1953. British conurbations in 1951. *Sociol. Rev., New Ser.*, **1,** 15-26.

— 1956. British conurbations in 1951: some corrections. *Sociol. Rev., New Ser.*, **4,** 91-7.

RUSSELL, J. C., 1948. *British Medieval population.* Albuquerque.

SMAILES, A. E., 1946. The urban mesh of England and Wales. *Trans. Inst. Brit. Geogrs.*, **11,** 85-101.

SMITH, C. T., 1951. The movement of population in England and Wales in 1851 and 1861. *Geogr. J.*, **117,** 200-10.

TAYLOR, E. G. R., 1938. The geographical distribution of industry. *Geogr. J.*, **92,** 22-39.

THOMAS, B., 1954. Migration and economic growth: a study of Great Britain and the Atlantic economy. *Nat. Inst. Econ. Social Res., Econ. Social Stud.*, **12.** Cambridge.

VINCE, S. W. E., 1953. Reflections on the structure and distribution of the rural population in England and Wales, 1921-31. *Trans. Inst. Brit. Geogrs.*, **18,** 53-76.

Note (p. 356) Large-scale growth at Ipswich, Northampton and Peterborough is now government policy and a new city is to built in north Buckinghamshire. Further expansion is envisaged for Portsmouth-Southampton and Swindon.

19

RURAL SETTLEMENT

FOR so small an area the British Isles reveal remarkable variety in forms and patterns of settlement. On the one hand, this is related to marked changes in physical geography within relatively short distances; on the other to successive movements of peoples—refugees as well as conquerors—from the continent. Struggles, some brief, others protracted, for political supremacy and the control of land have left their imprint in numerous defensive works of varying type and date and, not least, in the form and siting of settlement. In addition to major physical and cultural influences two common forces have contributed to the character of our rural settlements. One was the tendency towards nucleation, especially in the early stages when social and economic advantages led folk to cluster in hamlets or villages under the protection of a lord, a process further encoura ged by the persistent growth of population. Opposed to this was the desire of most landsmen to 'stand on their own feet' as owner or tenant of their own tract of land, though the fulfilment of their hopes, like the dispersion that resulted, often came only late.

Regional contrasts in rural life in the British Isles have always been strong and were heightened by events of the Industrial Revolution which brought urbanisation to former farming areas rich in coal and iron. Improvement of rural areas saw the rapid extension of walled and hedged fields over *champion* land and *runrig* alike with the enclosure of former common grazing. The swing from and-holding in common to individual ownership or tenancy induced many peasant farmers to live outside the village, hamlet, or clachan, while in some districts migration to distant new holdings was enforced by powerful land owners, especially in the Scottish Highlands, or encouraged by national policy seen in the work of the Congested Districts Board in Ireland. As the towns grew they engulfed old villages, hamlets, farmsteads, and fields. Improved transport facilities induced town workers to 'squat' in the countryside adding a new dormitory function to adjacent rural areas whose character now became intermediate between town and country. Thus a great variety of rural settlements sprang up within the British Isles, which the author has attempted to map and explain.

It should be emphasised that in Figure 47 the distinction between a village and a hamlet is based on size rather than function. Thus, a hamlet is taken to be a nucleated settlement, with or without a parish church, having from three to nineteen homesteads, i.e. dwellings with dependent buildings and ground. The term applies equally to the small clearing settlements of the Anglo-Welsh border (11E, Fig. 47) and East Anglia (13B) as to the clachans of Scotland and northeast Ireland. In contrast, a village is held to be a nucleated rural settlement of twenty or more homesteads, a large village being distinguishable from a small market town by its paucity of services. The term 'scattered homesteads' embraces isolated rural dwellings ranging from farmsteads and labourers' cottages to weekend bungalows and 'dormitory' houses. For Great Britain two densities are shown on Figure 47, varying from sparse (below fifty persons per square mile, 20 per sq. km.) to close, somewhat above that figure. For Ireland three densities are used, namely sparse (with normally below 50 persons per square mile), medium (50-100), and dense (over 100), to show the widespread distribution of isolated farmsteads and labourers' houses. Correlation of the symbols used for Ireland and Great Britain respectively is shown in the key to Figure 47. The extensive moorland tracts with virtually no permanent settlement are defined as lying over half a mile from a permanently-occupied building. Finally, urban areas are shown, with the addition of a separate symbol for *rururban* belts within which mining or industrialised villages and hamlets lie amid neglected fields and tracts of spoiled land.

Scotland

The mountain tracts of Scotland form one of the most thinly populated parts of Europe with extensive empty areas today, although prehistoric evidence indicates that this was not always so. In the *Western and Northern Highlands* (Zone 1)[1] the valleys and narrow coastal flats (1A) bear scattered farmsteads, crofts, and smallholdings today with many remains of an old basic stratum of *clachans*, a term strictly referring to the *kirk-ton*[2], but later loosely extended to the *ferm-toun*[2] as well (Fig. 48a). The clachan, or hamlet

[1]This region coincides closely with the area of true crofts as defined in 1886.
[2]It should be emphasised that in Scotland the element *-ton* and *-toun* does not indicate a town but merely a small nucleation, usually a hamlet and at most a village.

1 HIGHLANDS

NORTHERN

WESTERN

2 FORTH-MORAY

3 FORTH-CLYDE

4 SOUTHERN SCOTLAND

SHETLANDS

ORKNEYS

5 CUMBRIA

6 NORTHUMBRIA

7 LANCASHIRE

8 EAST MIDLANDS

22 N.E. IRELAND

21 DRUMLIN CRESCENT

28 DONEGAL DISTRICT

21 DRUMLIN CRESCENT

27 CONNACHT PENINSULA

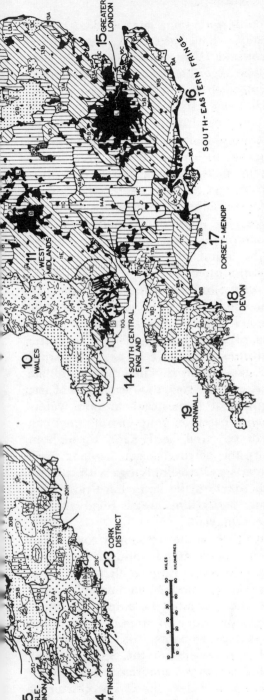

Map labels:
10 WALES · 11 WEST MIDLANDS · 14 SOUTH CENTRAL ENGLAND · 15 GREATER LONDON · 16 SOUTH-EASTERN FRINGE · 17 DORSET-MENDIP · 18 DEVON · 19 CORNWALL · 23 CORK DISTRICT · 24 S.W. FINGERS · 25 DINGLE-SHANNON

MILES / KILOMETRES

GREAT BRITAIN

	URBAN	EMPHASIS ON NUCLEATION	EMPHASIS ON DISPERSION
Extensive urban areas.	■		
Extensive rururban areas with mining or industrial villages interspersed with agricultural villages, hamlets and scattered homesteads.	▦		
Smaller towns.	:		
Predominantly villages with many scattered homesteads; occasional hamlets and market towns.		▥	
Intermediate area of villages interspersed with many scattered homesteads and hamlets; occasional market towns.		▨	
Predominantly hamlets with many scattered homesteads, occasional villages and market towns.		▨	
Close to medium density scattered homesteads with occasional hamlets, villages and market towns. Population density >50/sq. mile.			::::
Sparse scattered homesteads; some hamlets; few villages or market towns. Population density <50/sq. mile.			::
Virtually unpopulated upland, marsh, bog, dune or military training ground.			

IRELAND

URBAN / EMPHASIS GENERALLY ON DISPERSION	
Extensive urban areas.	
Extensive rururban areas.	
Smaller towns.	
Close stipple of scattered homesteads with numerous villages; occasional hamlets and market towns.	
Medium density scattered homesteads with numerous villages; occasional hamlets and market towns.	
Close stipple of scattered homesteads with numerous hamlets; occasional villages and market towns.	
Medium density scattered homesteads with numerous hamlets; occasional villages and market towns.	
Close stipple of scattered homesteads with occasional hamlets; villages and market towns. Population density >100/sq. mile.	
Medium density scattered homesteads with occasional hamlets; villages and market towns. Population density c. 50–100/sq. mile.	
Sparse scattered homesteads; some hamlets; few villages or market towns. Population density <50/sq. mile.	
Virtually unpopulated upland and bog.	

Fig. 47. RURAL SETTLEMENT, 1962.

of farming or fishing/farming folk with their land worked on the runrig system, is believed by many to have been the typical clustered settlement of many parts of Scotland, Wales and Ireland from perhaps as far back as the Early Iron Age. Before c. 1700 folk appear to have lived in simple hovels of earth and turf walls covered with heather and reed thatch which have left little trace today. After that date homesteads of stone and thatch were built, so fossilising the plan of some of the now depopulated clachans. Signs of heavy depopulation from the late eighteenth century to the present day are numerous. Though fishing has now declined, tourism has often strengthened the coastal nucleations. Gaelic and Norse place-names are common, as in the Outer Hebrides and Skye (1B) where old clachan units (e.g. Howmore, Fig. 48a) often remain amid long linear crofting hamlets with shepherds' huts and old abandoned shielings on the hills above. The island of Arran (1C), with many clachans in the south, is distinguished from the remainder of Zone 1 because it lacks true crofts. Similarly in the Shetlands (1D) a thin stipple of crofts with coastal fishing hamlets, many bearing distinctive Norse names, contrasts with the closer pattern of small farmsteads and linear hamlets of the Orkneys (1E). The better farming possibilities of the Caithness lowland (1F) are reflected in many crofts, smallholdings and sizeable farms with a number of late hamlets and villages dating particularly from the clearances of last century. Here, too, the grouping of homesteads around water-power gave rise to small *mill-touns*, based on grain or fulling, which form an important ingredient of rural settlement throughout eastern Scotland. Farther south the narrow coastal lowland (1G) carries a high density of farmsteads and smallholdings with clusters of true crofts in places, though many of the latter have now been abandoned or have changed their status. This area is relatively well served with market towns, like Dingwall.

South and east of the Moray Firth in the settlement zone called *Forth-Moray* (Zone 2) Norse place-names are rare and the dominant British-Gaelic names are overlain by many English elements, some springing from contacts between England and Alban during Norman times but which in general are later. Around the empty mountain core lies an upland fringe (2A) of widely scattered farmsteads, smallholdings, and occasional clachan remnants, but true crofts are rare except in the middle and upper valley of the Spey. Bothies and hunting lodges are sprinkled across the moorland flanks amid old shielings, while in the fretwork of valleys the recent clustering of folk around a hydro-electric station, distillery, saw-mill, affores-

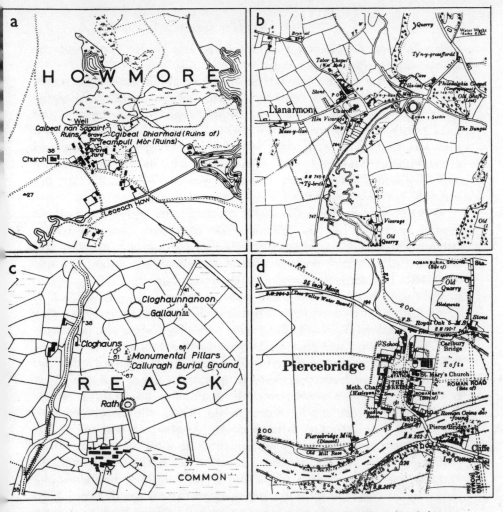

Fig. 48. EXAMPLES OF NUCLEATED RURAL SETTLEMENTS. (*a* and *c* based on, *b* and *d* reproduced from Ordnance Survey Six Inch maps; here reproduced at slightly different scales.)

(*a*) *Howmore, South Uist, 1878.* This Scottish clachan or kirkton with remains of ancient churches, chapels, and graveyards occupies a dry site on the boundary between the more fertile *machair* to the west and the low-lying bogland farther east. The settlement, whose name signifies 'great burial mound', was probably once a parsonage of Iona. Today fourteen stone-built crofters' cottages, many with thatched roofs, cluster to the south of the old well (now disused).

(*b*) *Llanarmon, Denbighshire, 1953.* This Welsh hamlet, with its early church dedication to St Garmon, provides a fine example of a *tir cyfrif* bond hamlet. As the centre of the medieval *commote* of Iâl, it formed the *maerdref* with the dwellings of the lord in the vicinity of *Tomen y Faedre* ('the mound of the maerdref'). Note the mill, which once served five outlying bond hamlets, and the later nonconformist chapels.

(*c*) *Reask, Co. Kerry, 1842.* This Irish hamlet, with

an orderly disposition of homesteads around what may be a partly infilled green, lies on an old lane between a stream (Reask = 'marshy place') and a tract of open common. Continuity of occupation for many centuries in this area is indicated by numerous standing stones, a large *rath*, with many *clochauns* (cloghauns), an old burial ground (*Calluragh*) with early Christian grave slabs and an inscribed cross-pillar on the site of an early cell.

(*d*) *Piercebridge, Co. Durham, 1924.* This shapely English broad-green village, occupying a dry river terrace at a convenient crossing of the Tees, is neatly placed within the Roman fort of *Magis*. After being re-occupied in Anglo-Saxon times the settlement was later included in a Danish wapentake embracing land along the Tees. Note the persistence of former Roman gateways as entrances into the village and the taking in of parts of the green as front gardens to the homesteads.

tation scheme or upstart tourist centre has partly redressed the drastic depopulations of a century or so ago.

Descending to the coastal belt (2B) with its more favourable farming conditions one enters a region of plentiful farmsteads, sometimes dispersed like the well-built *Mains*[1] (home farm of the local laird) or the more humble *cot*, but often clustered to form a *kirk-ton, ferm-toun, castle-ton, mill-ton* or perhaps a late planned street-village. Market towns with buildings grouped around the axis of a broad street, such as Keith with its Market Green, are liberally sprinkled throughout the area.

Within and around the main mining and industrial belt of central Scotland lies the *Forth-Clyde Rururban Zone* (3) where urbanised hamlets and villages affected by mining and industry still retain a girdle of fields and a scatter of farmsteads and smallholdings. A smaller but more fragmented urban and rururban district (4G) is also found in coal-mining and quarrying areas of Ayrshire, south Lanarkshire, and northwest Dumfriesshire, but apart from this most of *Southern Scotland* (Zone 4) is rural. Excluding the unpopulated higher portions, dispersed farmsteads are typical of most of this area. Similar sparse distributions occur in the upper dales and on mid-slopes of both the western (4E) and eastern uplands (4F), but the two regions are remarkably distinct in other ways. While Gaelic place-names predominate in the west, the eastern part of the region was strongly influenced by Anglian settlement as far as the Forth. Here English place-names abound, especially those ending in *-ton*[2]. A long tradition of nucleated settlement in villages and hamlets since Anglian times may in part explain the distinctive character of the Haddington area (4A) and the Tweed Valley (4B) whereas in similar favoured farming areas of the west close density farmsteads with occasional *kirk-tons* and *ferm-touns* occupy the Rhinns of Galloway and the Solway lowlands (4D), as well as the northern flanks (4C). Shapely villages with greens, some ancient, others more recently planned, appear to have penetrated the Anglian east from adjacent Northumbria (Zone 6) while many of the Border boroughs, such as Haddington and Peebles, may have developed their market area around an old green nucleus (Fig. 48d). Among other cultural transfers from Northumbria one may include the horse-wheel sheds and open horse-gins for grinding corn, while proximity to the war-torn frontier between Scotland and England

[1]The word is derived from Norman-French *demesne* (*demain*) with its strong feudal associations.

[2]Old English *tun* originally meant 'fence' or 'enclosure'. At an early date the meaning of 'enclosure around a homestead' had been extended to include a hamlet or village.

was reflected in great castles of the lords, the more humble pele towers of freemen farmers and in massive church towers.

England and Wales

Whereas in the east the extension of Northumbrian culture northward into Lothian was strong, in the west contrasts of human geography north and south of the Solway remained surprisingly sharp and not least in rural settlement. Once south of the border into *Cumbria* (Zone 5) villages and hamlets, many with greens, are freely scattered among the numerous farmsteads in region 5A with clusters of pele towers in region 5D. Yet north of the Solway dispersed settlement, with only an occasional hamlet, prevails, perhaps reflecting successive 'scorched earth' policies of long ago. Around the unpopulated core of Cumbria lies a girdle of scattered farmsteads (5E) bearing Celtic and Anglo-Saxon names interspersed with many Norse elements in *-thwaite*, *-garth*, and *-rigg*, giving topographic emphasis to 'dales'. By contrast, in the Vale of Eden (5B) with its many villages set amid stone-walled fields, Scandinavian names in *-by* dove-tail with English counterparts in *-ton*, *-ham*, and *-field*. Here the courtyard farmsteads boast massive, stone-built, slate-roofed hay barns. Farther south hamlets and scattered homesteads predominate (5E), while urban conditions characterise the Cumberland coalfield (5F). To the west the lonely Isle of Man bears a thin stipple of farmsteads, especially in the north (5H) with hamlets (often with distinctive *Balla*-[1] names) more numerous in the south (5G).

Scattered farmsteads, including some that sprang from monastic granges, are sprinkled loosely over the Pennine flanks and rounded Cheviot slopes (6D) of *Northumbria* (Zone 6), appearing again in the bleak North York Moors (6E). But widespread dispersion is generally rare in Northumbria where strong traditions of nucleated settlement appear to date at least from Anglian times. South of the Tweed hamlets with typical Anglo-Saxon place-names in *-ington*, *-ton*, *-ham*, and *-wick* predominate on the coastal lowland (6A) as far as Alnwick, with many large farmsteads, pele towers and occasional green villages, the latter increasing in number southward into region 6B (Fig. 48d). This region continues as far as the Wapentake of Sadberge where Danish village and hamlet names in *-by* and

---

[1]*Baile*, the Gaelic word for 'homestead', 'townland', 'township', and sometimes 'hamlet' appears frequently in Scotland as *bal*, *baile*, or *baillie*, in the Isle of Man as *balla* and in Ireland as *bally*. The Welsh *beili* and *baeli* are related to it.

-thorp reinforce the Anglo-Saxon elements in a broad belt (6C) running down the Vale of York to beyond the Humber. Open-field farming with co-aration was strong in this area until the enclosures, and the 'reversed S' corrugations of ridge and furrow are deeply inscribed particularly on the wetter claylands. The reversion of arable to pasture encouraged by religious and secular lords during the fifteenth and early sixteenth centuries saw the disappearance of many villages in the North and East Ridings and elsewhere, so that the present village pattern is often less dense than formerly. Even so, villages are often less than one and a half miles apart today. The pattern of close scattered farmsteads (6F) north of Hull is partly the result of depopulation, while that nearer Spurn Head reflects late reclamation. By contrast, the working of coal and iron, and the growth of industry on the Northumberland and Durham coalfield and on Tees-side (6G) have seen the urbanisation of many areas once rural.

In Zone 7, which embraces *Lancashire* and part of the upland flank of Yorkshire, urbanisation has been equally heavy particularly in the coal, textile, and engineering districts and along the coast from Liverpool to Lancaster. Among the upland cloughs of Rossendale (7B) small hamlets and isolated stone farmsteads, with names incorporating *delph*, *fold*, *wood*, *shaw*, *-worth*, *intake*, or *ridding*, predominate, while the less accessible and bleaker moorland flanks of Bowland Forest (7D) have only isolated farmsteads. In the richer farming areas near the coast emphasis changes from nucleated villages with mixed Anglo-Saxon and Scandinavian names around Morecambe Bay, the southern Fylde, and Ribblesdale (7A), to hamlets on the late-reclaimed mosslands of Overwyre (7C). Farther south still, close farmsteads and smallholdings occupy similar reclaimed lands behind Southport extending east to the Ormskirk potato district (7E).

A measure of continuity in form and pattern of settlement across the central Pennines is provided by the great corridor of Airedale with its many villages. The latter frequently incorporate a green, resembling in many ways those of the Vale of Eden, though in Lancashire such villages are rare. Immediately south of the Aire Gap the urban and industrial belts of the Pennine flanks almost straddle the watershed, being separated only by relatively narrow belts of limestone and gritstone country (7B) with occasional hamlets and scattered sheep-farms. The latter continue into the *South Pennines* (Zone 9) encircling the bleak waste (9C) from Black Hill to Kinderscout, but once into the Low Peak (9A) villages reappear in the limestone dales and even on the plateau itself provided water is available. Lead-mining, quarrying, lime-burning, and tourism have both strengthened and changed the old nucleations here, but rural hamlets are still plentiful, increasing in numbers southward around Ashbourne particularly on the shales and Keuper Marl of regions 9B and 11E.

The *East Midlands* (Zone 8), like Zone 6, is an extensive area of basic Romano-British, Anglo-Saxon, and Danish settlement stretching from the Humber southward along the Vale of Trent into the Northampton Uplands, but excluding the Fens. Its southern boundary coincides with the southern limit of strong Danish place-names. Close nucleated villages, many with greens, occupy the bulk of the rural area (8A) which was generally late enclosed despite the fact that it had suffered heavily in the de-populations of the fifteenth and sixteenth centuries. 'Empty' parishes, with perhaps a solitary church and a few farmsteads, are common, though signs of their more populous past still remain in tumbled mounds, old sunken ways, and in great 'Ewe Fields' and 'Town Fields' often set like islands amid a sea of aratral curves. In northeast Lincolnshire (8B) hamlets are typical of both the Wolds and the late-reclaimed coastal marshes, giving way to scattered farms around Louth (8F). Hamlets again predominate east of Grantham and Stamford, this region (8C) being terminated sharply on the east by a remarkable string of villages bordering the Fens. In the hunting country around Higham Ferrers (8D) the hamlets are interspersed with many ancient moated settlements which appear to be the remains of farmsteads established by prosperous freemen in woodland clearings soon after the Norman Conquest. Finally, a close stipple of isolated farmsteads occupies the damp Isle of Axholme (8E), with thinner distributions in the Dukeries and Charnwood Forest. Extensive rururban tracts (8G) are also to be found on the concealed and exposed coalfields and where iron-stone is worked, late clearing names like Woodhouse, Woodseats, and Wood Laithes being common.

In the flat black lands of the *Fens* (Zone 12) the rectilinear mesh of roads, banks, and drainage channels bounding the evenly spaced farms and smallholdings proclaims relatively recent reclamation (12B). Westward these modern 'centuriation' patterns terminate abruptly beyond the Roman Car Dyke where a remarkable chain of dry-point villages runs from Peterborough to Lincoln, paralleling those along the mid-slope, scarp-top, and scarp-foot of Lincoln Heath. Old 'island' sites, such as Thorney, Whittlesey, and Ramsey

lie scattered about the marsh and often had strong monastic associations that made their markets prosper. A well-marked belt (12C)
of Anglo-Saxon settlement with numerous villages occupies the
area between Spalding, Long Sutton, and Wisbech, with later
Marschhufendörfer, especially near the latter. Farther east again is
a narrow belt (12A) reclaimed before 1700 and having daughter
villages and hamlets like Holbeach St Marks and Holbeach Drove,
which appear to have developed from summer grazing sites established on the extensive marsh of the mother settlement of Holbeach
since Domesday times. Around historic Cambridge the attraction of
population during Romano-British and Anglo-Saxon times towards a convenient river crossing point on the southern edge of
the Fens encouraged the rise of villages (12D) as in the adjacent
regions 8A, 13A, and 14A.

The *West Midlands* (Zone 11) are strongly urban around Birmingham and Stoke but outstandingly rural in the west and south.
Settled rather late in Anglo-Saxon times and little affected by
Scandinavian colonisation, the Celtic roots of the area strengthen
as one moves westward. Thus, although Anglo-Saxon villages predominate on the plains bounding the Dee estuary (11A), between
Shrewsbury and Stafford (11B), around Lichfield (11C), in the
terrace belt flanking the Avon and on the late *champion* lands of the
Feldon of south Warwickshire (11D), hamlets and scattered homesteads are characteristic of the Cheshire mosslands, of late cleared
areas like the Forests of Arden and Feckenham, and of the broken
uplands of Herefordshire and western Shropshire (11E). Celtic
place-names become increasingly common the farther west one
goes, and the western boundary of Zone 11 coincides closely not
only with Offa's Dyke but also with the political and etymological
frontiers. Persistent defensive needs are seen in Celtic hill forts,
Roman camps, and Norman castles alike, in strong church towers
and numerous moated homesteads.

From its early Romano-British, Anglo-Saxon, and sporadic
Danish settlement, together with its prosperity in Domesday times,
one might expect *East Anglia* (Zone 13) to be a region of strong
village settlement today. Yet over extensive areas (13B) one finds
a landscape of loose hamlets and scattered farmsteads with later
squatting settlements on the former heavily-wooded, drift deposits.
The hamlets, which are often grouped around a large, amorphous
or sometimes triangular green, frequently incorporate the element
'Green' or 'Heath' in the place-name, as for example in Maypole
Green. As in parts of the Welsh Border, the churches, which often

have a distinctive round tower, sometimes lie isolated from the hamlets. An old tradition of isolated farmstead settlement may be seen in the many moated homesteads resembling those of the Forest of Arden and perhaps similarly datable to the twelfth and thirteenth centuries. By contrast, village settlement is strong in a narrow, anciently-occupied belt (13A) bordering the Fens, along the eastern shore of the Wash, and in three coastal lobes from Great Yarmouth southward. Southwest of Lowestoft and over the southern part of the Broads (13C) dispersion is again the rule though the density of farmsteads is much greater than on Breckland (13D).

The belt of strong village settlement that extends from Northumberland down the Vales of York and Trent breasts the Cotswold scarp and continues into *South-Central England* (Zone 14) with its predominant Anglo-Saxon place-names. Late medieval depopulation in part explains the frequency of hamlets in northern Oxfordshire and part of Buckinghamshire (14B), but once into the upper Thames Valley and the Vale of Aylesbury villages extend in a great arc (14A) to Cambridge and beyond, though terminating abruptly to the south at the Chiltern scarp. The Marlborough, Berkshire, and Hampshire Downs together with Salisbury Plain form a very distinctive settlement region (14C). Here there are very few hamlets, and the broken strings of valley villages, many with *-bourne* names, are separated by upland tracts either ploughed and grazed by scattered farmsteads or recently depopulated to make way for airfields, artillery ranges, and military camps.

One of the greatest densities of nucleated villages and hamlets in England occurs in the *Dorset-Mendip* area (Zone 17), with a great horse-shoe of villages (17A) extending through the Vales of Pewsey and Malmesbury. Here continuity of occupation has been strong since Romano-British times. Saxon place-names abound while the weight of Norman penetration is seen in numerous castle sites and by the addition of Fitzwarren, Budville, or Peverell to homely Saxon settlement names. West of Warminster, hamlets reappear on the clays and with scattered farmsteads are characteristic of the North Dorset Downs (17C). By contrast villages, many strongly influenced by tourism, are found in the South Dorset Downs and Isle of Purbeck (17B), whereas on the reclaimed tracts of the Somerset Levels (17D) farmsteads lie close, continuing more thinly across the slopes of Mendip (17E).

Since Cobbett's day the 'Great Wen' of London has stretched far into the surrounding belt of woodland, heath, and field to fashion *Greater London* (Zone 15) which now threatens to engulf much of southeast England. Dormitory squatting and industrial development around the urban core have produced a ring (15A) of suburban villages and towns extending beyond the Green Belt to Reading, Aldershot, Chatham, and Hertford. Beyond lies a generally well-wooded border zone (15B) having many hamlets, with names incorporating -*worth*, *wood*, *hatch*, *heath*, and *green*; numerous estates; a rash of farmsteads, houses, and bungalows; and a fair number of villages which in the Chiltern valleys assume long linear forms. Army camps, set in woodland clearings or on barren heath, further complicate the settlement pattern. As Figure 47 shows, the strength of hamlet settlement in the great triangular belt from East Anglia to the New Forest, thence narrowing to the borders of Devon, is remarkable, the pattern being broken only by the tentacular mass of Greater London. Characteristic is the woody arc (16B) from Newbury through the Wealden Forest Ridges to the *denns* of Kent, forming part of what has been called the *South-Eastern Fringe* (Zone 16). Here thin suburban squatting lies among late Saxon clearing names, homestead moats and shingled church spires. Past industrial activity based on timber as fuel is seen in reed-flanked hammer ponds and in names recording furnace, tiler, potter, and tanner. In Kent, with its tradition of strong Jutish settlement, the hamlets are set among orderly orchard trees with the tapering oasthouse an attractive architectural feature. London's influence on settlement persists throughout the South-Eastern Fringe even to the coastal strip of ports and resorts. Important gaps occur, however, in Romney Marsh and the Pevensey Levels, along the South Downs and also in the New Forest where scattered farmsteads (16C) now predominate, though William of Normandy may have destroyed some twenty villages and a dozen hamlets to make his royal forest here. Elsewhere clusters of old villages, many showing early Anglo-Saxon associations in their place-names and pagan cemeteries, appear in the Hastings area (16A), in east Kent and around Portsmouth, though here too, as in the Isle of Wight, the influence of industry or tourism has been strong.

Within the compact unit of *Wales* (Zone 10) unpopulated tracts and areas of isolated homesteads (10A, B, C) cover many square miles. No longer do we believe, as did Meitzen and others, that these *Einzelhöfe* set among small fields, sometimes irregular or squarish, sometimes strip-like, have been the traditional pattern since the Early Iron Age. Instead, emphasis is placed today on the early existence of hamlet clusters, akin to the clachan and the continental *Drubbel*; with arable infield and pastoral outfield.

370

Some sprang up around the cells of itinerant Celtic 'saints'; others grew by natural accretion, many being recognisable in medieval times either as loose girdle-hamlets of freemen with their home-steads disposed around a block of open, quilleted, arable land, or as compact hamlets of bondmen holding symmetrical strips in an open-field shareland (e.g. Llanarmon, Fig. 48b). By the fifteenth and sixteenth centuries both these types of hamlet were splintering into scatters of large enclosed farms, to which were later added lesser farms and smallholdings from the final enclosures of the last two centuries. Among the Celtic place-names that predominate in Zone 10 today the element *llan*, meaning a religious enclosure and later a church, is very common; to this may be added other names like *eglwys*, *betws*, *glas* (*clas*), and *capel*. Centuries later in areas like Snowdonia (10B) where upstart hamlets grew into gaunt villages and occasional ugly towns, a new religious factor, Non-conformity, brought into being the chapel which in turn gave spiritual and choral unity to places like Bethesda set amid the dark slate quarries.

In the frontier region west of Offa's Dyke the relentless pressure of Anglo-Saxon peasant and Norman knight alike upheld minor nucleations within both the Englishry and the Welshry, though even here dispersion is the keynote today compared with the dominant hamlet patterns east of the Dyke (11E). Over the High and Middle Plateaux embracing regions 10A and 10B the density of isolated farmsteads is often very low, but becomes much closer on the peripheral low plateaux and undulating plains. Once again place-names such as *tyddyn* (single homestead) high-light the ground patterns, while implications of former transhumance appear in *hendref* (old township or winter home) and *hafod* (summer dwelling). Similarly, the imprint of the squatter is seen in whimsical names like *ty un nos* (one night house), Clod Hall, and Morning Surprise.

The cultural shatter-belt of the Anglo-Welsh border swings sharply round through Monmouthshire, continuing along the Vale of Glamorgan to St Brides Bay. The scattered hamlets and fortified church-towers of Monmouthshire (10E) still resemble those of Herefordshire, but the place-names remain on the whole over-whelmingly Celtic. The force of Anglo-Norman penetration westward into 'Little England beyond Wales' is seen in numerous nucleated villages, many with a castle and a typical English name, that extend right across the Vale of Glamorgan into the Gower peninsula and western Pembrokeshire (10G). It is difficult to assess the influence of earlier Scandinavian settlement in these western shorelands with place-names like Tenby and Swansea, particularly when Anglo-Norman hamlets (10F) bearing other 'foreign' names like Jameston, Hodgeston, and Cosheston have been superimposed, as in remote Pembrokeshire. Here, too, Anglo-Norman manorial influence brought lowland open-field husbandry with co-aration to this favoured farming area, and may have introduced late green village forms to places like Reynoldston and Maenclochog. The grid of urban and rururban valleys within the South Wales Coalfield deserve special mention, as also do the old lead-mining hamlets inland of Aberystwyth (10D) and the woollen hamlets around Talybont or Llandyssul, but we must now look beyond the Bristol Channel at the Southwest Peninsula.

South of the Bristol Channel, a waning of Celtic culture again occurred after the tide of Saxon colonisation broke against it. Whereas the Romans had achieved little against the Dumnonii, the colonising force of Wessex was funnelled steadily westward into the Southwest Peninsula to spread Saxon settlement names thickly across Devon and westernmost Somerset. Yet beyond the Tamar infiltration quickly slackened, leaving Cornwall as a strong Celtic outpost. The settlement pattern that developed in *Devon* (Zone 18) was still very different from those of the English Lowland Zone, being a hybrid showing adjustment to contrasting physical, social, and economic conditions. Thus, nucleated villages (18B) of no particular form extend westward in a narrow coastal belt having a close association with fisher-farmer communities of the past and with the tourist industry of today. Similar distributions extend inland along the Exe and Yeo, border Barnstaple Bay and run from Wiveliscombe to Bampton. Apart from these and the several towns and ports, nucleation takes the form of hamlets occupying the eastern neck (18A) of the peninsula, the flanks of Exmoor, the Quantocks, and Dartmoor. An understandable preference for sheltered valleys is revealed by the many *-combe* names, while early clearing is commemorated in numerous *-leigh*, *-worthy*, and *-wood* names. Elsewhere close scattered farmsteads (18C) predominate, many bearing late names like Tythecott and Smythacott, with a thinner stipple on Exmoor, the Brendons, and around Dartmoor (18D).

Similar patterns continue from Devon into *Cornwall* (Zone 19) whose Saxon name emphasised the survival of the Welsh in 'Cornavia'. Here, not only do Cornish place-names predominate but Cornish as a Celtic dialect was spoken until the eighteenth century.

Where villages (19A) occur today, they are often related to mining and quarrying around Cambourne and St Austell or represent former fisher-farmer clusters on the coastal platforms now swept by tourism. Around Bodmin with its sparse sheep farms (19D) lies an arc of hamlets (19B) whose names recall those of Wales and Brittany. For example, the element *tref* (township, homestead, hamlet) appears frequently, as in Treskinnock, Trehausa, and Tremaine, while the peregrinations of Celtic 'saints' underlie St Glevias, St Clether, Perranzabuloe, and Zennor (St Senara). Similarly, near Fowey names like Lansallos and Lanteglos bear further witness to the power of the Celtic church. West of Bodmin is a close pattern of isolated farmsteads (19C) with occasional villages and hamlets particularly on the '400-foot platform' (120 m.) that terminates in the ultimate bastion of Land's End.

Ireland

The family farmstead is the basic ingredient of Irish settlement today, but this has not always been so. It is now supposed that either during or soon after the period of *raths*, *cashels*, and nascent *bailes* (townlands), native clustering of primitive farmsteads and cottages to form hamlets with a primitive rundale system coupled with strong pastoralism occurred, while along the coast fisher-farmer communities probably shared boats as well as land. The resulting hamlets probably closely resembled those of Wales and the *clachans* of Scotland. Apart from these native clusters, including also those around religious cell and monastery, larger nucleated settlements ranging from villages to small towns were in general grafted on to the Irish landscape by invasion, commencing with the Norse coastal towns from Dublin to Cork and being continued by feudal towns and villages of the Norman period; finally in Tudor and Stuart times strong English and Scottish plantations were added. Foreign occupation sustained for so long brought vast areas of land into the hands of a favoured few, so that before the great famine of 1845-7 eighty per cent of Irish peasant holdings were under fifteen acres. The subsequent redistribution of land by the Congested Districts Board, the Estates Commissioners and now the Land Commission, has contributed in no small way to the extensive stipple of farmsteads shown on Figure 47.

Medium density farmsteads (many with over 100 acres) and labourers' houses now predominate on the better drained plains (20A) of Zone 20, for convenience called *Leinster*, although it is not precisely co-terminous with the ancient kingdom. Here population density averages 50-100 per sq. mile (20-40 per sq. km.), dropping to below fifty on the boglands of Allen (20B), in the upper Suir, on the flanks of the Galty and Ballyhoura Mountains and around historic Tara. Strings of individual homesteads straggle along the narrow esker ridges, while the old importance of adjacent water-meadow (*cluain*=clon) and distant summer cow-pasture (*buaile*=booley) is seen in typical Irish names like Clonavoe, Cloncreen, Boolageelagh and Bolabeg. While the Norse influence on settlement was slight away from Dublin, Wexford, and Waterford, the Anglo-Norman imprint is stamped indelibly in the villages (20E) and hamlets around Thomastown[1] (Co. Kilkenny) and especially in the fascinating group of hamlets (20C) around Licketstown, Ballygorey, and Doornane. In some of these (e.g. Doornane) the fine courtyard farmsteads appear once to have been grouped around a small central open space (*faiche*=green), recalling the *Sackgassendorf* so well suited to joint tillage and herding. By contrast, nearby Mooncoin is a fine street-village, resembling many Stradbally (*Sráidbhaile*=street settlement) villages and hamlets elsewhere. Street-villages and market towns are also common around Lough Derg (20G), inland from Dublin (20D), west of Tipperary (20F) and in separate, narrow coastal strips from Waterford to Dundalk (20H) where industry or tourism have infused new life into old fishing, farming, and trading settlements. Finally one must mention the arc of hamlets and scattered farmsteads (20C) that extends from Wicklow to Waterford, terminating in the strong Anglo-Norman district of Licketstown. On the inland side of this arc lies Ferns, once capital of the Kingdom of Leinster, but now despite its market and cathedral a quiet place of only some 600 souls. It is typical of many such Irish 'towns' that once knew better days and is best described as a 'market village'.

Northward into Ulster the historical ingredients of settlement are little changed, but the great physical transition to the more fertile *Drumlin Crescent* (Zone 21) is associated with a remarkably even pattern of close farmsteads (21A) stretching from Sligo Bay to Strangford Lough, the emphasis being on dry-point 'island' sites above the pastoral damp hollows. In the fragmented upland (21B) between Lough Erne and Lough Allen farm densities are lower, as also in the lake-studded depression from Upper Lough Erne to Cavan. Hamlets and occasional market towns, often with castle,

[1]There is a striking similarity between the Anglo-Norman place-names here and in the Pembrokeshire district of southwest Wales.

abbey, or humble creamery, are evenly scattered throughout the Drumlin Crescent with a narrow coastal belt of old fishing villages (21C), turned holiday centres, in the Ards peninsula and north of Carlingford Lough.

Whereas the preceding zone spans the frontier of 1925, *North-East Ireland* (Zone 22) lies almost entirely in the political unit of Northern Ireland whose strong Protestant and Presbyterian allegiance, compared with overwhelming Roman Catholicism in the Republic, introduces a powerful regional distinction between church and chapel in settlements north and south of the border. The native stratum of hamlets (or clachans[1] as they can rightly be called here) remained a distinctive element of the rural landscape until last century since when the splintering of hamlets and fragmentation of great estates have spattered the area with farmsteads, ranging from close density in the valleys of the Bann and lower Foyle (22A) to sparse in the uplands of Sperrin and Antrim (22C). Weak Anglo-Norman colonisation brought the small defensive town and perhaps a few villages to some coastal areas, but the great period of English and Scottish settlement occurred in Tudor and Stuart times. The influence of such late founded towns and villages is well seen in a great belt (22D) from Loughs Neagh to Erne, some having distinctive 'new' names like Charlemont, others being grafted on to pre-existing Irish settlements like Dungannon and Eniskillen. The element 'Newtown' features prominently in the place-names of Ireland, many Planters' Towns arising at this time. Thus, what is now the small market town of Newtownstewart took its name from Sir William Stewart who acquired it in 1628. Less spectacular, but equally important, were the stout farmsteads of English and Scottish 'pioneers' that set names like Englishtown and Scotshouse among the lowly Irish cabins.

Turning to the southwest and west, rural settlement in the *Cork District* (Zone 23) reflects many of the features already discussed above, but the weight of Anglo-Norman colonisation and of later planting slackened considerably westward into the uplands of Kerry. Along the coast successive occupations from Viking to Cromwellian times have produced a belt (23C) of small ports, castle towns, and villages now much affected by tourism, or by industry as around Cork. Intruders who pressed inland saw many advantages in nucleation and this may explain in part the groups of villages (23D) around centres like Buttevant whose aggressive

---

[1] Although the word 'clachan' is not known in modern Irish it does appear in dialect in northeast Ireland, perhaps having been introduced by Scottish settlers.

Norman name perpetuates the battle-cry of the Barry family *'Boutez-en-avant'*. Between Ballineen and Macroom a belt of hamlets (23E) appears to mark a hybrid region within which native hamlets, still plentiful in the peninsulas farther west, have survived alongside intrusive elements like Castletown and Crookstown. Finally, serving the medium density (23B) to close density (23A) farmsteads in the valleys of the Blackwater, Lee, and Bandon are scattered villages and small market towns centred economically on the creamery.

Helped by the potato and coastal fishing, the carrying capacity of rural Ireland in terms of population during the eighteenth and early nineteenth centuries was truly remarkable. With a total population in 1841 of over eight million, almost double that of today, congestion and malnutrition became acute in infertile, small-farm areas during periods of famine, especially 1845-50 and particularly in the western peninsulas. Here the native Irish stratum remained strong and coincidence with the *Ghaeltacht* today is very close. But with the exception of Galway-Shannon (Zone 26) these were economically the poorest parts of Ireland in 1891 when the Congested Districts Board was established to cope with the problem of persistent rural overpopulation despite the alleviation that had followed mass emigration. Movement of population to new compact farms carved out of great estates has led to the break-up of many 'native' hamlets and occasional villages, but the shrunken remnants of former fisher-farmer nucleations can still be clearly seen discontinuously from Bantry Bay to the Mullet peninsula of Mayo with an outlier around Fanad in Donegal.

In the *South-Western Fingers* (Zone 24) sparse farmsteads, many bearing *bally-* and *booley-* names, occupy the flanks of Macgillycuddy's Reeks and the Caha mountains (24A) changing to medium density (24B) around the small market towns of Bantry and Kenmare, the latter founded only as late as 1670 by Sir William Petty. North of Bantry close clusters of hamlets (24C), strongly Irish in character, follow the narrow coastal belt to reappear in *Dingle-Shannon* (Zone 25). Here in the Dingle peninsula, promontory forts, raths, clochauns, and early Christian sites record the strength of native occupation long before the coming of Norse sea-rovers to Smerwick and Limerick, or the setting up of an Anglo-Norman barony (e.g. Reask, Fig. 48c). As population grew, hamlets (25D) were to jostle for shelter and space reaching their greatest density perhaps just over a century ago. For example, at Dunquin the remains of five hamlets, each strongly nucleated with old fisher-farmer single-storey thatched houses, face Great Blasket Island once the home of three hundred folk, but now completely empty. Co-operation in fishing probably extended to farming, and may well be an important factor in the tradition of nucleation here. East of Brandon Bay close farmsteads (25C) occupy the narrow coastal flat, declining to average density courtyard-farms in the limestone plains (25B) and so to sparse on the harsher Coal Measure uplands (25A). Market villages and towns are also numerous in Co. Limerick, many displaying O'Donovan, Desmond (Fitzgerald) or later Tudor and Cromwellian influence.

Medium density homesteads (26B) now stipple the grits and limestones around the Fergus inlet of *Galway-Shannon* (Zone 26), becoming much more scattered around Slieve Callan, Elva, and Aughty (26A), but two belts of hamlets along or near the coast deserve special mention. One (26C) takes in a virtually unplanted area from Loop Head to Liscannor Bay; the other (26D) occupies the great karst plain, dry or wet according to the changing water-table, from Lough Corrib over to the market town of Gort. Around the lower Clare is a larger and even more remarkable group, of which Kiltullagh was an orderly street-green hamlet last century.

Proceeding westwards into the *Connacht Peninsula* (Zone 27) a close pattern of late farmsteads and splintered hamlets lies along or near the coast road in the stern granite country bordering Galway Bay (27D). In the belt from Cashla Bay to Gorumna Island the close mesh of irregular, stone-walled enclosures or 'gardens', often scarce an acre in extent, together with the spattered debris of farmsteads past and present, conjures up a vivid picture of the congestion and poverty of a century ago. The wonder is that land and sea, here so closely knit, contrived to support such a throng of fisher-farmer hamlets for so long. From Streamstown Bay along the rocky coast to Benwee Head hamlet patterns continue, but inland the transition to sparse farmsteads (27A) around the metamorphic mountain masses is sharp. In the more sheltered, drift-covered plains (27B) east of Lough Mask the density of farmsteads increases, becoming close again as one approaches the outskirts of the more favoured drumlin belt east of Lough Conn (27C).

Finally, in the *Donegal District* (Zone 28) the Celtic component still remains strong today. Savage Norse attacks were here seldom accompanied by settlement, nor did the Anglo-Normans venture far beyond Lough Swilly, but the plantation of Ulster and the succeeding Cromwellian settlement brought considerable alien,

Protestant influence to the native hamlets especially in the more sheltered and fertile east. Emigration and the redistribution of land during the last century have fragmented the old hamlets, except for a small group around Fanad Head (28E), and the scattered farm is characteristic of most parts today. Densities are understandably low around the Blue Stack and Derryveagh mountains (28A), medium along Lough Swilly and Rossbeg (28B), in the drift plains of the Foyle (28C) and Donegal Bay (28D) where market towns are many. Along the coastal strip from Gweebarra Bay to Inishowen Head farmsteads again prevail, some of the old thatched houses still having the *cailleach* and wall-bed similar to those in the black houses of the Hebrides and providing yet additional evidence of remarkable cultural continuity throughout Atlantic Highland Zone areas of the British Isles.

Within the British Isles a bountiful Nature has provided rich variety in rocks, landforms, and soils, presenting Man with a challenging range of opportunities and limitations according to his technological skill and strength of purpose. But it has not been left to a single company of actors to strut without interruption upon this stage. A succession of players differing in race, religion, and language, in ways of life and in organisation, has moved across the scene. When such groups were numerically small and their pressure on land still weak, strong social or economic forces were generally required to induce them to cluster permanently, but by the Dark Ages at least hamlets or villages were to be seen in many areas. In the more physically favoured Lowland Zone these were likely to be larger and closer than in the Highland Zone. For the ordinary peasant the change from land-holding in common to holding in severalty came generally late and was particularly associated with political stability, population pressure, new means of livelihood, and even ideas of economic planning at landlord or national level. Thus in Wales the break up of bond and free hamlets began in the later Middle Ages, while in Scotland the great changes were often delayed until the mid-eighteenth century and in Ireland to as late as the 1880s. In sharp contrast, although in England scattered farmsteads spread around the old villages and hamlets following early or late enclosure, in general the old nuclei still remain remarkably stable features of the rural landscape today.

References

BERESFORD, M. W., and ST JOSEPH, J. K., 1958. *Medieval England: an aerial survey*.

BOWEN, E. G., (ed), 1957. *Wales*. Part II, Historical Geography.

BUCHANAN, R. H., 1958. Rural change in an Irish townland, 1890-1955. *Advanc. Sci.*, **56**, 291-300.

EKWALL, E., 1960. *The concise Oxford dictionary of English place-names*, 4th edn.

EMERY, F. V., 1962. Moated settlements in England. *Geogr.*, **47**, 378-88.

EVANS, E. E. *et al.*, 1959. Rural settlement in Ireland and western Britain. *Advanc. Sci.*, **60**, 333-45.

FAIRHURST, H., 1960. Scottish clachans. *Scot. Geogr. Mag.*, **76**, 67-76.

FLATRÈS, P., 1957. *Géographie rurale de quatre contrées Celtiques—Irlande, Galles, Cornwall et Man*.

FREEMAN, T. W., 1960. *Ireland*, 2nd ed.

GAILEY, R. A., 1962. The evolution of Highland rural settlement. *Scot. Studies*, **6**, 155-77.

GLEAVE, M. B., 1962. Dispersed and nucleated settlement in the Yorkshire Wolds, 1770-1850. *Trans. Inst. Brit. Geogrs.*, **30**, 105-118.

HARRIS, A., 1961.*The rural landscape of the East Riding of Yorkshire, 1700-1850; a study in historical geography*.

HOUSTON, J. M., 1948. Village planning in Scotland, 1745-1845. *Advanc. Sci.*, **5**, 129-32.

HUGHES, JONES, T., 1959. Landlordism in the Mullet of Mayo. *Irish Geogr.*, **4**, 16-34.

JOHNSON, J. H., 1961. The development of the rural settlement pattern of Ireland. *Geogr. Ann.*, **43**, 165-73.

JOHNSTON, J. B., 1914. *The place-names of England and Wales*.

JONES, E., 1951. Some aspects of the study of settlement in Britain. *Advanc. Sci.*, **8**, 59-65.

JONES, G. R. J., 1953. Some medieval rural settlements in north Wales. *Trans. Inst. Brit. Geogrs.*, **19**, 51-72.

— 1960. The pattern of rural settlement on the Welsh border. *Agric. Hist. Rev.*, **8**, 66-81.

JOYCE, P. W., 1913. *Irish names of places*, 3 vols.

MCCOURT, D., 1955. Infield and outfield in Ireland. *Econ. Hist. Rev.*, **7**, 369-76.

MOISLEY, H. A., 1962. The Highlands and Islands: a crofting region? *Trans. Inst. Brit. Geogrs.*, **31**, 83-95.

O'DELL, A. C., and WALTON, K., 1962. *The highlands and islands of Scotland*.

PROUDFOOT, V. B., 1959. Clachans in Ireland. *Gwerin*, **2**, 110-22.

RAVENHILL, W. L. D., 1955. The settlement of Cornwall during the Celtic period. *Geogr.*, **40**, 237-48.

SYLVESTER, D., 1949. Rural settlement in Cheshire. *Trans. Hist. Soc. Lancs. and Chesh.*, **101**, 1-37.

THOMAS, J. G., 1957. Some enclosure patterns in central Wales. *Geogr.*, **42**, 25-36.

THORPE, H., 1949. The green villages of County Durham. *Trans. Inst. Brit. Geogrs.*, **15**, 155-80.

— 1961. The green village as a distinctive form of settlement on the North European Plain. *Bull. de la Soc. Belge d'Etudes Géogr.*, **30**, 93-134.

UHLIG, H., 1961. Old hamlets with infield and outfield systems in western and central Europe. *Geogr. Ann.*, **43**, 285-312.

WATSON, W. J., 1926. *History of the Celtic place-names of Scotland*.

20

TOWNS

By any standards Great Britain is the most urbanised of countries (Smailes, 1961), the great majority of its inhabitants living in towns, nearly half of them in nine vast agglomerations that each contain more than a million people (Robinson, 1953, 1956). More than this, all but a tiny minority partake of services that require regular and frequent visits to towns (Smailes, 1946). Among more than a thousand functioning towns that can be distinguished, very considerable diversity of origin as well as a wide range of functional emphasis are represented, yet British towns in their historical development have shared a common, insular tradition. It is natural that in so urbanised a country as Great Britain towns should be peculiarly expressive of the national way of life, and that they should contribute in large measure to the distinctiveness of the British scene. They are more than usually significant elements of the geography of the country.

It is the purpose of this chapter to examine their character and structure and to note the chief variants in functional emphasis and morphology that are present. The old-established towns of England, Wales, Ireland, and Scotland were rooted in or introduced into different cultures, which for some time developed independently, and other regional differences both in geographical setting and historical development are expressed in the towns of different parts of Britain. But the transforming influences of the past two centuries, which have been responsible for the major growth of towns and which make the predominant contribution to the townscape today, have largely been shared. Ireland, however, lacking the endowment of material resources to participate in the industrial revolution as did the main island, has remained much more rural. The towns of the Irish countryside certainly play an important rôle in the life of its rural society, but, as the economic and social development of Great Britain has diverged, the Irish town has become increasingly distinctive, and in recent decades political separateness has emphasised the differences. Although much in its antecedents resembles urban development in other parts of Britain, in Ireland the town is now set in a very different frame of reference. With far more of an old, pre-industrial order persisting, the very connotation of the word 'town' must be something different in Ireland.

Functional bases

Industrialisation began earliest in Britain and has proceeded further than in any other country in removing people from agricultural pursuits. The vast increase in the population of the main island of Great Britain (more than five-fold since 1801), which was made possible as industrialisation proceeded, has been accompanied by an advance of prosperity that has found expression in the transference of an increasing sector of the employed population from production to service occupations, which now absorb a larger proportion of employment than in any country except the U.S.A. The process of urbanisation associated with this economic and social revolution has been responsible first and foremost for increasing the size of old-established settlements by accretions of non-agricultural population, but many new towns have also come into being. Indeed, the transformation of manufacturing processes began so early, and was so far advanced before the development of railways made possible the easy movement of the coal upon which the factories depended, that the scale of creation of new industrial towns on and near the coalfields in the period before 1840 was quite exceptional. Since then, the creation of completely new towns, as distinct from the enlargement of settlements, has been much less associated in Britain with manufacturing industry than with the extension of mining and the colonisation of the coastline. The reason is that the siting of factories did not need to be dissociated from established nuclei of settlement, but on the contrary sought the transport services that developed in relation to the latter.

The old towns that date back before the eighteenth century were predominantly market towns of the agricultural countryside, together with the ports through which the foreign trade and much of the internal trade of the country were effected. The largest cities were seaports, such as London and Bristol, and inland towns, such as York and Norwich, whose markets were especially important and which had grown as centres of organisation of handicrafts. In contrast, the towns that have emerged and developed within the last two or three hundred years include many whose bases are manufacturing, mining and resorts. During the Victorian period railways played a decisive part in their growth or emergence. Railways were no less important for the new ports created for new cross-Channel links, for the modern organisation of the fishing industry, and especially to serve as outlets for newly-exploited portions of coalfields. Laid out at the terminus of the 1830 extension of the Stockton and Darlington line, Middlesbrough is noteworthy as the first town to owe its creation to a railway.

For the most part, however, railways did not pioneer urban settlement in Britain. The railway system was provided to serve established centres of population, and railways brought modern industry to enliven old country towns and enhance their functions. The scale of factory employment was such that even a modest share of industrial development was enough to enlarge greatly the old towns and alter their occupation structure. The benefits brought by railways, however, were not bestowed indiscriminately on all towns of the old order. If a town's prosperity did not justify pro-vision of a railway service so that it was left aside, and only equipped later, if at all, by means of a spur, it stagnated. The railways did not so much create entirely new geographical values as re-inforce, albeit selectively, the established road nodality. It was usually when a town was not prosperous that it failed to attract a railway, and this in turn sealed its fate. Railways greatly extended the grip of towns upon the surrounding areas, and the additional nodality they conferred extended the centralising power of favoured towns at the expense of their smaller, less well-situated neighbours. Thus the increasing provision of central services was related to a larger scale of urban mesh as modern transport developed.

The coming of railways thus confirmed the decline of many old market centres, while it extended the economic base and enhanced the service functions of others. Manufacturing industry and central services were the accessions of functions responsible for the growth of towns, extending town areas and at the same time effecting extensive replacement and re-organisation in their old kernels. In densely settled tracts of mining and industrial activity on the coalfields the railway system promoted the emergence of service centres that had few, if any, antecedents as rural market towns, though they often acquired markets as they assumed the collection of food produce from their surroundings for the local concentration of population. With the proliferation of mines and factories, and of attached housing for their workers, increasingly close-set or coalescing tracts of industry and housing produced veritable conurbations, the chief foci of which came to rank among the major service centres of the country. Early attainment of large size, usually by exceptional concentration of manufacturing industry, in the pre-railway period, asserted the status of towns such as Birmingham, Manchester, Sheffield (which became corporate boroughs with the reforms of the 1830s), and also ensured their progressive amassment of central services that strengthened their regional importance.

Broadening of their functional bases has thus been especially characteristic of the growth alike of the old-established towns that have been able to play their part in the modern order and of the leaders among newer towns created by industry and resort development. Yet specialised towns, whose origin and subsequent growth have remained narrowly based upon mining and industry on the one hand or catering for visitors on the other, are prominent features of British urbanism. When the relative proportions of the two essential ingredients of urban employment—industry and services— are used as indices for functional classification, these specialised towns appear with exceptionally high or exceptionally low ratios of industrial workers as compared with those engaged in services, whereas the urban norm shows a much more balanced structure. Furthermore, there are in Britain many single-base towns (Smailes, 1943), heavily dependent upon a single type of industry, in some cases represented even by a single unit, as compared with a diversity of factory employment, or else dependent upon catering for a seasonal influx of visitors as compared with a permanent residential population of commuters or retired people. Such extreme lack of balance is most frequently found among small- or medium-sized towns, though there are extensive tracts of sprawling mining settlement in parts of the coalfields that are practically completely dependent upon mining, an exclusively male occupation, with other industries hardly represented, and services reduced practically to the urban minimum.

The mining community is both the extreme and by far the commonest type of ill-balanced economic and social structure represented in Britain. The typical colliery settlement, whether called a town by its designation as an Urban District or not, has more than half its occupied population engaged in mining, and in many cases the proportion rises to two-thirds. This means utter dependence upon one industry, and it is not surprising that such mining areas were the blackest spots in severity and intractability of unemployment during the inter-war period of chronic industrial depression. Although great efforts have since been made to attract and direct light manufacturing industries to these districts, their dependence upon mining has not been greatly mitigated, and the post-war return of prosperity is primarily a measure of full employment in the basic industry. In many parts of the British coalfields, however, the presence of manufacturing industry, deriving from the early phases of the Industrial Revolution, reduces dependence upon mining, and indeed it provides manufacturing towns in old mining areas where mining is well-nigh dead.

Extreme specialisation is also shown by many of the textile towns of Lancashire and the West Riding, by the Potteries, the footwear manufacturing towns of Northamptonshire, and the slate-quarrying settlements of north Wales, and by more scattered individual towns that rely upon other industries, or upon railway works or military establishments, including naval dockyards (Smailes, 1943).

Numerous resorts that depend narrowly upon the holiday industry, and have not become broadened as residential centres, present another class of excessively-specialised towns, the economic disadvantages of which are especially manifest in their deficiency of male employment and the heavy incidence of off-season under-employment.

It must be emphasised, however, that larger towns, whether industrial or service in their primary basis, rarely show the more extreme forms of specialisation. As they grew they usually attracted additional functions and experienced a considerable broadening of their economic bases. In many cases the functional labels suggestive of specialised character that are commonly applied to British towns refer more properly to the origin or one-time character than to the present-day activities, and do less than justice to the present-day range of functions. 'University town' is such an incomplete and misleading appellation. That Oxford and Cambridge are cities with University institutions that have played a major part in their urban development is indubitable, but the adjective is a singularly inadequate description of their character as functioning towns to-day. In relation to Aberystwyth and St Andrews, and, to a less extent, Durham, the designation is perhaps more meaningful, but in its application elsewhere the term can mean little more than that a university is present as one of many subsidiary ingredients.

In many coastal towns, not only has a resort function super-seded port activity, the resort has increasingly developed a resi-dential character dependent upon a permanent population rather than upon seasonal visitors. This emphasis at Bournemouth is widely recognised, but it is less generally appreciated that the post-war growth of Blackpool represents such a trend and has been accompanied by a cessation of hotel development. Although broadening of the functional basis is especially characteristic of urban growth, some towns are strictly epifunctional (Aurousseau, 1921) and now depend upon functions quite different from those of former times, their earlier activity having declined to the point of disappearance. Their present-day activities are replacements, not additions, and their continued urban character has been rendered possible only by the development of a new economic base. In Britain the most common types of such functional succession are represented by (a) industrial towns that have taken the place of mining settlements or ports, (b) resorts that have superseded commercial or fishing ports, (c) residential towns (sometimes with some accession of administrative functions) that have superseded resorts (the typical succession from towns founded as spas), and (d) suburban service centres that were formerly market towns but whose one-time agricultural surroundings have become suburbanised.

The urban hierarchy

In Britain today a simple, clear-cut dichotomy of town and country, and of urban and rural settlement, such as administrative boundaries and related Census data might suggest, exists neither socially nor physically. The reality instead is an urban-rural continuum, within which towns may be distinguished as the foci where central services tend to concentrate, differing in this way from the intervening tracts where the essential differences are simply those in density of buildings and degree of transformation of countryside into built-up areas. It is at such points of concentration of central services within the texture of settlement that developed urban functions and the essential character of modern townhood in Britain are to be recognised. In England and Wales they have been identified on the basis of their institutional equipment (Smailes, 1944). They include about 470 fully-equipped centres, together with another 250 only slightly deficient in their range of equipment, and they correspond with remarkable consistency with the 695 nodes of the system of public bus transport investigated by Green (1950). In Northern Ireland we should recognise 24 fully-equipped centres, and another 10 that may be admitted as towns, and again there is close agreement with the 32 bus-centres identified by Green (1949). It seems justifiable therefore to accept the figure of 235 bus-centres in Scotland

(Fleming and Green, 1952; O.S., 1955) as a substantially correct indication of the number of towns in Scotland.

In Eire, where towns are generally much smaller and less well equipped, and the urban integration of society is much less advanced, the same criteria for the recognition of towns cannot apply. The more uniform functional bases of Irish towns as essentially rural service centres, and the more open and evenly-spaced mesh of these service centres would suggest a closer correlation between urban rank and population size, but close matching with towns of the main island is invalid. It must suffice here to note that Eire has fewer than one hundred distinct 'towns' with populations of more than 1,500 inhabitants, and only half of these have as many as 3,000 inhabitants each (Freeman, 1950, esp. Fig. 24).

A total figure of rather more than one thousand towns is thus suggested for the British Isles, but difficulties of definition, some of which have been noted, make precision impossible. Apart from problems of independent ranking that are presented in conurbations and in the beaded resort development strung out along considerable stretches of coastline, there are several examples of town pairs, towns in such close proximity that they share certain services and divide district functions, so that in their relations with the surrounding area they are in part competitive, in part complementary. Some of these pairs of towns are like twins in sharing a common origin and in their functional resemblance, e.g. Camborne and Redruth, Sandown and Shanklin, Windermere and Bowness, Margate and Ramsgate. Others present striking contrasts in their date and mode of origin and development and in their economic bases. It has often happened that a new industrial, resort, or residential town has appeared close to an old-established town, but far enough away to maintain its administrative and often its physical distinctness. Examples of the proximate siting of old market town and modern industrial town are Fenny Stratford and Bletchley; Glastonbury and Street; Higham Ferrers and Rushden; Nantwich and Crewe; Pembroke and Pembroke Dock; Stony Stratford and Wolverton; Stockton and Middlesbrough; Bo'ness and Grangemouth.

Newer resort and residential settlements near old ports or market towns are exemplified at Baldock and Letchworth; Gloucester and Cheltenham; Knaresborough and Harrogate; Lancaster and Morecambe; Poole and Bournemouth; Reigate and Redhill; Warwick and Leamington. The Medway Towns present a remarkable triple group, the dockyard settlements of Chatham and Gillingham having grown up alongside the old cathedral, port, and market city of Rochester. In some cases separation by a river that is a county boundary contributed to the double development, having helped to perpetuate the administrative separateness of the towns that face each other across the river, as with Linslade and Leighton Buzzard, Widnes and Runcorn, Newcastle and Gateshead, Dundee and Newport[1].

Implicit in our definition of modern townhood in Britain and our recognition of the special character of towns as service centres is the idea of status and rank in an urban hierarchy (Smailes, 1944; Carruthers, 1957), though the urban scale, like the social scale, is continuous and gives little scope for the recognition of many distinct steps. Incontestably supreme at the top of the hierarchy is London but, beneath its dominant position, twelve other cities show many features of a metropolitan character. First there are the national capitals, Dublin (the capital of an independent State), Edinburgh, Belfast, and Cardiff, with varying degrees of independent control of their respective territories. But Birmingham, Bristol, Glasgow, Leeds, Liverpool, Manchester, Newcastle, and Nottingham are other cities that are also outstanding as regional centres and focusing-points of provincial life, a status recognised over and over again by their selection as regional headquarters alike for Government departments and private organisations operating on a national scale. They are all centres of major conurbations, in most cases the focus of a local concentration of the order of a million or more, and they exercise a profound influence over much wider areas.

Including the metropolitan cities named above, about 130 urban centres (Smailes, 1944) in England and Wales are of clearly-recognisable higher status in urban equipment and regional importance than the general run of towns, and in the United Kingdom as a whole there are between 150 and 160 'cities' in this special sense. They are seats of more centralised services and their spheres of influence in some respects embrace the primary fields of surrounding towns of lower rank. Ireland has only 13 urban centres with as many as 10,000 inhabitants each (Freeman, 1950), and not more than eight could possibly qualify as 'cities', though several others, with comparatively small populations, undoubtedly stand out above the general run of Irish country market towns as regional centres of greater importance.

The numbers of towns and cities given above do not include

[1] It will be noted that there are great disparities in size between members of some pairs cited above, as well as between different pairs.

the subsidiary shopping centres in Greater London and in the major provincial cities, where a wide range of services, catering for the immediate day-to-day needs of the population, are provided at service centres located within the extensive residential zones that surround the highly-specialised, non-residential, commercial core. Like the centres of more clearly distinct towns, they have presented a profitable field for colonisation by chain-stores, banks, and cinemas, groupings of the same business concerns whose premises increasingly command town centres throughout Britain and characterise their townscape. The structure of Greater London has been examined from this standpoint by G. Hartley, who has recognised and graded nearly three hundred shopping centres outside the central core of City and West End (Smailes and Hartley, 1961). These suburban centres are not dissimilar in functions, as in appearance, to town and city cores elsewhere in the urban mesh of Britain, and the most important among them, such as Croydon and Kingston, have a service equipment that is comparable with that of the cores of major provincial cities.

Urbanisation has permeated British society, bringing a growing adventitious element of townsfolk into the countryside, people who have moved out of the towns to seek country residence in retirement or who live there while travelling to and from urban employment, and also carrying colonisation of some urban institutions beyond those service centres that we recognise as fully-developed towns. Banks, shops, and cinemas have all been introduced into the texture of settlement on a more diffused scale, so that below the grade of full towns there are many auxiliary centres, partially equipped and providing their immediate localities with a more limited range of services. Some of these are nascent towns, but others are the decayed towns of an older order, equipped with only a limited, incomplete range of modern urban institutions. Among the market towns, craft centres, and ports of the urban mesh of pre-industrial Britain, before modern communications were developed, many fossil remnants persist into the contemporary scene. Their markets defunct, their crafts superseded, their ports dead, these settlements have failed to grow like their more prosperous rivals, and the past century has seen little addition to their townscape, either in its extent or by way of replacement of the old fabric. They are shells from which urban activity has largely departed, and they have been occupied by few of the institutions through which modern townhood functions. While the centres of active towns become increasingly alike as old buildings make way for standardised forms

388

of shops, banks and cinemas, built of mass-produced materials in replicated styles, these fossil towns appear the more pronounced in their individuality, local character, and old-world attractiveness. They are museum pieces and places of retreat, offering escape from modern town or suburban life into a more peaceful and gracious, if less highly-mechanised, setting.

Town nuclei

Just as elsewhere in Europe generally, the old-established towns of Britain were associated with points of relative security in a troubled countryside, where urban functions could be discharged under the protection of lord and castle. Their siting was almost invariably governed by the existence of opportunities for establishing good defences, and usually by the pre-existence of a stronghold.

The Romans had first brought urban life to Britain, but their towns were confined to the civil zone of their occupation, in the English Lowland, and it is very doubtful whether later towns on Roman sites represent the continuous survival of urban functions. More probably the urban lights flickered out as Roman civilisation and order withdrew. The later resuscitation of some, but not by any means all, Roman towns followed their selection (as that of other sites occupied by the Romans for purely military purposes) by newcomers for the establishment of their own strongholds. The latter were the real gathering points for fresh towns. It was not unnatural that the shells of Roman settlements should often serve this purpose, for they were usually well-chosen vantage points, and the roads that were provided to serve them persisted to give the nodality that was so vital for urban growth. But the Roman towns needed to be reborn in order to take their place in the medieval urban pattern, from which that of the present derives. At some important centres of the Roman system, such as Silchester, rebirth did not happen, and even at Verulamium it was not the abandoned Roman site that became the nucleus of a medieval town but the abbey established across the valley on a hill where was the reputed scene of St Alban's martyrdom.

Most Roman towns, and many other Roman fortified sites, took their place in the medieval urban mesh of England, leaving an imprint of varying degree upon the layout of the heart of the medieval town, which might inherit and retain the same *enceinte*, as did London, or the Roman axial street-system, which is so prominent a feature of Chichester and Colchester. There were, however, only some fifty towns in Roman Britain, and other sites occupied in Roman times as camps could not provide more than a small minority of the number needed for the close-set, local urban mesh of the Middle Ages, which was also more widespread than that of Roman Britain.

The great majority of medieval market-towns were attached to castles. The older among these dated back as 'burhs' to Anglo-Saxon and Danish foundations, but Norman castle-building added many more. In their shelter traders found favourable conditions for their peaceful activities, and here lords could bring profit to themselves by promoting trade. In part towns emerged by a process of spontaneous growth as the essential urban functions gathered, but in part urban character was deliberately planted and nourished. Especially was this so in Wales, Scotland, and Ireland, where trade had few early roots and where the native, largely-pastoral societies were without an urban tradition. Round the western shores, Norse trading posts were the germs of towns, notably in Ireland, but it was the Normans who laid the main foundations of urban development in these countries, using towns, established beside their castles, as instruments of their penetration and occupation of conquered territory (Carter, 1957; Freeman, 1950, esp. Fig. 15). The Anglo-Norman towns of Wales and Ireland were settled by immigrants who ministered to the needs of the garrison troops, traded with the natives and generally promoted the intrusion of Anglo-Norman culture into the surrounding countryside. The towns were the plantations of an alien culture. In Scotland, too, burghs established by the royal house were similarly conceived as agents of royal authority in the countryside, and copied English models, both in their physical construction and in the municipal charters they received (Mackenzie, 1948; Dickinson, 1961). Their first trading communities were foreigners, English and Flemish. By the fifteenth century many Scottish barons had followed the example of the king and of feudal lords in England and Wales in granting market rights and patronising urban development, so that to the 33 royal Scottish burghs were added ten times as many new foundations (Houston, 1944).

The activities of monastic houses in promoting trade, as well as the relative security provided by attachment to sacred places, were responsible for abbeys becoming the gathering points of several other towns, such as St Albans, Beverley, Bury St Edmunds, Ripon, Hexham, St Andrews. It is important, however, to distinguish between settlements, such as Newcastle upon Tyne, that had monastic houses as prominent constituents and true abbey towns, which owed their genesis to abbeys, the precursors of any urban development.

Not all places that were equipped with market rights during the Middle Ages achieved active markets and the towns to which they gave rise, and not all places privileged by incorporation as boroughs came to act in any real sense as towns (Stephenson, 1933). The economic and physical reality did not always match the title, which often hopefully anticipated an urban character that in fact never materialised. Special franchises and privileges were undoubtedly characteristic of medieval townhood but their provision in itself proves nothing. They did not necessarily bring townhood with them, for not all were endowed with a sufficiently-advantageous geographical situation to enable them to hold a place in the urban mesh. They might be still-born or short-lived as towns, yet the privileges with which they were invested persisted for centuries. It was not until the reforms of the 1830s that such empty trappings were swept away and the abuses to which they had given rise were brought to an end.

Not only was the medieval town characteristically attached to a pre-urban nucleus whence it initially derived its protection, it acquired as the seal of its development its own defensive wall. In Scotland this was often no more than a crude palisade or earthen mound with ditch, but in some form or other a defensive perimeter gave clear-cut definition to the medieval town. Wall and charter were symbols of the physical and legal separateness of the town and its burgess community.

The invulnerability from external attack vouchsafed to Britain by the girdling sea and the early establishment of a strong central government in England and Wales discouraged renewal of the medieval town walls as these fell into decay, nor was extended walling called for to protect extra-mural extensions that grew up, especially after the sixteenth century. Sometimes there had been some medieval extension of the first walls to bring in early annexes, but for the most part the space enclosed by quite early walls was ample to accommodate a considerable increase of population by progressive infilling, and when at last considerable extra-mural suburbs did appear, maybe as a result of industrial accretion, the need for defence had largely passed. Even London, the scene of the greatest urban growth and extension, never acquired an outer *enceinte* beyond the line of its medieval walls, themselves on the site of those of Roman times. The plantation towns (Camblin,

1951) established after the conquest of Ireland in the early seven-teenth century provide an exceptional group of later walled towns, and in England a few naval dockyard towns, such as Portsmouth and Chatham, also offer isolated examples of later walling. In this respect British towns stand in striking contrast with those on the Continent, where walling was repeatedly renewed and extended and town fortifications became increasingly elaborate in response to the problem presented by improved artillery. Well into the nine-teenth century the extension of Continental towns was shaped by walls in ring-like fashion.

Apart from towns whose rise took place early enough to ensure that they were once walled, there are many pre-modern towns which came into existence with the development of trade, handi-craft industries, or with early mining in the Palaeozoic rocks of west and north Britain, that were never walled. Many market centres have a long history of immature urban development so that although their roots date far back into the Middle Ages, with early grants of market rights, the emergence of full urban character came slowly and they never acquired a wall. In modern times, when the economic bases for urban growth have multiplied, new towns have developed not about nuclei that point to defence as a prime consideration, but in association with whatever features, whether spas, mines, mills, harbours, resort 'estates', canal or railway junctions, that might induce a clustering of population and pro-vision of services on a considerable scale. Their morphological development in consequence has differed profoundly from that of old-established towns.

Although use of water-power might draw factories to rural sites, and virgin stretches of sandy beach that were of no previous value for maritime settlements might attract resort developers to establish estates on the coast, more often the urban growth for which industry and resorts were responsible was accretionary. Advantage was taken of the incipient nodality of a pre-existing settlement, and also of a modicum of labour supply and service provision already present there. This happened not only when factories and housing for their workers were attached to market towns and ports of an older order, but also to mining settlements, new ports and new transport nodes. Similarly resorts became attached to older spa nuclei and on the coast to old ports whether fishing or commercial, or to agricultural villages that happened to lie there.

Where the genesis of a new town was the development of a new economic base on a virgin site, the initial housing that was provided, albeit on a modest scale, then became the nucleus of what developed into a town. Infrequently in the case of mining and industrial settlements, but more often with new ports and resorts, the original lay-out was conceived and designed as a new town. Other planned towns were directly associated with the development of the rural economy in hitherto-backward areas, notably the 'demesne' towns of Scotland and Ireland.

When it is remembered what a great diversity of sites is added to this diversity of nuclei, it is not surprising to find that the inner areas of British towns especially display great individuality. This applies even among towns that may be relative newcomers to urban rank. The kernel, as the oldest part of the town, tends naturally to be the most complex, with the greatest range of features inherited from different morphological periods. Rarely, however, does it form a large proportion of the whole built-up area of today. Most of the townscape has been added in the last century or so, as the accelerating process of urbanisation has been accompanied by the development of urban transport, so that towns have sprawled increasingly in loose, tentacular extensions. Surrounding the kernel areas, the integuments of nineteenth and twentieth century growth are much more uniform, dominated by the extensive development of a few forms that give the widespread textures of terrace-ribbing and villa studding, with block clumping recently making a limited contribution for office accommodation in city centres and for high-density residence in place of congested slums (Smailes, 1955).

As long as urban circulation remained largely pedestrian, compactness was of the essence of the nature of town growth. Thus, before the old town was appreciably extended, its open spaces, which were often considerable in the medieval town, were filled in to the point of repletion. The typical burgess plot had a narrow frontage on the highway, which quite early tended to be lined with contiguous buildings. The street façade these provided was interrupted only by narrow passage ways, but behind was extensive open space in the form of aggregates of the long, narrow tails of the individual plots. In course of time these were increasingly built over, and the gardens and orchards of larger town properties, including those of the religious orders that were dissolved in the middle of the sixteenth century, were similarly carved up and packed with cottages and workshops. The fission of plots and complication of the pattern of urban land units ultimately reached a stage when con-

393

solidation became a pre-requisite of re-development by modern buildings. Such resolution of the old pattern, with clearance of buildings and re-shaping of property boundaries, marks the completion of what Conzen calls the burgage cycle. The process that he has traced in detail at Alnwick (Conzen, 1960) must be widely represented in old towns throughout Britain.

Extensive replacement of old buildings by Georgian street façades, accompanied by filling in of spaces in the rear hitherto left vacant, was characteristic of the growth of town prosperity in the eighteenth century. It provided many British towns with much eighteenth-century fabric, within the framework of an elaborated medieval plan. There might be some simplification of urban thoroughfares to improve circulation by vehicular traffic, but towns in which extensive re-organisation of the medieval plan was effected were the exception. Subsequent piecemeal replacement by modern commercial buildings, as central services have increasingly ousted residence from town centres, with modern renewal of decayed fabric, have effaced legacies of the burgage cycle. In some towns the transformation has recently been greatly assisted by war-time devastation or by civic redevelopment schemes.

It is quite usual, however, for some of the old town to survive as an enclave or enclaves. Especially does this apply to the precincts of great church and castle, but in more exceptional cases the whole or a large part of the old town may persist as a fossil shell, aside from the commercial core of the modern town. More usually modern business district and old kernel overlap. The degree of correspondence is very variable, but is rarely complete. Quite commonly the modern shopping and commercial centre transgresses beyond the old town, while leaving some of the latter as an enclave. Conditions of physical site and the position of the railway station, which is not unrelated, are especially responsible for such re-centring or asymmetrical extension of the commercial core.

The structure of the modern town

Figure 49 is a schematic representation of British town structure, related especially to an old-established county town. Divergences from it must often be attributable to different conditions of site, with other important peculiarities introduced by accidents of land ownership. Persistence of open space in and near the heart of the town in the form of islands or wedges is a feature that especially reflects such individual peculiarities. On the other hand the early

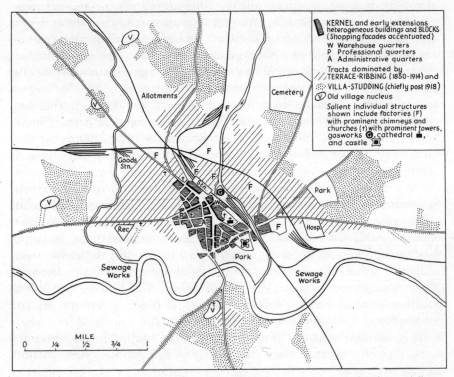

Fig. 49. A SCHEMATIC REPRESENTATION OF BRITISH TOWN STRUCTURE, related especially to an old-established county town.

possibility of dispensing with town defences in Britain and the absence of provision of those elaborate defences that included bastions and a belt outside the wall where building was forbidden are responsible for the general absence of boulevards. The spacious inner ring roads, so typical of Continental towns, where they occupy space quite lately freed by removal of such town defences, find very few counterparts in Britain. Here urban kernel and integuments are continuous. The girdle of open ground, somewhat encroached upon now by barracks, that separates Old Portsmouth from its urban extension which has spread over Portsea island, is a rare representative in Britain of such a boulevard zone.

Early town markets in Britain were often accommodated in streets by means of a slight widening or in a larger space at a road fork, though some towns had spacious market squares that have been retained. Known as 'Diamonds', such squares are a regional characteristic of Ulster towns (Camblin, 1951), an integral feature of the plan of the Plantation towns and a town-planning 'improvement' of the eighteenth century in other towns that had not been planned earlier. As street markets became increasingly congested and inadequate, covered produce markets were provided nearby by municipal enterprise in the course of the eighteenth or nineteenth centuries in prospering British towns, and livestock markets were moved some distance from the congested centre and commonly attached to the new railway. Market halls, crosses, and tolbooths of various ages, displaying the distinctive style of period and region, often survive as residues in town centres.

A noteworthy expression of Great Britain's insularity is the flowering of towns along her coastline. In no country do seaside towns play so important a part in the urban scene. The story of their rise is a well-worked field of social history and recently attention has been given to their typology (Barrett, 1958). Differing considerably among themselves in site conditions, notably as between their occupation of cliffed or flat stretches of coastline, and in the relative emphasis upon different facets of their functions, all are distinctive by reason of the importance of the sea-front as a morphological element. It assumes primacy with the commercial core, which typically lies adjacent to and immediately behind the front.

On the sea-front amenities inherited from the pre-railway age are mainly natural features of the coast and sometimes preserved open space. Much of the special equipment accumulated on the sea-front, including piers, pavilions, bandstands, and amusement parks, as well as its minor urban furniture, was provided during the half-century before the First World War by the local municipality as it acquired increased powers.

Some seaside towns were comprehensively planned before any building began, while in others growth has been controlled by the operation of restrictions upon the forms of development permitted. Such places especially provide the resorts and residential towns that have a 'select' character. But there have been wide differences in the degree of orderly development and control, and some seaside towns are the epitome of unregulated enterprise. Often there is a clear difference between 'select' and 'popular' parts of a seaside town, with access from railway station to beach and the siting of amusement parks playing a large part in locating the latter.

Holiday accommodation in the form of hotels and boarding houses, naturally a distinctive element of any resort, is a less promi-

Table 21. British Town Structure

	Growth phase	Functional zone	Function-form relation	Relief	Fabric materials
KERNEL	Old town	Enclave(s)	Residues	Architectural dominants e.g. castle-towers, church spires	Traditional, or imported stone
		Commercial CORE with prongs outside kernel. Ousting of residence	Extensive replacement or new façades	High buildings: point blocks; rugged profile; irregular street cornice	Concrete, replacing traditional
INTEGUMENTS	Late 18th and early 19th century	Decayed inner zone of mixed use. Workshops, cramped factories, warehouses, high density residence (slums and high flats); railway space	Conversion rather than replacement	Low buildings; little relief except churches; terrace housing in formal lay-outs; some replacement with flat blocks	Mixed
		Professional and administrative quarters	Converted houses		Brick or stucco and slate
	Railway age before 1914	Industry and tightly-packed housing mixed	Some conversion but mainly obsolete forms still in use	Terrace-ribbing with factory and neo-Gothic church salients Gas-holders	
	Railway and automobile age since 1919	Industry and housing segregated	Forms conforming to current functions	Villa-studding	Brick (much Fletton), rough cast, and tile. Much foliage
		Villa housing in open, bourgeois suburbs and municipal estates Spacious factory lay-outs	Chain-store façades in shopping centres	Intermixture of roofs and tree tops Factory scaling: low buildings with extensive continuous roof surfaces. Power-station chimneys and cooling towers	
		Village enclaves			Traditional
	Urban fringe	Interim development; residential ribbons and outliers; urban utilities, e.g. cemeteries, sewage works; amenity space and surviving farmland, allotments and market gardens.			

Note—In Scotland residence in inner integuments is represented mainly by high tenements, exclusively in stone. Tenements continue as important building forms after 1919 and rough-cast brick buildings only recently modify the stone tradition.

nent feature of seaside towns that have always relied mainly upon day trippers or of others that are primarily residential. It is an element which, with changes in holiday habits, is rarely expanding today, whereas extended provision of housing may be continuing fast. Where this is so the functional basis of the seaside town is clearly swinging from resort to residence, a feature of the post-war growth of Blackpool and many other traditional 'resorts'.

Reflecting the related factors of functional emphasis and age-span of town growth, there are variant types of town structure that show a widespread occurrence. Their grouping into types depends upon a comparable representation of the different morphological periods and their characteristics that are set out in summary form in the accompanying table (Table 21).

There are other distinctive features which are regional, rather than individual or specially associated with a functional emphasis. The 'Diamonds' of the Ulster towns have already been mentioned. In Wales the strength of Nonconformity and at the same time its fissive tendencies are manifested in the proliferation of chapels, which are a specially conspicuous feature of the Welsh townscape. When there has been a local tradition of building in stone, as obtained throughout much of Highland Britain, its use may have persisted on a more extensive scale into the later phases of building and even up to the present. Brick buildings are very latecomers in the urban scene in Scotland, and the bricks are usually concealed by rough-cast.

In a modern industrial town, where there is no old kernel the commercial core will have developed by invasion of commercial premises at the expense of the area of mixed industry and housing. In such a town more effective penetration by the railway right to the centre will be likely; indeed, the railway station and tracks may provide the skeletal framework, not merely of the outer sectors, but even of the town core itself.

Resorts that experienced considerable growth in the late eighteenth and early nineteenth centuries, and contemporary town extensions that are sometimes well represented elsewhere as gentry and well-to-do tradesmen built themselves substantial town houses, have prominent tracts of Georgian houses covered with stucco. They have lasted well and, although no longer convenient for single-family residence, persist as boarding houses, professional houses and offices, or are divided into flats.

In contrast to the variety of the central areas, a few forms dominate the extensive integuments that surround them (Smailes,

1955). Drab terrace housing, a debasement of its urbane and dignified Georgian models, was the prevailing form that added large areas to British townscapes during their vigorous extension in the nineteenth century. Some of the worst products of workers' housing, built a century or more ago, before by-law legislation enacted certain minimum standards for public health, survive in varying proportions as uncleared slums. They include the notorious back-to-back and tunnel-back dwellings that are so common in industrial towns in several parts of the country.

Suburban villa housing, no less characteristic of the urban sprawl since the First World War, although it is everywhere represented, is far less conspicuously an ingredient of industrial towns in those parts of the country, such as the coalfields and old industrial areas, that have experienced stagnation or depression during much of this century. In these towns modern building is much more predominantly municipal than in the prosperous towns of southern Britain that have been the scenes of most rapid growth in recent decades. Here the garden city or garden suburb model, its prototypes at Letchworth (1903) and Hampstead (1907), with plots of generous size only very partially occupied by buildings, has imprinted its stamp upon great areas of townscape. If its ideal has been a marriage of town and country, its achievement has more often been the creation of a neuter suburbia.

Victorian philanthropic organisations, first to tackle slum clearance in blighted areas of cities, began to rehouse slum dwellers *in situ* in high-density building blocks. Later, however, as slum clearance and provision of extra housing for workers have been increasingly carried out by municipal enterprise, the new housing has been chiefly in the form of peripheral housing estates. Resembling the garden surburb ideal in emphasis upon horizontal extension, these are only a little less lavish than private villadom in use of land. In Scotland the tradition of tenement housing, with three to five storeys, was early established and prevailed throughout the nineteenth-century industrial growth of Scottish towns. It was followed by municipal housing schemes, and other types of working-class housing were only tardily introduced and are proportionately less represented.

Shortage of land within municipal boundaries has not always been adequately met by boundary extension and this has certainly stimulated the recent erection of costly high blocks of flats in some of the largest and most crowded cities. Tower blocks of flats are much more expensive to provide than two-storey dwellings in open, peripheral estates and, except for those built for the wealthy minority who are able to pay the necessarily-high economic rent, they involve subsidisation from general taxation. Horizontal spread, so characteristic a feature of modern urban growth in Britain, has a sound cost basis and is not merely an expression of the social models that prevail. On the other hand, as Birch and Coppock have shown, it creates a serious problem in eating into agricultural land.

The current problem faced by the great cities of Britain, and above all by London, of finding accommodation for numbers of people considerably in excess of any planning provision within their municipal areas, is a consequence of pressures of growth related to national shifts of employment and of the needs for slum clearance and replacing housing destroyed during the war. This problem of 'overspill' has been tackled by building out-boundary estates, by the creation of New Towns, and by the expansion of selected established towns as reception centres for planned migration of industry and workers.

Although out-boundary estates are often referred to as satellite 'towns' and in the nature of things do not bear the parental name, they are only to a very limited degree independent for employment and services. They are primarily housing estates which, except for local government, are hardly less bound up with the nearby city than are tracts of suburban housing within the municipal boundary. They are suburbs rather than towns.

Most of the towns created under the New Towns Act of 1946 (Edwards, 1956; Pocock, 1960) are in a different category in that they are planned groupings of residence, work-place, and service-unit, located at what was regarded as a sufficient distance from city centres to allow them to function independently as towns. Eight of the original fourteen New Towns that were designated lie in a ring round London at distances of between 20 and 30 miles (30 and 50 km.) from Charing Cross. They were established with the express intent of making a contribution to the decentralisation of industry and housing from London beyond a preserved zone (Green Belt) of countryside. In their case, work as well as homes have been moved and community services commensurate with the local population have been provided. It is in this co-ordinated provision of all three elements—work, housing, and services—that the post-war New Towns are distinctive as compared with other current urban developments, although their forerunners may be discerned in the enlightened town-planning carried out by the nineteenth-century industrialists who created Saltaire, Bournville, and Port Sunlight. The New Towns are examples of social and economic as well as of physical planning and are built on the principles of segregation of factories and housing, and separation of more centralised services that are provided in the town centre from others that are more appropriately provided in residential neighbourhoods. The grouping of housing and primary services in neighbourhoods is a cardinal feature of their lay-out. Since the establishment of the first crop of New Towns immediately after the Act, the Government has been slow to countenance additions but Cumbernauld, 12 miles from Glasgow, was begun in 1955, and subsequently Skelmersdale (1961), 12 miles from Liverpool, and Livingston (1962) and Dawley (1962), 30 miles from Glasgow and Birmingham respectively have been initiated, while others are proposed[1].

Facilitated by the Town Development Act of 1952 (Dickinson, 1962), towns that are conscious of some present deficiency in their economic structure and are hopeful of benefiting from an accession of employment have provided an alternative to town creation by assisting planned dispersal from major concentrations of population. Such is the magnitude of the problem, however, that creation of more new towns and promotion of more town-expansion schemes must be envisaged as contributing together to a loosening of the excessive concentration of urban population that at present obtains in Great Britain.

The distinction between urban and rural settlement, for long blurred in Britain, is rapidly becoming more so as similar building forms spread everywhere and the homes of a motorised people, who share the same technologically-advanced culture, colonise the countryside between the older settlement nuclei, the residences of long-distance commuters intermingling with those of local rural workers, from which they are in many respects indistinguishable. Town and countryside merge together as settlements increase not so much by multiplication of towns that appear as distinct entities as by the sprawl of suburbs and roadside accretions. Model New Towns there are in twentieth-century Britain, but Subtopia is the norm, the prevailing manifestation of our contemporary culture upon the face of the country.

[1] Subsequently development under the Act has also been undertaken at Redditch and Runcorn, two earlier industrial towns, and at Washington, between the conurbations of Tyneside and Wearside. In Northern Ireland, too, special legislation in 1965 initiated Craigavon, a new town development to link the existing towns of Lurgan and Portadown, south of Lough Neagh.

References

AUROUSSEAU, M., 1921. The distribution of population. *Amer. Geog. Rev.*, **11**.

BARRETT, J. A., 1958. *The seaside resort towns of England and Wales.* (Ph.D. thesis, University of London.)

CAMBLIN, G., 1951. *The Town in Ulster.* Belfast.

CARRUTHERS, I., 1957. A classification of service centres in England and Wales. *Geogr. J.*, **123**, 371-85.

CARTER, H., 1957. Urban Settlements, in *Wales*, ed. E. G. Bowen, 157-81.

CONZEN, M. R. G., 1960. Alnwick, Northumberland, a study in town-plan analysis. *Trans. Inst. Brit. Geogrs.*, **27**.

DICKINSON, G. C., 1962. Overspill and town development in England and Wales, 1945-71. *Town Plann. Rev.*, **33**, 49-62.

DICKINSON, W. C., 1961. *Scotland from the earliest times to* 1603.

EDWARDS, K. C., 1956. The New Towns in Britain. *Nott. Univ. Surv.*, **6**, 7-19.

FLEMING, J. B., and GREEN, F. H. W., 1952. Some relations between town and country in Scotland. *Scot. Geog. Mag.*, **68**, 2-12.

FREEMAN, T. W., 1950. *Ireland.*

— 1959. *The Conurbations of Great Britain.*

GREEN, F. H. W., 1949. Town and country in Northern Ireland. *Geography*, **34**, 89-96.

— 1950. Urban hinterlands in England and Wales: an analysis of bus services. *Geogr. J.*, **116**, 64-88.

HOUSTON, J. M., 1944. The Scottish Burgh. *Town Plann. Rev.*, **25**, 114-27.

MACKENZIE, W. M., 1948. *The Burghs of Scotland.*

ORDNANCE SURVEY, 1955. *Local Accessibility maps of Great Britain*, 1 : 625,000 (2 sheets).

POCOCK, D. C. D., 1960. The growth of British New Towns. *Tijdschr. Econ. Sociale Geog.*, **51**, 2-9.

ROBINSON, G. W. S., 1953, 56. British conurbations in 1951. *Sociol. Rev.*, **1**, 15-26; **4**, 91-7.

SMAILES, A. E., 1943. Ill-balanced communities, a problem in planning. *Case Stud. Nat. Plann.*, ed. E. A. Gutkind, **2**, 226-47.

— 1944. The urban hierarchy in England and Wales. *Geography*, **29**, 41-51.

— 1946. The urban mesh of England and Wales. *Trans. Inst. Brit. Geogrs.*, **11**, 87-101.

— 1955. Some reflections on the geographical description and analysis of townscapes. *Trans. Inst. Brit. Geogrs.*, **21**, 99-115.

— 1961. The urbanisation of Britain, in Problems of Applied Geography. Polish Acad. Sci., Inst. Geogr., *Geogr. Stud.*, **25**, 131-40.

SMAILES, A. E., and HARTLEY, G., 1961. Shopping centres in the Greater London area. *Trans. Inst. Brit. Geogrs.*, **29**, 201-13.

STEPHENSON, C., 1933. *Borough and town, a study of urban origins in England.*

21

CULTURAL GEOGRAPHY

National areas

THE British Isles show a considerable cultural complexity, and offer a variety of languages, thought, and traditions which are basic to many of its peoples. This diversity, which is more often expressed socially than politically, underlies the identity of several 'national' groups other than the English: the Scots, Welsh, Northern Irish and Irish and Manx. The degree to which these groups have maintained their identity will be discussed later. First something must be said about their origin and evolution, and about the cultural characteristics that still distinguish them one from another.

The division of the British Isles into Highland and Lowland zones, described earlier in this book, underlies the feeling of separateness that is felt by the people of Wales, Scotland, Ireland, and the Isle of Man, in contrast with the English. The division figured most prominently in the formative stages of the national groups. Roman civil influences rarely went beyond the Lowland zone; only its military arm extended into Wales: even this came to a halt in the midland valley of Scotland, and Ireland remained uninfluenced. More fundamental changes followed the Roman period in Lowland Britain, such as its peopling by Germanic tribes. These changes, again, had little direct impact on the Highland zone, though in the seventh century the Anglo-Saxons drove wedges westward to the Irish Sea and to the Bristol Channel, thus effectively separating Cornwall, Wales, and north Britain, three Celtic areas that had much in common, including the Brythonic language. Although Brythonic—basically the Welsh language—held its own in Wales, it soon died out in southern Scotland and north England; in the southwest it lingered on, and Cornish was spoken until the end of the eighteenth century before it was finally submerged by English.

In 790 the King of Mercia recognised the limits of the English advance westward by building Clawdd Offa (Offa's Dyke), which is approximately along the line of the modern political boundary of Wales, and in this way he also acknowledged the identity of a separate people. The Welsh were only a loosely-grouped collection of clans, but they had a common language, had retained a Celtic church which strongly resisted the influence of Canterbury, and had a common enemy! Welsh cohesion was helped by the codification of laws under Hywel Dda (c. 920-50), and by temporary political unification under Gruffydd ap Llewelyn (1055-1063), so that on the eve of the Norman conquest Wales was approaching nationhood. Its independence during the next 250 years was maintained because the Norman marcher landships were ineffectual in subduing the country, particularly the west and the northwest. Even the Edwardian conquest of 1282 and the creation of six shires in the recalcitrant west had little *social* effect.

The accession of Henry VII (Henry Tudor), who was of Welsh descent, was the beginning of the end of an independent Welsh nation. His son, Henry VIII, systematised the union in 1536, so that Wales would be 'forever incorporated, united and annexed' with England. The marcher country was reorganised into six new shires, to which was added Monmouthshire, thus completing the county pattern which has remained unchanged. Not only was anglicisation intensified by English becoming a fashionable language (for many Welshmen had followed Henry Tudor to London), but under Henry VIII efforts were made to stamp out the language by compelling all office holders to speak English and by making Welsh illegal in courts of law. Unwittingly the Tudors saved the language they tried to suppress by sponsoring the translation of the New Testament and Prayer Book into Welsh (1567) in order to enforce the Protestant creed. By 1588 the entire Bible had been translated, and a language that had almost become a patois was given dignity and a new lease of life.

The full significance of these events did not become obvious until the educational and religious revivals of the early eighteenth century. These were based on the Welsh Bible, and the eventual outcome of the religious revival of 1735-51, namely the establishment of a Calvinistic Methodist church, gave Wales the nearest equivalent to a national church. It may well be that in such circumstances secular education was neglected: so much so that a report of 1846 strongly advocated sweeping away the Welsh language as it was an impediment to educating the people. The consequent overhaul of the educational system, leading to a new secondary school system and to a 'national' university, was certainly English in character and language.

Like the Welsh, the early Scots had in common a language (Gaelic), the Celtic church, and the clan system. In 1034 Duncan succeeded in uniting four kingdoms north of the Tweed, and the resulting nation was to persist for seven centuries. The southernmost parts of Scotland, once Brythonic but by now cut off from their Welsh contacts, were rapidly assimilated in an English culture, partly by the efforts of the Scots kings themselves. But Scotland was always strong enough to fight off English efforts at conquest. Eventually, in 1327, England acknowledged the independence of Scotland under Robert I, and the equality of both nations was confirmed when James VI of Scotland, by virtue of his being a Protestant, was asked to become James I of England. His departure to London further increased the assimilation of the Scots and the anglicisation of southern Scotland. But the Highlands were still singularly free from English influences.

Still acting as an independent nation, the Scots, having accepted a union of crowns in 1603, in 1707 accepted a union of parliaments, retaining only some distinctive elements of their own such as a separate legal system. By this time southern Scotland was thoroughly anglicised. The major change which was still to come was the cultural transformation of the Highlands after 1745. The clan system was destroyed and the Gaelic language quickly receded. Although Scotland, not unlike Wales, underwent a religious and educational revival in the eighteenth century it was accomplished in the English language. The Bible was not translated into Gaelic until the beginning of the eighteenth century, and there was an absence of associated literature. When Scottish literary culture blossomed it was in the lowlands: its centre was Edinburgh: its language was English. But there was still enough distinctiveness and national feeling for the Scots to identify themselves as a separate nation.

The emergence of the Irish as a nation was more complex than that of the Welsh or the Scots. It is impossible to separate the early cultural history of Scotland and Ireland. The Irish sea acted, not as a barrier, but as a centre, ringed by Celtic cultures and enabling the peoples around it to keep in close communication. This condition persisted for many centuries: even as late as the eighteenth century it was easier for a squire's son from west Wales to be educated at Trinity College, Dublin, than at Oxford or Cambridge. Irish sea links were strong from the earliest history of man in Britain, but of all the links those between the north of Ireland and Scotland were the strongest.

In Ireland the upland fringes tended to be centres of population, emerging as four kingdoms in the fourth century—the four historic provinces, Ulster, Connacht, Leinster, and Munster. Although quite separate they were culturally akin in having a common Gaelic language. There was, however, a strong tendency to distinguish the north from the south, the former being mainly historic Ulster; even the Christianisation of Ireland was so divided, centering on both Armagh and Cashel. The links of the southern part of Ireland were mainly with Wales, and people moved freely between the two countries: though after the Norman conquest these links became Anglo-Irish rather than Welsh-Irish. The northern links, between Ulster and western Scotland, were even stronger, and continued much longer. The O'Neill domination of Ulster became complete in the fifth century, and there immediately followed a movement of Gaelic peoples across the North Channel. These completely dominated the Isle of Man, where the Gaelic language became modified into Manx, as well as Argyll and the west of Scotland. The success of this Gaelic penetration of Scotland was the result of intimate and continuing contacts: its spread was closely tied to the conversion of the Picts to Christianity, for Iona, the centre of Scottish Christianity in the sixth century, was an outlier of Irish Gaelic culture. Thus the west of Scotland and the north of Ireland became one culture region, with an identical language, literature, and religion. Not until the tenth century did the languages begin to diverge, and in literate form there was nothing to distinguish them up to the seventeenth century.

The subsequent social history of Ireland is dominated by movement into the island from England and Scotland. The Anglo-Norman conquest was partial and piecemeal, and its lack of unification led to the gaelicisation of the barons themselves. The real English colony was a bridgehead, varying in extent, around Dublin itself, from which influence sometimes spread over much of southern Ireland: but even this influence was largely confined to towns and cities. Ulster was only marginally influenced by the Anglo-Normans. Contacts, friendly and otherwise, were with Gaelic Scotland. At the end of the fourteenth century the Lordship of the Isles included the Lordship of Antrim, and Scots influence became indelible.

It was the Tudors who began the real conquest of Ireland, but the greatest resistance was put up in the Gaelic north, and only terminated with the 'flight of the earls' (1607), which marked 'practically the end of a distinctive culture'. Much of the earls' confiscated lands were parcelled out to Scots nobles, the beginnings of the Scots colonisation of the seventeenth century. James's plantations also caused the movement of many English families into Ulster.

Meanwhile the older English colonists in the south, partly by virtue of being Roman Catholics and so cut off from Protestant England, were merging with the native Gaelic Irish: but it was the latter who lost their language, so that the Catholic fusion which was to be the basis of the future independent Ireland was mainly English-speaking. One of the paradoxes of the Irish struggle for independence after the union of 1801 was that it was never based on the native language: its ideas were always expressed in English. During the nineteenth century Gaelic was actively discouraged and education spread entirely through the English language. Strangely enough, therefore, the greatest struggle to preserve political identity arose in the anglicised parts of Ireland. The real difference that made the south militate against the union with England was religious. But in this respect Ulster, with its very strong Presbyterianism—the result of Scottish links—was ready to break with the remainder of Ireland. Partition rests on a religious split. But it was a strange solution that compelled the Unionist north to accept its own parliament because it was unwilling to accede to Home Rule mediated through Dublin. And so, in 1921, two states emerged, Northern Ireland, closely linked with Westminster, and the Irish Free State, eventually to be called the Republic of Ireland.

This very brief glance at the evolution of the national groups within the British Isles has emphasised cultural changes, processes that are still continuing as English influence erodes the diminishing characteristics distinguishing the different groups. Those tied to language suffer most: religious differences remain little changed. It is true, of course, that the claim to be Scots or Welsh extends far beyond a knowledge of the native language: there is a feeling of belonging to the land rather than to the culture, recognising only the vaguest of traditions and falling back on a sentimental attachment that need only be evoked on special occasions. Nevertheless an essential part of the social geography of the British Isles today concerns what remains of the Celtic languages in Wales, Scotland, and Ireland, and the strength of Roman Catholicism in Ireland. These are elements that can be mapped and are a fair indication of the deeper differences that still characterise the several national groups of Britain.

Language areas

The Celtic languages in Britain are spoken by about 1,400,000 people. Welsh is the strongest and Gaelic the weakest. One can discount Manx, which is spoken by no more than a handful of people; although its use at the official opening of the Manx parliament is a reminder that it was once basic in the autonomy of this group of people. A century ago Manx was spoken by half the population of Man: today it is little more than a text-book language. Cornish has been a dead language for nearly two centuries.

The table shows the number and percentage with a knowledge of the three main Celtic languages.

Table 22.

	Able to speak native languages		Monoglot native speakers		Total Population
Welsh (1961)	656,022	26.0%	26,223	1.0%	2,518,711 (age 3 and over)
Irish (1946)	588,725	21.2%	—	—	2,771,657 (age 3 and over)
Gaelic (1961)	75,508	1.46%	1,079	0.02%	5,178,490

The figures in the table refer only to persons living in the country where the language is spoken. There are relatively few Gaelic or Irish speakers outside Scotland and Ireland but a considerable number of Welsh speakers live outside Wales. In the English conurbations alone there are over a quarter of a million people who were born in Wales, a proportion of whom are able to speak Welsh: this is confirmed by churches in England in which services are conducted entirely in Welsh. The census does not enumerate Irish speakers in Northern Ireland, since the total number of people able to speak Irish is insignificant.

Furthermore the figures refer only to ability to speak the language and give little indication of the extent to which the language is spoken, read, or written. The vast majority of Celtic speakers can also speak English. The number of monoglots is very small and is likely to diminish still further until it is reduced only to those children who have not yet acquired English. Practically all native-speaking children become bilingual during their schooldays. The extent to which their native language is used afterwards depends on many circumstances, but even if it is retained as a language to be spoken at home, the vast majority of influences—newspapers, periodicals, books, radio, and television—is in English.

Less than one Scotsman in sixty speaks Gaelic. Even in 1881 only a quarter of a million spoke it (less than 7%), and only 44,000 were monoglot. These low figures reflect the thorough anglicisation of Scotland even before the nineteenth century. Gaelic has long been restricted to the highlands and the islands and has long ceased to be a national language. Even in the west and northwest Gaelic now dominates only the islands. In only one mainland parish is Gaelic spoken by over 70%, and this, in Ross and Cromarty and facing Skye, is probably the most isolated in the country. Gaelic-speaking Scotland has a sparse population, and continues to lose people by migration. Gaelic persists partly because of the isolation of the west and because the west is predominantly rural. Towns are centres of English influence, but they are few. In Skye, Gaelic is losing ground around the town of Portree, the largest urban centre in the western isles. In the remainder of Scotland the number of Gaelic speakers is small, but in the populous counties of the lowland valley an insignificant percentage may well hide a considerable number. For example, it hides the fact that in 1951 Lanarkshire had nearly 14,000 Gaelic speakers, 12,556 of them in Glasgow. This was a great contrast to the national capital, Edinburgh, where there were only 2,221.

Gaelic clings to the outermost island fringes of the west. Similarly Irish has its last strongholds on the extreme Atlantic peninsulas. In the last century Irish was in a much stronger position than Gaelic: one reason was the comparative density of the population in the west before the famines. It is probable that half the population could speak Irish in 1800. That this was cut to 23·3% by 1857 was due mainly to the great losses by death and migration from the predominantly Irish areas during the 1840 famines: but this should not hide the fact that the language was declining in the face of increasing anglicisation. Little was done to arrest this until after the establishment of Ireland as an independent state in 1921. Then the politicians turned, most of them very belatedly, to the language as one of the symbols of the new state. It became the national language, with English 'equally recognised as an official language'. In the 1937 constitution English was called the 'second' official language' for the simple reason that the Irish could not do without it. In the meantime Irish was taught compulsorily in schools, a knowledge of Irish became essential in all state appointments, and special economic and cultural aid was given to the Irish-speaking west. The figures for 1926, 1936, and 1946 must be dealt with cautiously. They show a relative increase between 1911 and 1926, and an absolute increase between 1926 and 1936. However, both total number and percentage are lower in 1946.

Table 23.

	1901	1911	1926	1936	1946
Number of Irish speakers	619,710	553,717	540,802	666,601	588,725
Percentage	19.2	17.6	19.3	23.7	21.2

The numbers have certainly increased, particularly in the younger age groups, but the extent to which this has meant the resuscitation of the language remains to be seen. As far as school children are concerned, knowledge of Irish has been compared with knowledge of French in English schools. Many more persons can claim a knowledge of the language, but Irish-speaking is decreasing in the natural Irish-speaking areas of the west.

This western area, known as the Ghaeltacht, includes all the western peninsulas, parts of Donegal and distal Connacht and Munster. It is divided into two parts, the Fior Ghaeltacht, defined as that area where more than 80% spoke Irish in 1925, and the Breac Ghaeltacht where between 25% and 80% spoke Irish in 1925. The 1946 figures show that these areas have greatly retracted. The predominantly Irish areas (over 70%) are now restricted to the coast of Donegal, west Mayo, south Galway, the peninsulas of Kerry, with two small outliers in counties Cork and Waterford. In the Fior Ghaeltacht there was a decline in Irish speakers between 1936 and 1946 of 14·8%; in the Breac Ghaeltacht it was 23·6%, compared with a general decline of 7·6% in the whole of Ireland. During the same period the population declined by 6·1% and 5·6% in the Fior and Breac Ghaeltacht respectively. The changes, therefore, are not due to migration only, but largely to the fact that the older people who are fluent Irish speakers are dying out. Most of the western counties show very considerable losses of Irish speakers, four of over 20%, but this is partly compensated by increases in the centre and east of between 11·7% and 21·8%. This is a reflection of the teaching of Irish in schools, but it certainly hides a real decline: for estimates of the number of Irish using the language as an everyday medium are as low as between 25,000 and 35,000. This accords more with the absence of a newspaper in Irish—even the extreme nationalist papers are in English—and the strong feeling against the compulsory teaching of Irish in schools.

Welsh is in a much stronger position than either Gaelic or Irish, although decline has also characterised this language, particularly in the last half century. The language was ignored in the educational policy of the second half of the nineteenth century. In 1871, when Welsh was spoken by a vast majority of people in all but the border areas, and south Pembrokeshire and the Gower, an observer noted that 'not a single instance of a Welsh school has come to my notice: . . . where the school is being used as a means of eradicating the Welsh language, the pulpit has proved its staunchest friend'. This is a reference to Welsh nonconformity, for 2,338 of the 2,781 dissenting chapels in Wales at that time conducted their services in Welsh. It was not until the Education Act of 1944 that Welsh was given an equal footing with English in the schools of Wales.

The continued decrease has lessened very slightly in the last decade, the change between 1951 and 1961 being $-8 \cdot 2\%$ compared with $-21 \cdot 4\%$ between 1931 and 1951. But the number of monoglots has decreased rapidly and the percentage of children between 5 and 15 who speak Welsh has decreased (from 21% in 1950 to $17 \cdot 6\%$ in 1961). It remains to be seen whether a change of attitude will affect the trend. For ability in Welsh is now almost a status symbol, and since the war over 50 Welsh schools have opened in the most anglicised areas, a spontaneous response to the problems of a declining language. It would need a social revolution, however, to reverse the overwhelming anglicisation of today.

The distribution of Welsh-speaking in Wales shows several influences that have been operating for at least a century, some for very much longer. (a) The most longstanding influence is the pressure from the English border country which became anglicised after the Anglo-Norman conquest, and which is particularly marked along the river valleys, such as the Severn and the Wye. (b) Similarly south Pembrokeshire, Gower, and the Vale of Glamorgan have been anglicised from medieval times. (c) Industrialisation in the last century, with its attendant migration, brought anglicisation to the coalfields of Glamorgan and south Cardiganshire and to Flintshire. (d) Most outside influences have been nurtured in towns, and for hundreds of years urbanisation has meant anglicisation: this is true even in the north and west, but it is particularly marked along the north Wales seaboard where holiday resorts cater for the industrial areas of northwest England.

There is still a very considerable area where Welsh is spoken by more than 70% of the population: there are large areas where the percentage exceeds 90%. This is the upland core of Wales together with its western slopes facing the Irish Sea. A remarkable

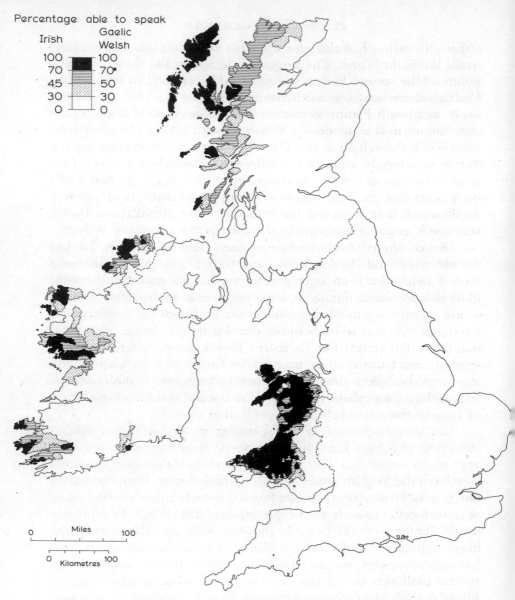

Percentage able to speak

Irish	Gaelic Welsh
100	100
70	70
45	50
30	30
0	0

0   Miles   100

0   Kilometres   100

Fig. 50. PERCENTAGE OF POPULATION. ABLE TO SPEAK IRISH, GAELIC, OR WELSH.

feature of Figure 50 is the sharp break between English-speaking Wales and Welsh-speaking Wales, which Bowen would call 'Le Pays de Galles'. Two things should, however, be borne in mind. The first is that the map shows contiguous administrative areas, not necessarily contiguous communities, and these are in sparsely-populated upland country. The second is that percentage figures hide the very considerable numbers of Welsh speakers in the most anglicised parts of Wales: for example there are 201,000 able to speak Welsh in Glamorgan, not many less than the total (216,000) in the four most Welsh counties, Anglesey, Merionethshire, Cardiganshire, and Carmarthenshire.

A surprising feature is the comparatively little change in this distribution in the last decade—or even since 1931. The encroachment of the anglicised area has been small, sometimes only a parish in a decade, sometimes stationary, although there does now seem to be a danger of Welsh Wales being split into north and south by a salient of anglicised country. The paradox of a very slowly diminishing Welsh-speaking area and a more rapidly decreasing number is partly explained by the fact that rural Wales is losing population, and probably losing its most anglicised groups, leaving the older folk and children who have not yet acquired English as a second language. Increasing population always means a decrease in Welsh-speaking, for such areas in Welsh Wales often signify an army camp or a new industrial centre, both types of development temporarily bringing in more English speakers. It has also been pointed out that territorial changes may have more or less come to a halt, and that the effect of English will now be seen linguistically as the Welsh adopt more and more English words and phrases. Increasing bilingualism in Welsh Wales may well be a forerunner of anglicisation.

Religious areas

The variety of religious beliefs in the British Isles presents a much greater problem of description and distribution than that of languages. This is partly because statistics for the various denominations are collected separately and on widely differing bases. Nor is there a clear-cut link between religious groups and national groups. The episcopal Church of England, regarded as a state church although it has never had its position legally defined, is by far the most dominant denomination in England, its baptised members numbering about 27 million—i.e. about 66% of the total population. The established church in Scotland is not the episcopal church, which has about 108,000 members, but a free church, the Church of Scotland, presbyterian in government and claiming 1,316,000 members. The episcopal Church in Wales was disestablished in 1920, but has only 200,000 communicants. Nonconformism, and more particularly Calvinistic Methodism, is more the 'national' church. The Church of Ireland, disestablished since

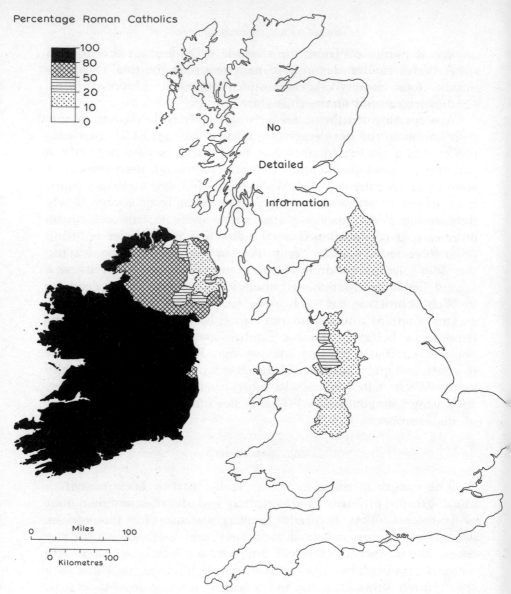

Percentage Roman Catholics

100
80
50
20
10
0

No

Detailed

Information

Miles
0   100

0   100
Kilometres

Fig. 51.   PERCENTAGE OF THE POPULATION WHO ARE ROMAN CATHOLICS.

1869, has 350,000 members, a small number compared with the Roman Catholic church. This very broad equation of episcopalian England, presbyterian Scotland, methodist Wales, and Roman Catholic Ireland is confused by the number of smaller denominations, some of whom have united to form the Methodist Union, Congregational Union, Baptist Union, and Presbyterian Churches. These together claim about 1,700,000 members who are distributed throughout the British Isles, though they are numerically very weak in the Republic of Ireland. In addition there are 400,000 Jews, and many smaller denominations among whom the Unitarians (20,000) and Society of Friends (20,000) are strongest.

Differences within the Protestant denominations being less than differences between them and the Roman Catholic church, all that will be attempted here is a brief glance at the strength and distribution of the latter, more particularly as it underlies the national identity of Ireland and is a critical social and political factor in the life of Northern Ireland.

The total membership of the Roman Catholic church in the United Kingdom (i.e. excluding the Republic of Ireland), is estimated as $4\frac{3}{4}$ million, but this includes the child population which is rarely included in other denominational figures. The proportion in the total population is small—1 in 12—but nevertheless rapid growth has characterised this church since the middle of the last century. Statistics are rare, but a rough guide is given by these figures: there were less than 500 priests in 1850, 3,833 in 1910 and 6,741 in 1955: there were about 1,000 chapels in 1875, 1,891 in 1914 and 2,821 in 1949. This increase is closely linked with immigration of Irish labour from the earlier part of the nineteenth century onwards. Even in 1841, the percentage of the population born in Ireland was very high in southwest Scotland, Tyneside, and Lancashire. The period 1841-61 saw a peak of Irish migration; not only was the drift enormously exaggerated by the famines, but increasing industrialisation encouraged constant movement. The vast majority were Roman Catholics, for the famines hit Ulster lightly and Belfast had its own industries to attract the farm labourer. Immigration has continued. In 1961 there were 600,000 Irish-born in England and Wales and 700,000 in Scotland. In 1951 there were 33,500 Irish-born in Manchester, 23,000 in Liverpool, 8,000 in the West Midlands. The distribution of Roman Catholics is related to the urban centres nearest Ireland where work was available during the last hundred years. The heaviest concentration in England is around Merseyside—the major point of entry—followed by the Manchester region and Tyneside. Elsewhere the proportion varies between about 5% and 10%, though in Wales and the West Country it is as low as 3%. Detailed figures are not available for Scotland, but nearly 17% of church marriages took place in Roman Catholic chapels, and we can accept this as an approximate overall figure. But the distribution is uneven, Glasgow and the southwest showing a very marked concentration, possibly as great as that in Merseyside.

Ireland is the stronghold of Roman Catholicism. So dominant

is the church here that one must look for the exceptions, for the inroads of Protestantism from the east. There is one such area around Dublin, but even here Protestantism is between 20% and 50% only. Protestantism becomes an important factor only in Ulster. Protestant minority groups of between 20% and 80% extend beyond the boundaries of modern Northern Ireland to include eastern Donegal and northern Monaghan (these two counties, together with Cavan belonged to the historic province of Ulster but were not included in Northern Ireland in the 1921 partition treaty). But the 'Protestant north' is only a relative term, for in most of Northern Ireland over 50% of the population is Roman Catholic. Only Antrim and north Down are overwhelmingly Protestant (80%-90%), the former completely dominated by Presbyterian Scots (with the interesting exception of the northeast glens which had such close Gaelic connections with Scotland in pre-reformation times), and north Down dominated by the English. The latter's influence can be seen southwestward along the Lagan valley into north Armagh. Belfast, having drawn so much of its population from the interior during its industrial expansion, has a much higher proportion of Roman Catholics than the surrounding countryside.

On the basis of this distribution the north could make out a case for a Protestant majority only if the total population of all the six counties was taken into account. The Free State, as it was then, accepted the retention of so many Roman Catholics by the north only as political expediency and in exchange for certain financial concessions. It has never forgotten the Roman Catholic majority of counties Londonderry, Tyrone, and Fermanagh. In these counties the distributions of either sect is very uneven, with small intermixed areas where one denomination or the other is in a marked majority. The social difficulties that arise under these circumstances tend to be solved partly by degrees of segregation and partly by conforming to patterns of behaviour, easily identifiable and acceptable on both sides. Segregation is most marked in Belfast itself and has in the past led to a great deal of tension and to periodic rioting. Periods of tension lead to greater segregation, whereas the easing of tension promotes greater mixing.

The fundamental differences of political and economic life on either side of the boundary between the Republic of Ireland and Northern Ireland tend to be forgotten because superficially life is much the same. But movement has naturally become restricted. Most of the very numerous roads that cross and recross the boundary are closed to motor traffic, for comparatively few are approved and have a customs check. During the war all roads were sealed and this had far-reaching consequences for communities that had once lain astride the border but were now divided. Social differences hardened as Protestant minorities on the southern side diminished. And as state administration covers increasing aspects of life, e.g. educational and health services in the north, so, gradually, the social pattern becomes more identified with the political.

Nationalist movements

It was suggested earlier that language and religion were two cultural elements basic to the original 'national' differences within the British Isles. Difference of language has now become so weakened that national identity need not necessarily depend on it. In Scotland and in Wales political independence is past history and social peculiarities must be evoked to differentiate one group from another. Reaction against English hegemony, especially the translation of cultural differences into political terms and into demands for independence, has been comparatively recent, and not very effective. Towards the end of the nineteenth century, when the question of Irish home rule dominated most domestic issues in Westminster, Scotland and Wales were also vigorously putting forward their claims. There was a feeling that Westminster was too far away to be either sympathetic or efficient in governing these two countries. These demands reached a peak during the 1914-18 war, and in 1919 a conference was convened to examine possible solutions. Significantly, the basis of discussion was not the national separateness of Scotland and Wales, but the possibility of federal control following some degree of devolution. Nothing came of this conference—except the birth of nationalist movements in Scotland and in Wales which are now prepared to fight the issue on purely political grounds. Scotland, with a long tradition of independently controlling her educational and legal systems, was granted a Secretary in 1885. Since 1920, in addition to a Secretary of State there has been a Minister of State for Scotland and three parliamentary under-secretaries, together responsible for controlling agriculture and fisheries, education, health, and home affairs: the day-to-day running of these offices is done in Edinburgh. Wales has its own departments of health and education in Cardiff, but is represented at ministerial level only by the Minister of Housing and Local Government.

While the devolution of Scotland and Wales was still being debated, Ireland solved the same problem by force, and an Irish Free State was established in 1921. The relations between it and the United Kingdom have been modified until, by the constitution of 1937, it became a completely independent republic. As we have seen, religion was a basic element in this breakaway. Inside Ireland the religious schism of the north is the only social factor that has been strong enough to recreate an international boundary in the British Isles. As a result of this, Northern Ireland was forced to accept a large degree of self-government, however contrary this was to its own desire for continuing the union with Great Britain, because it was the only alternative to accepting government from Dublin. Consequently it has a much greater control over its home affairs than any part of the United Kingdom, although it also sends twelve members of parliament to Westminster. It is a paradox that that province of the United Kingdom most eager to remain tied to London should have the greatest degree of independence.

Thus it can be seen that in national sentiment, religion, and language forces exist that divide the British Isles into more or less distinct cultural areas. At the same time it is evident that these divisions are, in the main, growing less strong, as they give way to a more uniform way of life throughout the Isles.

References

BOWEN, E. G., 1959. Le Pays de Galles. *Trans. Inst. Brit. Geogrs.*, **26**, 1-24.

CENSUS, IRELAND, 1953. *Census of Population of Ireland*, 1946, Vol. III, Irish Language.

CENSUS, SCOTLAND, 1961. *Census of Scotland*, 1961, Preliminary Report, Table VIII.

CENSUS, 1961. *Wales (including Monmouthshire)* 1962, Report on Welsh Speaking Population.

COUPLAND, R., 1954. *Welsh and Scottish Nationalism: A Study*. London.

HESLINGA, M. W., 1962. *The Irish Border as a Cultural Divide*. Assen (Netherlands).

RAVENSTEIN, E. G., 1879. On the Celtic languages in the British Isles. *J. Roy. Statist. Soc.*, **42**, 579-636.

ROMAN CATHOLIC YEAR BOOK, 1962. London.

22

THE BRITISH ISLES IN THEIR WORLD CONTEXT

THE unravelling of the world map, achieved during the last five hundred years, changed very advantageously the value of the geographical position of the British Isles. Geographical position can be rated a valuable asset, though perhaps not always, as one American geographer (Semple, 1911) believed, the supreme geographical fact in the history of any country or people. How much the relative position of the British Isles has improved during modern times can be measured, to some extent, by reflecting on the shortcomings of their location during the three or four millennia of human history that preceded the exploits of the Great Age of Discovery.

Ultima Thule

During this long period, which embraces the cultural advances from the Megalithic through the Neolithic to the Early Iron Age, the British Isles occupied a peripheral position on the oceanic edge of the known world around the Mediterranean basin, beyond the shelter of the landlocked seas and remote from those areas where civilisation had precociously developed in Nilotic Egypt and the Near East. Cultural currents moved slowly westwards along natural routes by land as also by the seaways, so that the peoples of the British Isles acquired successive cultures belatedly, being in the main merely recipients of external stimuli. Exceptionally, and hardly expectably, these islands did on occasions generate indigenous cultures with some success, as notably in the Bronze Age when artifacts of gold and of bronze made their way eastwards from Ireland to continental Europe and later in the Early Iron Age when the Celtic Christian Church spread its influence from Ireland to Britain and even to Gaul and Germany.

The impact of imperial Rome on Britain testifies also to the way in which the geographical position of the British Isles dwarfed their importance as part of the known world of classical antiquity. Julius Caesar came, saw—and withdrew: the effort required for the conquest of Britain's 'continental angle', its most populous, developed, and organised southeastern corner, seemed then not worth while. The security of Gaul, and perhaps, too, Britain's sources of lead, may have justified the successful conquest initiated in A.D. 43 by the Emperor Claudius. Yet it is significant that no sustained attempts were made to conquer the Highland zones of either Wales or of Scotland north of the Central Lowlands. Moreover, although (as Tacitus relates) Agricola believed that Ireland could have been conquered and held by a single legion and a small force of auxiliaries, he wisely never put his optimism to the test. And to the Roman soldiers who manned the northern defences of Britain behind the walls of the emperors Hadrian and Pius Antoninus, their service must have seemed somewhat comparable with that of British troops in more recent times on the northwest frontier of India—involving virtual exile in the wilderness.

It is not without interest that the position of Ireland, if we can believe Tacitus (Mattingly, 1948), was assessed by the Romans more highly than that of Britain. 'Ireland', he wrote, 'lying between Britain and Spain, and easily accessible also from the Gallic sea might, to a great general advantage, bind in closer union that powerful section of the empire . . . Its approaches and harbours are tolerably well known from merchants who trade there'. Whatever its geographical inaccuracies, this statement throws light on an interesting fact of location. Whereas eastern, if not southern Britain faced the less developed northern part of Gaul, the 'barbarian' (i.e. non-Roman) world beyond the lower Rhine, and the wastes of Scandinavia, southern and eastern Ireland flanked a sea route from the Mediterranean Sea which appears to have been frequented for some two thousand years before the Roman Empire. Ireland was reached, with the aid of the prevailing sou'westers, by sailings along the coasts of Iberia and then by short sea passages from Brittany via Cornwall. Moreover this westerly route continued northwards through the Irish Sea to western Scotland and beyond, and, as has been shown, served as an axis of an Atlantic Zone in the British Isles characterised at many periods, from prehistory onwards, by cultures distinct from those developed on the lowlands of Britain.

New horizons

The British Isles long remained dependent on continental Europe, from which they received immigrant colonisers and conquerors, and thus languages, religion, and social and political institutions. Insularity spelt detachment but not isolation; indeed by means of the local seaways parts of Britain were linked at times politically with parts of Scandinavia and of France. With insularity went the development of seamanship but foreign trade fell into the hands of aliens, notably the Venetians and the Hansards, before English seamanship made strides in the fifteenth and sixteenth centuries. Nor, too, did the small territories of the British Isles prove conducive to political unity: Scotland held itself politically and in some measure culturally apart from England which absorbed Wales and held only eastern Ireland under its direct rule. The political and economic strength of the English kingdom favoured to some extent by its proximity to the Continent but above all by its superior geographical endowment for agriculture and settlement, stand out clearly at the end of the Middle Ages, although it did not become a strong sea state, poised for world-wide adventure, until the creation of a navy in the seventeenth century. For it should be emphasised that it was not insularity so much as sea power that protected and fostered the development in security of the English economy and culture.

By this time the maritime gates to a greatly-expanded world—in part newly discovered but in part merely made accessible by new oceanic routes—had been flung wide open thanks to the persistent, practical, and enlightened enterprise above all of Portuguese and Spaniards, but also of Italians, Dutchmen, Englishmen, and others. New and challenging opportunities were presented for the British Isles to play a more positive role in world affairs: indeed England ultimately became the principal beneficiary of the Iberian discoveries. For the Atlantic Ocean had long proved a barrier, sealing off the European oecumene; it was breached only partially when Scandinavian seamen moved west to Iceland and Greenland and when, by the fourteenth century, Iberians had reached the islands of Madeira, Canaries, and the Azores. The northerly Atlantic routes provided no break-through, for the technical difficulties of Arctic navigation denied an effective northwest or northeast route to the Orient. But the achievements of Columbus and his successors and of Portuguese navigators transformed the relative location of the British Isles which, no longer a cul-de-sac, assumed an excellent position within the land hemisphere at the northern gateway into Europe from the New World and to the populous and civilised Orient. Thanks to the successful initiative of west Europeans in navigation and exploration, western Europe rather than southern Asia was able to exploit the new opportunities to overseas expansion. Thanks, it would seem, to the greater economic, demographic, and political strength of England, it was this part of the British Isles that became a protagonist in world affairs in the eighteenth century.

In order to assess the present position of the British Isles in the world, it is necessary to recall some of the events of more recent centuries. First, account must be taken of the fact that only by stages did the British Isles come to be organised as a single political unit—the United Kingdom of Great Britain and Ireland—which, however, was modified in the early 1920s when the greater part of Ireland moved towards independence. Now, as the Republic of Ireland, its position must be considered separately from that of its greater neighbour. Second, if only to measure the reduced status that the United Kingdom now assumes, it should be recalled how, like Europe itself of which it was a loosely-attached part, it came to occupy a dominant position in the economy and politics of the world.

The boastful exaggeration of Bartholomew Anglius in the thirteenth century contained a measure of truth: thanks to its mineral and agricultural resources, England was (he thought) 'the plenteousest corner of the world, so rich a land that it needeth no help of any land, though every other land needeth help of England' (Kimble, 1938). Certainly, within the British Isles, it has always over-topped Ireland and Scotland in men and resources, though less so before the major industrial developments and migrations of the nineteenth century. At the first census of 1801, out of a total of 15·7 millions, Ireland accounted for perhaps 5·2 millions, Scotland for 1·6, and England and Wales for 8·9: to this last, Wales contributed less than 0·6. Subsequently the preponderance of England's population has become more clearly marked and, in this century, this has become most evident in the English Lowland. There, during 1921-61, the population increased by about 8·5 millions—equivalent to 80% of the increase recorded for Great Britain during these years. In contrast, because of the outflow of population, Scotland recorded only a trifling increase in numbers —from 4·88 millions in 1921 to 5·18 millions in 1961. During these years too the population of Wales was virtually constant: 2·66 millions in 1921 and 2·64 millions in 1961.

Although England's poorer neighbours warded off assimilation by England and succeeded in preserving traditional elements of their own cultures (Chapter 21), they could not resist the English language which became the common speech throughout the British Isles. In agriculture the ideas of the English 'improvers' were taken up, and England's industrial revolution transformed the Isles. Understandably, then, it was English political and legal institutions and practices that came to spread so widely, and influence so much of the world so greatly. This is not to say, with Bartholomew Anglius, that England was so innately strong that it could with ease so markedly affect the culture of a large fraction of the world, notably by colonisation and overseas conquest. Indeed, as a small country with larger and more powerful rivals in continental Europe, it maintained its independence and effected its commercial and imperialistic expansion only by resort to skilful diplomacy and by the exercise of naval power, when its strength lay more in the quality of its seamen than that of its ships. *The Influence of Sea Power upon History, 1660-1783*, by the American Captain Mahan in 1890, laid bare this important factor. But if so much of the British achievement has an essentially English cast, it is noteworthy that in its greatest days—during the two hundred years before the First World War—England was strengthened by its partnership with Scotland in the United Kingdom. This partnership created by the Act of Union of 1707, has meant that British effort has sprung from Anglo-Scottish co-operation in all fields—in the inventions of the Industrial Revolution, in overseas settlement, conquest, and administration, as in all branches of the economy. The attachment of Ireland to the United Kingdom was a dubious accession of strength if only because this represented an imperialistic expedient resented by Irish nationalists and doomed to failure, although England gained substantially through Irish immigration and Irish recruitment in the armed forces. It is noteworthy that, when four empires in Europe collapsed during and after the First World War and the British Empire survived intact in all continents, the only secession from it was that of Ireland close by.

From Empire to Commonwealth

Maritime exploration, commerce, and power lie behind the creation of the British Empire. It was scarcely, as one historian argued (Seeley, 1911), built up in a fit of absence of mind, nor was it wholly due to direct political policy and action. Some who have noted a connection between Protestantism and the rise of capitalism may look for explanations in British individualism, self-discipline, and restraint which fostered initiative and adventure as well as the pursuit of unrestricted private profit. Certainly in their attempts to maintain political independence and to exploit trade opportunities

England and the United Kingdom in turn challenged successfully in war their powerful rivals—Spain, Holland, France, and Germany. England gave up the policy of seeking territories on the Continent in favour of seeking military allies there who could help in defence and give her freedom for operations overseas.

The Empire came to include the two familiar types of holding: new temperate lands suited to European settlement, as in North America, and inter-tropical and sub-tropical lands of prime interest for trade and investment, as in the West Indies, India, and Africa. In this case the flag tended to follow trade, as in India where until the Mutiny of 1857 affairs were in the hands of the East India Company, and as in western Canada where the Hudson's Bay Company pioneered and held territories until 1870. Clearly the economic motive, and with it strategical considerations well understood by maritime traders, were uppermost, stimulating efforts that proved highly rewarding economically and politically. The British took the lead in the technological achievements of the 'industrial revolution' so-called which led to 'cheaper quantitative production' (Nef, 1956). They were thus able to offer an increasing range and flow of manufactures to newly-found markets which supplied return cargoes of high value, made up of goods scarce or unobtainable in western Europe. The relative cheapness of oceanic freight also was a permanent advantage. Imperialism as it developed and extended involved the British, not always as they wished or intended, in assuming governmental responsibilities in overseas territories. One dark side of British activities was a large share in the trade in African slaves and their use on plantations, although it was Britain that took the lead in the eventual abolition of the Slave Trade (in 1807) and of slavery within the Empire in 1833.

By the end of the Napoleonic wars (1815) British imperial power reached its zenith, though it had been reduced by the loss of the thirteen American colonies in 1783. Had British statesmanship averted this loss, as later it averted the loss of Canada, the capital of the empire, as Adam Smith (1775-6) contemplated, might well have ultimately moved from England to North America. But this set-back did not prevent the continuance of British territorial expansion, in Australasia, Asia, and Africa. Indeed, between 1870 and 1900, 4·75 million square miles (12 m. sq. km.) with a population of 88 million people were, if Egypt and Sudan are included, added to the Empire (Hobson, 1938).

Distinguishing features of British imperialism were first, that it did not usually seek cultural and ethnic assimilation, and

424

further, at least during the years since the famous Durham Report of 1839, that it aimed at helping dependent nations towards autonomy and ultimately independent statehood. Admittedly the pace of this process was often rated too slow and the British Government was continually reacting to pressures from the colonists themselves, yet the dependent peoples were sharply different in cultural levels and social organisation, as indeed in ethnic character. This is not the place to attempt to present a balance sheet of British imperialism; doubtless there were mistakes, failures, things left undone, and ugly incidents. On the other hand, economic gains were in some measure shared and the British legal and administrative systems were applied, and won respect. Liberal thought and democratic institutions were introduced by stages in response to the local initiatives of dependent peoples. The scale of the problems faced, notably in the field of education in countries so populous and poor as India and in others so backward and also poor as British Africa, have been grasped only in quite recent times. The whole imperial system, controlled by the United Kingdom parliament and bound economically to the United Kingdom by reason of its ascendancy in industry, commerce, and finance during the nineteenth century, was remarkably flexible, so that 'colonies' came, in many different degrees, to take part in their own internal affairs.

The idea of creating a federated Empire, with parliamentary representation in London, was never seriously taken up. However, when in 1914 King George V declared war on Germany, the whole of the Empire, including the self-governing Dominions, was at war. The sovereignty of the Dominions was also then limited in that they lacked their own direct representation in foreign countries: foreign affairs remained a responsibility of the metropolitan country. As to imperial defence, while the United Kingdom bore the main burden, a principle, adopted in 1909, ensured the co-ordination and co-operation of United Kingdom and Dominion forces.

The change from Empire to Commonwealth is surely a very remarkable phenomenon. The record of history might well suggest that as empires rise, so they fall, thus disintegrating into parts that tend to be subject to a new empire-builder. Yet, although the First World War brought grave losses in men and in wealth, this war was won and the British Empire survived intact, except that the greater part of Ireland left the United Kingdom as the Irish Free State in 1921. It became a republic in 1937 but withdrew from the Commonwealth only in 1948.

The term 'The British Commonwealth of Nations', which is

nowadays shortened to 'The Commonwealth', has come into use during the last generation to replace the term 'The British Empire', as 'empire' and 'imperialism' tended to acquire opprobrious over-tones and became also misleading. The Commonwealth has its legal foundation in the Statute of Westminster of 1931 which granted full sovereign status to the then Dominions of Canada, Australia, New Zealand, and South Africa. Membership of the Common-wealth is therefore held by those former countries of the British Empire that, having achieved independent statehood, have chosen to remain closely associated. They either recognise the British Queen as also theirs or, at the least, recognise her as Head of the Commonwealth. This term is also used less surely to include those remaining (and mainly insular) territories that are in varying degrees dependent on the United Kingdom and receive financial help under the Overseas Resources Development Act (1948) and the Colombo Plan (1950).

The process of change from Empire to Commonwealth was gradual until recently: the lesson of the delays in handing over power to India, Burma, Ceylon, and Cyprus, has been learnt. But this process of liquidation has been regarded constructively and much careful preparation has been made before a new State emerges with some reasonable chance of maintaining its viability (Carrington, 1961). Since 1947 the former Dominions and new entrants to the Commonwealth are properly known as 'members'—and the United Kingdom becomes merely senior member. Despite the fact that Burma chose not to join, and despite the withdrawal of Ireland and the Union of South Africa and the failure of the West Indies Federation, to survive and seek membership, Com-monwealth membership had increased to thirty by 1968. New mem-bers attending the Commonwealth Conference in 1962 included Cyprus, Jamaica, Trinidad and Tobago, Nigeria, Sierra Leone, and Tanganyika. The Rhodesian Federation, self-governing but not wholly independent, and destined to break up, was also represented. It is not surprising that an increased diversification of interests and attitudes was noted at this conference. These have markedly increased in more recent years as a result of the addition of many new African mem-bers.

It is not easy to explain why so many nations, so different in stature and culture, and now so strongly nationalistic in sentiment, should choose to remain in close co-operation with the United Kingdom—and with each other; nor indeed to assess the role of the Commonwealth which embraces between a fifth and a quarter of mankind, multi-national in character and so world-wide in distribution. Clearly it does not fit into any recognised political category. It is in no sense a super-state, nor is it clearly what Hartshorne has called, 'an international organisation at a higher level' such as NATO. It has no common foreign or defence policy and no formal organisational blueprint, although it rests on a large number of enactments of the United Kingdom parliament (Jennings, 1948), of which the Statute of Westminster is the most important. It is subject to strains and stresses within; various centrifugal regional forces operate, such as that which binds Canada closely to the United States and the ANZUS treaty binding Australia, New Zealand, and the United States. Certainly British power is no longer sufficient, nor has it been in this century, to provide common defence in all theatres. Nor indeed has the United Kingdom assumed this responsibility—except to its dependent territories—since 1937, although it has specific commitments of importance to specific Commonwealth members (Carrington, 1961).[1] Yet, improvised though it is, the Commonwealth has meaning and reality. The precise reasons for its cohesion and effectiveness are various. Sentiment, based on community of blood, culture, and history may explain the adherence of Australians, New Zealanders, and Canadians, although less than half of the last named are of British male descent. There is no such bond of sentiment for Asian and African members and reasons must be sought in their partial acceptance of British political ideas and of the English language, economic advantage, the need for friends in an unquiet world (and some would say a common interest in cricket!). The Commonwealth provides for the continuous exchange of information, notably on foreign and business affairs, for periodical consultations at Commonwealth Conferences, co-operation within an extended area of peaceful inter-relations, and for some degree of co-ordination and co-operation in defence: it may well be thought, on the basis of mutual services rendered in the past, that the Commonwealth would show a high degree of unity in face of major danger from outside.

A valuable practical aspect of the Commonwealth was that it allowed a fair measure of inter-migration. Britain traditionally allowed free entry to citizens of its Empire, as indeed to aliens seeking sanctuary. The Imperial Conference of 1918 decided that

[1]Thus the United Kingdom has engaged to defend Malaya, is together with Canada, a member of NATO, and, together with Australia and New Zealand, maintains the so-called Commonwealth Strategic Reserve in the Malayan region.

each country should establish its own control of immigration, but Britain alone left the door wholly open to immigrants from the Dominions, the British colonies, and Ireland. The several independent members of the Commonwealth control immigration in various ways, although in general entry is accorded freely to United Kingdom citizens. Nearly seven millions emigrated from the British Isles to the Dominions between 1812 and 1914. More recently, notably since the end of the Second World War, the United Kingdom has received an influx from the Commonwealth and from the Republic of Ireland, valuable to the economy since this has helped to make up losses by emigration, mainly to the former Dominions. During the years 1946-59 no less than 685,000 Commonwealth and Irish citizens settled in the United Kingdom (fully half of whom were Irish). In 1960 immigrants into the United Kingdom totalled 236,000, but emigrants had declined to 130,000.

Although the employment situation was sound, the Government was concerned at the sharp increase in the proportion of coloured Commonwealth immigrants. These were mainly from the West Indies, especially from Jamaica, 200,000 of whom were settled in London, Birmingham, Liverpool and elsewhere, and whose entry numbered 54,000 in 1960 and 70,000 in 1961. Further, Indians and Pakistanis were entering in 1961 at the combined rate of about 40,000 a year. The scale of this inflow caused alarm and hence a complete reversal of policy was made by the Commonwealth Immigrants Act of 1962 which empowered the government to regulate the entry of Commonwealth citizens—especially in relation to employment opportunities—as indeed it already regulates alien immigration. Entry into the United Kingdom was made even more difficult by measures taken in 1968.

The Sterling Area

Another aspect of Commonwealth co-operation relates to the Sterling Area. The precise etymology of 'sterling' is doubtful, although it originally meant a coin of true weight. The pound sterling of the United Kingdom, convertible for gold at a fixed rate and backed by the strength of its economy, came to acquire and hold the highest reputation for financial stability. The Sterling Area was formally created only in September 1939 at the start of the Second World War, but the conditions which made this practicable had long existed. Before the First World War sterling was widely used in international trade and finance by the countries of the British Empire as also by many others outside it. The British banking system had spread its activities widely and the City of London, as the world's principal banking centre, held sterling accounts for many countries, and had come to provide the leading bankers' bank and many foreign exchange, investment, shipping, and insurance services. Even when, in 1931 during the 'great depression', the United Kingdom abandoned the gold standard so that sterling became a managed currency, though convertible for gold (at the variable gold-market price), the Dominions and a dozen foreign countries freely chose to join the so-called 'sterling bloc'. The creation of the Sterling Area had in mind the serious difficulties, especially that of conserving foreign purchasing power, which the Second World War was bound to present. Its membership was—and remains—large. Today it includes all members of the Commonwealth, except Canada whose trade is more closely bound to that of the United States, as well as the South African Republic, Ireland, Burma, Iceland, Jordan, Libya, Kuwait, and British-protected Sheikdoms of the Persian Gulf. In all, these constitute 8·4 million square miles (21·8 m. sq. km.), or one-sixth of the inhabited world, and 750 million people, about a quarter of mankind. Accordingly, a quarter of international trade, more than the share of any other such area (e.g., the Dollar Area), is accounted for by the Sterling Area, and this trade is virtually world wide.

The successful functioning of the Sterling Area during the Second World War and its survival are tributes to its convenience, efficiency, and flexibility as a means of conducting international business. It is clearly a free association of countries and neither a self-sufficient nor an integrated economic unit. Nor is it a free trade area which, like the Common Market, has a common tariff against the outside world. By the Ottawa Agreements made between independent members of the Commonwealth in 1932, the United Kingdom abandoned free trade, and the system of imperial preferences was greatly extended, so that the Commonwealth became a partly enclosed system vis-à-vis the outside world. Little organisation has been set up specifically to manage the Sterling Area's affairs. There are only a fact-finding committee of experts (the Sterling Area Statistical Committee created in 1947) and a committee at a higher level (the Commonwealth Liaison Committee), both of which meet in London; the latter interprets current situations and exchanges views, while both make preparations for the periodical meeting of Finance Ministers to discuss matters of major policy. Clearly the Sterling Area is firmly based on the common interest that springs from economic inter-dependence. It owes much, too, to the fact that the British Empire was *inter alia* 'a web of submarine telegraph cables' and that such practical conveniences survive. Further, although its relative stature in industry, commerce, and finance has lessened, the United Kingdom still remains a large producer of manufactured goods and a large market for primary products—foodstuffs, agricultural raw materials, petroleum and metals. In some commodities the Sterling Area is the world's outstanding supplier—in jute, mica, tin, gold, diamonds, raw rubber, wool, tea, cocoa—to name the chief. In contrast, it has notable deficiencies, for example, of petroleum, newsprint, soft and hard wood, cotton, and tobacco.

Another common ground between the Commonwealth members of the Area is the high share of their national incomes that is derived from international trade: higher, for example, in India than in the United States where inter-regional trade is so considerable. United Kingdom trade with the overseas members of the Area is large: these supply 40% of its imports and receive a slightly smaller share of its exports. However, the maintenance of sterling as a reserve currency has exerted so serious a strain on the United Kingdom that it sought and received help in this task in 1968 from international bankers.

English and the Englishry

Two evident marks of the part the British Isles has played in the world are the numbers and distribution of people of British stock resulting from emigration and settlement overseas and, related in part to this, the widespread use of English as a native or auxiliary language.

Of English it has been said (Wrenn, 1949, p. 9) 'it is one of the easiest languages to speak badly but the most difficult to use well' and, even if it may not be properly regarded as the international auxiliary language of the world, it is the one most widely used. Modern English grew out of Middle English, itself a development from Old English (or Anglo-Saxon), first spoken and recorded within the English Lowland, and took shape only about A.D. 1450. As such, it had some way to go before it became (with regional dialect differences) the written language of the whole country (say by A.D. 1600) and also by c. A.D. 1800 its spoken language. By stages the language of the English Lowland spread into Corn-

wall, Scotland, Wales and Ireland and in recent times only deliberate nationalistic efforts preserve Irish (Gaelic) in the Republic of
Ireland and Welsh in Wales as literary and spoken languages.
Notwithstanding certain special difficulties that present-day English
presents, notably a non-phonetic orthography that looks back to
late Middle English and to Early Modern English, it has several
advantages that have favoured its extended use: its few and simple
inflexions and its remarkable power of receiving and assimilating
vocabulary from many external sources. Thus it is a heterogeneous,
highly 'mixed' language, with a wide vocabulary to which Latin,
Greek, Norse, French, Dutch, and many other languages have
contributed. Singularly little in contrast survives in English from
the Celtic languages, which were once spoken throughout the British
Isles: so persuasive and pervasive became the language of the nation
that predominated in population numbers, material resources,
and political power.

The wide distribution of English speech, which helps to some
extent to break down the barrier of language in a now small and
closely-knit world, would appear a somewhat permanent effect of
centuries of British overseas colonisation, commerce and imperialism, and no 'artificial' language, such as Esperanto, has challenged
it successfully. Publications, the cinema and broadcasting are
doubtless instruments that confirm and extend its use which continues for purposes of education, administration, and commerce
in certain countries where it is not the native language. American
missionary enterprise in the Far East and British initiatives in, and
services to, higher education in India, Africa, Hong Kong, Malta,
Jamaica, and elsewhere have established its use as a vehicle of
thought and study. In all, about one-tenth of mankind, in the
United States and in the Commonwealth, speak English as their
native language. These make up what has been called the 'Englishry'
(Fawcett, 1941), about five-eighths of whom live in the United
States, which clearly has much culturally in common with the
Commonwealth from the sharing of English literature and speech.
To these must be added many others, in Europe, Monsoon Asia,
the U.S.S.R., and Africa, who learn English as a foreign language.

Commonwealth educational conferences that met at Oxford (in
1960) and at Delhi (in 1962) were concerned with positive measures
to promote the use and proficiency in English by establishing
postgraduate scholarships and facilities (in Britain) for teacher-
training in English, largely for those whose native tongue is not
English. And if in recent times the attraction and prestige of the

United States have much to do with the choice of English as a foreign language, the basis for its wide range of usefulness had already been laid during the last three centuries of British history.

The Republic of Ireland

In an account of the British Isles, Ireland needs separate consideration. Ireland has been partitioned since 1921 when the international boundary was drawn across it in the north to divide off largely-Protestant Northern Ireland, which enjoys autonomy within the United Kingdom, from the greater part of the island (26 of its 32 counties), forming the predominantly Roman Catholic Republic of Ireland, an independent State outside the Commonwealth. The economic contrasts between this Republic and the United Kingdom, even allowing for its relative size—it is only 28% of the latter in area—are striking and have become more so during the last hundred years. The reasons, which may be sought in physical and cultural geography, are not easy to evaluate fully. Although well endowed for agriculture—given the extent of its lowlands and the nature of its maritime climate—the Republic lacks coal resources. On the other hand, manpower was relatively considerable, for the population in 1851 was double that enumerated a century later and clearly Ireland has enjoyed the alleged advantages of much the same geographical position as that so well exploited by Great Britain.

The contrast between the Republic and the United Kingdom is reflected in population numbers: Ireland 2·9 millions and the United Kingdom 55·5 millions (1967), as also in the proportions of the working population engaged in agriculture: in the Republic of Ireland over 30%: in the United Kingdom 4%. The Republic continues to be a country of net emigration: the island as a whole sent millions overseas, especially to the United States. Emigration to Britain has been strong during the last two centuries of industrial expansion. Indeed, since the 1930s Britain in the main has provided the new homes.

The political position of the Republic is not without anomalous features. Despite its independent political course, it remains within the Sterling Area and stands in the closest economic association with the United Kingdom which is a market for 90% of its exports and supplies rather more than half of its imports. It enjoys, by treaty, special trade preferences in the Commonwealth and a guaranteed market in the United Kingdom where its citizens assume non-British but also non-alien status.[1] The Irish enjoy free entry and between 1946 and 1959 an average of 25,000 emigrated into Britain each year, and anomalously, it is believed, their free entry will be little if at all prejudiced by the Immigrants Act of 1962. The Irish are free also to join the armed forces of the Crown, as hundreds of thousands did while their country was neutral during the Second World War. A member of OECD, the Republic has held to its neutrality since this was first proclaimed in 1939, so that during the ensuing war, the Royal Navy was denied the use of its ports; it has thus avoided membership of NATO. On the other hand, it assumes the responsibilities of United Nations' membership.

The United Kingdom and the World

The United Kingdom's application in 1961 to join the European Economic Organisation, familiarly known as the Common Market, marked a new departure in policy. Changes in this century have emphasised the relative reduction in Britain's political, economic, and demographic strength. The rapid rise in this century of the economy, manpower, and military might of the United States and the Soviet Union transformed the geopolitical situation by substituting two 'Great Powers' where eight could be so rated in 1914 (Toynbee, 1948). Although the United Kingdom escaped defeat in the two world wars, it suffered severe economic losses, not only of men, but also of large overseas investments, by material destruction at home and at sea, and by the sundering of market ties. Its survival, notwithstanding its own all-out efforts, underlined the degree to which it had become dependent on the United States and its former Dominions, and without the great financial help of the United States and Canada it could not have achieved such a remarkable economic recovery. Further, its political power in the world fell sharply with the passing of the empire, especially with the loss of India, Pakistan, Ceylon, and more recently, Malaya. It was thus deprived of those great strategic bases and resources that gave reality to its world-power status and rested on naval control of the Mediterranean—Red Sea—Indian Ocean route. Earlier in this century it had already yielded naval control in the Caribbean and Far Eastern waters to the United States and Japan

[1] The special relationship of the Republic to the United Kingdom is reflected in the fact that Irish affairs there fall to the Commonwealth Relations Office, not to the Foreign Office.

respectively. Its position of power and influence in the Middle East, too, was lost with the ending of its mandates in Palestine, Iraq, and Jordan, and with its withdrawal of troops from the Suez Canal zone.

Illustrative of Britain's changed status since the Second World War is United States' control of the Mediterranean by means of the Seventh fleet and air bases in Spain and Libya, as also of Far Eastern waters principally by means of the Sixth fleet. Similarly, the defence pact known as ANZUS, entered into by Australia, New Zealand, and the United States in 1952, recognised the modern realities of Pacific power. Nearer home the creation, with the implied ultimate objective of political union, of the Common Market, which combines France, the German Federal Republic, Italy, and the three Benelux countries into a working trade unit, in scale, manpower, and resources approaching the United States, was a challenge to Britain from powerful, progressive, and friendly neighbours.

'England', wrote André Siegfried, 'is as a ship moored off the coast of Europe, always prepared to weigh anchor.' This alleged ambivalence is more apparent than real. British imperial defence—and it stood the severest tests—rested on a foreign policy designed to preserve the security of the homeland and of the ocean routes. To this end, in the attempt to maintain the balance of power, Britain sought allies everywhere but consistently sought them on the Continent and tried so to organise them as to prevent an aggressor from dominating it, and in particular, from occupying the Channel ports. Indeed, British power, although globally it had much success, turned many dangerous corners in a European involvement which might well have more than shaken a well improvised system of defence; yet Britain never attained that primacy in Europe exerted by Germany between 1871 and 1890 (Webster, 1950). Nor did it ever retreat to a strictly isolationist policy in Europe. Indeed, it took the initiative in effecting the Brussels Treaty of 1948: from this developed the North Atlantic Treaty Organisation which realistically brought North Atlantic strength to bear on the problem of west European security and thus of world stability. But this effective defence alliance has not as yet justified the original hopes that it would give rise to a real Atlantic community, physically united by the 'Midland Ocean'.

Much has changed since the United Kingdom produced one third of the world's manufactures, as it did in 1870, indeed, since 1913, when its share amounted to one seventh. Britain's share of registered tonnage of shipping declined from 45% in 1900 to 16%

in 1960. Its industrial output has grown slowly since the Second World War ended, and less fast than that of its Common Market neighbours. Although full employment and high living standards have been generally maintained, industry in Britain reveals clear weaknesses. The National Economic Development Council has been set up to remedy these and to plan for expansion. Britain has lost many striking advantages it formerly enjoyed and exploited: British coal is no longer cheap, many industrial locations related to changed conditions are no longer economic, and competition is strong and widespread. Further, despite striking original contributions, such as penicillin, the jet engine, and Hovercraft, Britain has become very dependent on foreign research and development. Insufficient research, inadequate management, which does not include enough of those who are technologically and scientifically trained, faulty investment policies—these, together with an obsolescent infrastructure—are the weaknesses that have to be overcome (Burn, 1962).

Similarly, although it remains one of the greatest commercial nations, its share of world trade has shrunk with increasing competition. Staple industries, like shipbuilding and textiles, have lost their former importance, but other specialised manufactures, notably motor vehicles, aircraft, machinery of many kinds, and chemicals, have increased in relative stature. Further, during the years 1950 to 1961 the United Kingdom's exports to the Commonwealth declined from 50% to 39%, while with European countries they increased from 25% to 32%. Britain's dilemma in 1962 was whether entry into the Common Market, which might seem to offer both economic and political advantages, and is favoured by the United States for political and defence reasons, could be achieved without prejudice to Commonwealth partners and to its European associates in the European Free Trade Association, popularly known as 'The Outer Seven' (although, with Finland's accession, it numbers eight). But if these difficulties could be overcome, Britain was ready to contemplate ultimate political unity with the Six. It seemed well cast also for the rôle of a bridge in the forging of the Atlantic partnership with the United States which President Kennedy desired. In 1963 Britain's application failed, as again in 1967, yet the British Government still wishes to write this fresh page of history believing that 'This new Europe will be a great power, standing not alone, but as an equal partner in the Atlantic Alliance, retaining its traditional ties overseas and fully conscious of its growing obligations towards the rest of the free world' (Heath, 1962).

435

References

BURN, D., 1962. Investment, innovation and planning in the United Kingdom. *Progress*, **49,** no. 274.

CARRINGTON, C. E., 1961. *The Liquidation of the British Empire*. London.

FAWCETT, C. B., 1941. *The Bases of a World Commonwealth*. London.

HEATH, E., 1962. Lord Privy Seal's speech to the Ministerial Council of Western European Union in London, 10 April, 1962. *The Times*, 13 April, 1962.

HOBSON, J. A., 1938. *Imperialism*, 3rd ed. London.

JENNINGS, I., 1948. *The British Commonwealth of Nations*. London.

KIMBLE, G. H. T., 1938. *Geography in the Middle Ages*. London.

MATTINGLY, H., 1948. *Agricola*, section 24. Tacitus on Britain and Germany. New translation. London.

NEF, J. U., 1956. *Cultural Foundations of Industrial Civilization*. Cambridge.

SEELEY, J. R., 1911. *The Expansion of England*. London.

SEMPLE, E. C., 1911. *Influences of Geographical Environment on the basis of Ratzel's System of Anthropology*. New York.

SMITH, ADAM, 1775/6. *An Inquiry into the Nature and Causes of the Wealth of Nations*.

TOYNBEE, A. J., 1948. *Civilization on Trial*. Oxford.

WEBSTER, C. K., 1950. *United Kingdom Policy*. London.

WRENN, C. L., 1949. *The English Language*. London.

INDEX

Abbevillian culture, 178
abbeys, 389, 390, 391
Abbotsford, 216
Aberdeen, 23, 276, 285, 320, 329, 354
— readvance, 144
Aberdeenshire, 138, 172, 185
Aberdeen-Angus cattle, 13, 266
Aberystwyth, 21, 269, 372, 384
Acheulian culture, 178
Act of Union (England and Scotland), 203, 210, 217, 405, 423; (England and Wales), 203, 404
administrative centres, 218
afforestation, 206, 209, 217, 255, 257, 362, 364
agricultural innovations, 209-14, 221, 222
— regions, 24, 222, 266
agriculture, 12-13, 21, 23, 25, 26, 34, 76, 85, 86, 175, 182, 195, 196, 208, 209, 210, 223, 224, 229, 231, 233, 238, 241, 242, 247, 254-5, 256, 257, 258, 260-1, 263-75, 276-8, 284, 287, 303, 306, 317, 331, 334, 336, 342, 354, 381, 417, 421, 422, 432
— regional specialisation in, 222, 266
Agrostis, 216
aircraft industry, 13, 317, 435
Aire, river, 75
Airedale, 366
Aire Gap, 138, 366
air-masses, 53, 56
air pollution, 29, 71
air-ponding, 58
airports, airfields, 253, 329, 369
air transport, 329
Aldershot, 370
Allen, Lough, 77, 126, 374
Allerod period, 136, 139, 144, 158
alluvium, 95, 96, 102, 247, 255, 326
Alnwick, 365, 394
Alpine race, 9
— structure, 6, 100, 102, 107
Alston Block, 106
Altaid structural alignment, 100
aluminium, 85, 296
Ancholme valley, 207
Andover, 113, 356
Anglesey, 97, 98, 119, 413
Anglican church, 1
Anglo-Norman place-names, 374
— towns, 390
Anglo-Saxon place-names, 365, 366, 369, 370, 372
Anglo-Saxons, 7, 10, 11, 15, 51, 166, 190, 198, 199-201, 202, 204, 206, 214, 218, 371, 390, 403, 430
Anglo-Saxon settlement, 27, 367, 368
Angus, 268, 302
anhydrite, 285
anthracite, 290
anticlines, 104, 105, 106, 107
anticlinorium, 104, 105, 107
anticyclones, 53, 56, 58, 60, 69, 71, 166

Antonine Wall, 194, 420
Antrim, County, 181, 300, 301, 304, 306, 311, 406, 416
— Hills, 375
— lavas, 119
— plateau, 99
apples, 268
arable farming, 208
— land, 172, 204, 207, 209, 212, 213, 214, 215, 230, 242, 269, 274, 366, 370, 371
arbutus, 9
architecture, 183, 286
Arctic char, 7
Arctic Front, 155
Ardnacrusha, 85
Ards peninsula, 375
Arenig mountains, 132
Argyll, 14, 119, 153, 186, 191, 205, 274, 406
Armagh, County, 406, 416
Armorican structural alignment, 100
Arran, 145, 362
artifacts, 177, 180, 187, 188
Arun, river, 76
ash, 182, 186, 198
Ashbourne, 367
Ashford, 356
astrolabe, 42
Atlantic climatic period, 162, 163, 164, 178, 180, 181
— fringe, 15
— Ocean, 3, 4, 5, 17, 75, 116, 154, 160, 162, 163, 173, 181, 182, 272, 421
— zone, 180-96, 420
atlases, 31, 42, 51, 52, 56, 65
atmospheric instability, 61
— pressure, 53
Aurignacian culture, 178
Avebury, 14, 186
Avoca, river, 77
Avon, river (Bristol), 77, 96, 117; (Warwickshire), 75, 77, 96, 136, 141, 368; (Wiltshire-Hampshire), 76, 275
Avonmouth, 321
axes, 178, 181, 182, 188, 190, 204
axial belt, 250, 259, 300, 301, 333, 351
Aycliffe, 356
Aylesbury (ducks), 267
Aylesbury, Vale of, 369
Ayr, 322, 354
Ayrshire, 2, 144, 270, 302, 345, 364
— cattle, 13, 266, 270
— coalfield, 289, 291
— seed potatoes, 267
Azilian culture, 181

Bagshot, 209
Bagshot Beds, 115, 209
Bala, Lake, 78
Baldock, 386
Ballineen, 376